NORTH POLE

SOUTH POLE

NORTH POLE

SOUTH POLE

Bernard Stonehouse

A Guide to the Ecology and Resources of the Arctic and Antarctic

PRION

First published in the United Kingdom by PRION,
an imprint of Multimedia Books Limited,
32–34 Gordon House Road,
London NW5 1LP.

Editor: Anne Cope
Design: Patricia Houden
Picture research: Charlotte Deane
Cartography: Malcolm Porter
Production: Hugh Allan

British Library Cataloguing in Publication Data
Stonehouse, Bernard 1926–
North Pole, South Pole: A guide to the ecology and resources
of the Arctic and Antarctic.
1. Arctic. Sub-Arctic regions 2. Antarctic
I. Title
998

ISBN 1-85375-056-5

Printed in Hong Kong by Imago

❄

Author's note

This book is one traveller's view of the polar regions. As a young ecologist I worked mostly in the Antarctic. Not until my middle years did I discover the Arctic, in northern Canada and Alaska. It was rather like discovering that there is an opposite sex, and I am grateful that the discovery did not come too late for me to enjoy it.

My studies are based at the Scott Polar Research Institute, a wonderful centre for interdisciplinary polar research in Cambridge, England. This book has been helped by several of my colleagues, who may recognize some of their own views. They should in no way be held responsible for my versions of them.

B. S.

CONTENTS

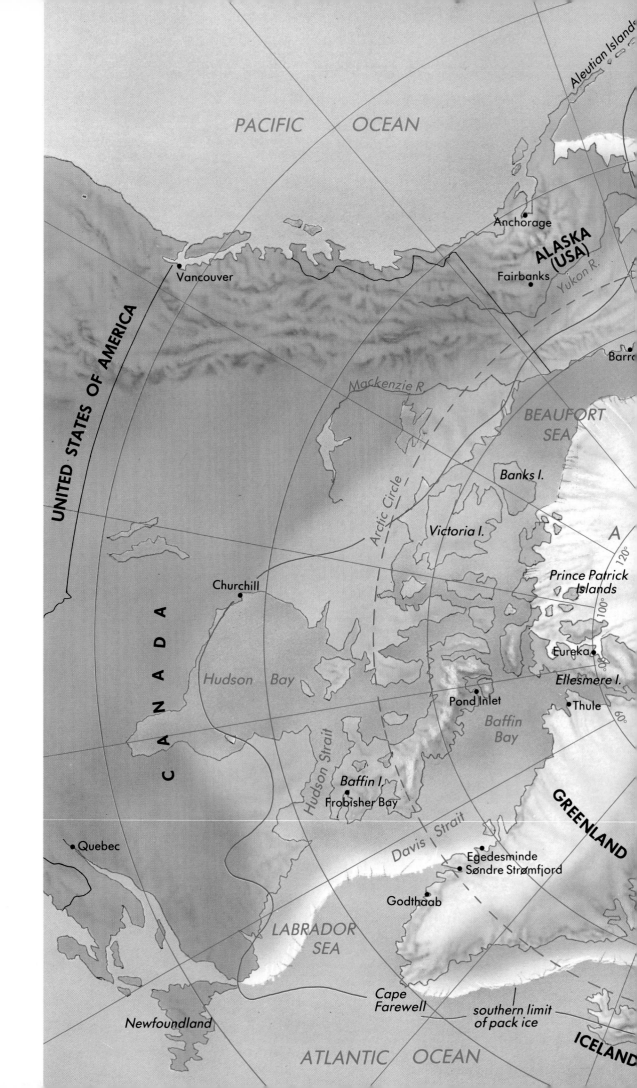

PACIFIC OCEAN

Aleutian Islands

Anchorage

ALASKA (USA)

Fairbanks

Yukon R.

Barro

BEAUFORT SEA

Vancouver

UNITED STATES OF AMERICA

Mackenzie R.

Banks I.

Arctic Circle

Victoria I.

Prince Patrick Islands

A

120°

Churchill

100°

CANADA

Eureka

80°

Ellesmere I.

Thule

Hudson Bay

Pond Inlet

Baffin Bay

60°

Hudson Strait

Baffin I.

Frobisher Bay

GREENLAND

Quebec

Davis Strait

Egedesminde
Søndre Strømfjord

Godthaab

LABRADOR SEA

Cape Farewell

southern limit of pack ice

Newfoundland

ICELAND

ATLANTIC OCEAN

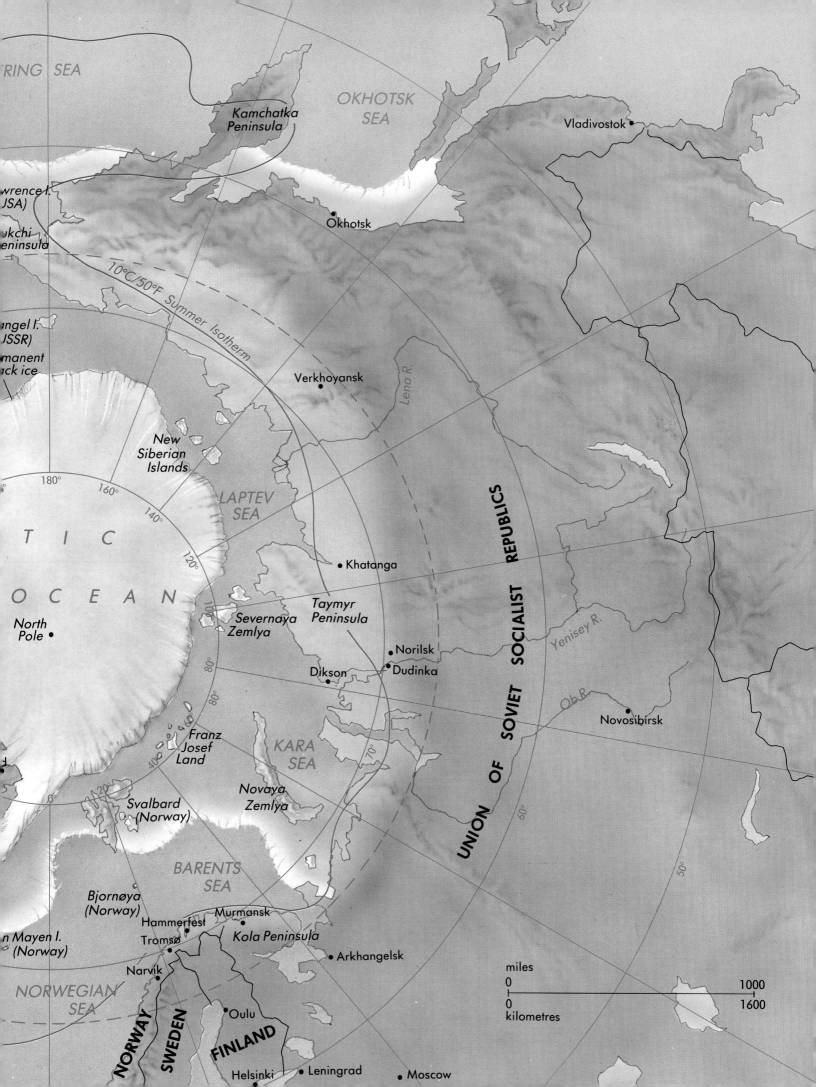

RING SEA

OKHOTSK
SEA

Kamchatka
Peninsula

Vladivostok •

wrence I.
USA)

Okhotsk •

ukchi
eninsula

10°C/50°F Summer Isotherm

ngel I.
USSR)

Lena R.

manent
ck ice

Verkhoyansk •

New
Siberian
Islands

180°

160°

140°

LAPTEV
SEA

120°

UNION OF SOVIET SOCIALIST REPUBLICS

TIC

Khatanga •

OCEAN

Yenisey R.

North
Pole •

Taymyr
Peninsula

Severnaya
Zemlya

Norilsk •

80°

Dikson • Dudinka •

80°

Ob R.

70°

Novosibirsk •

Franz
Josef
Land

40°

KARA
SEA

60°

Novaya
Zemlya

Svalbard
(Norway)

50°

BARENTS
SEA

Bjornøya
(Norway)

Murmansk •

Hammerfest •

Kola Peninsula

n Mayen I.
(Norway)

Tromsø •

Arkhangelsk •

Narvik •

miles
0   1000
0   1600
kilometres

NORWEGIAN
SEA

NORWAY

SWEDEN

FINLAND

Oulu •

Helsinki •   Leningrad •   Moscow •

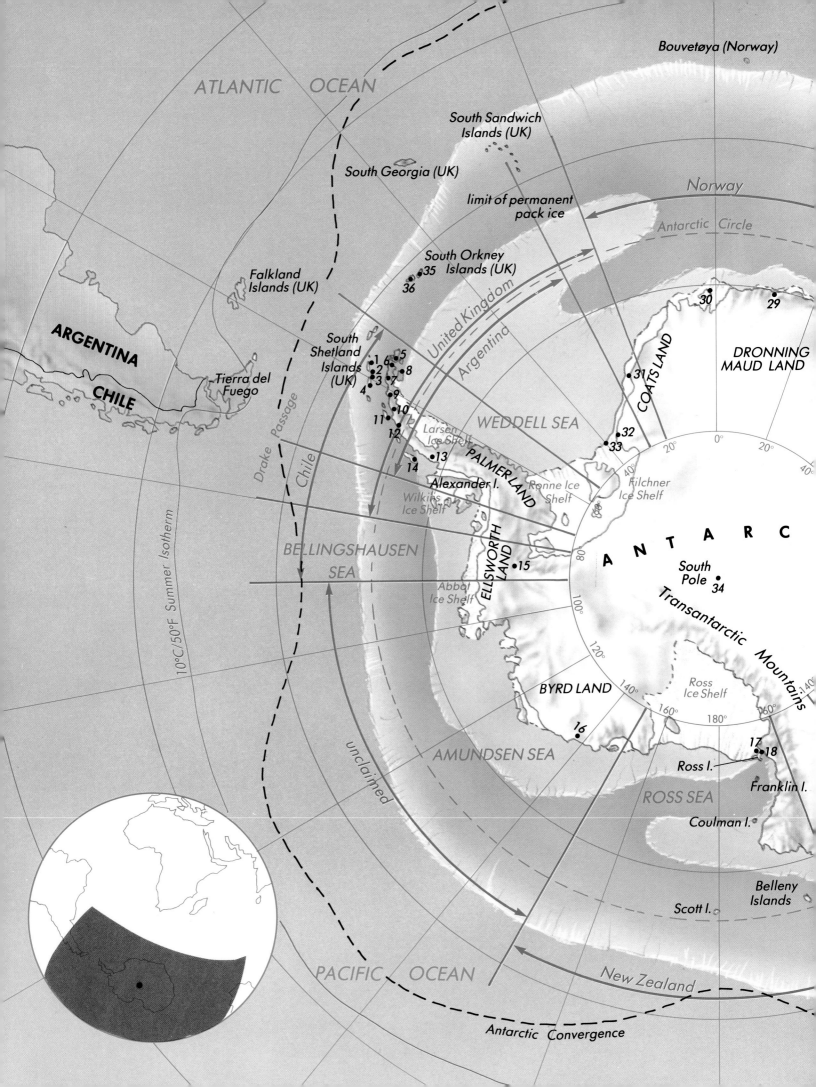

ATLANTIC OCEAN

Bouvetøya (Norway)

South Sandwich Islands (UK)

South Georgia (UK)

limit of permanent pack ice

Norway

Antarctic Circle

South Orkney Islands (UK)

•35
•36

Falkland Islands (UK)

United Kingdom

Argentina

•30   •29

DRONNING MAUD LAND

COATS LAND

South Shetland Islands (UK)

1 •6 •5
•2 •8
•3 •7
4 •9
•10
11 •12

•31

WEDDELL SEA

•32
•33

ARGENTINA

CHILE

Tierra del Fuego

Larsen Ice Shelf

PALMER LAND

Ronne Ice Shelf

Filchner Ice Shelf

•13

14

Alexander I.

Wilkins Ice Shelf

0°   20°   40°

ANTARC

Drake Passage

Chile

•15

ELLSWORTH LAND

South Pole •34

Transantarctic Mountains

BELLINGSHAUSEN SEA

Abbot Ice Shelf

80°

100°

10°C/50°F Summer Isotherm

BYRD LAND

120°

140°

Ross Ice Shelf

140°

•16

160°   180°   160°

•17
•18

Ross I.

Franklin I.

unclaimed

AMUNDSEN SEA

ROSS SEA

Coulman I.

Belleny Islands

Scott I.

PACIFIC   OCEAN

New Zealand

Antarctic Convergence

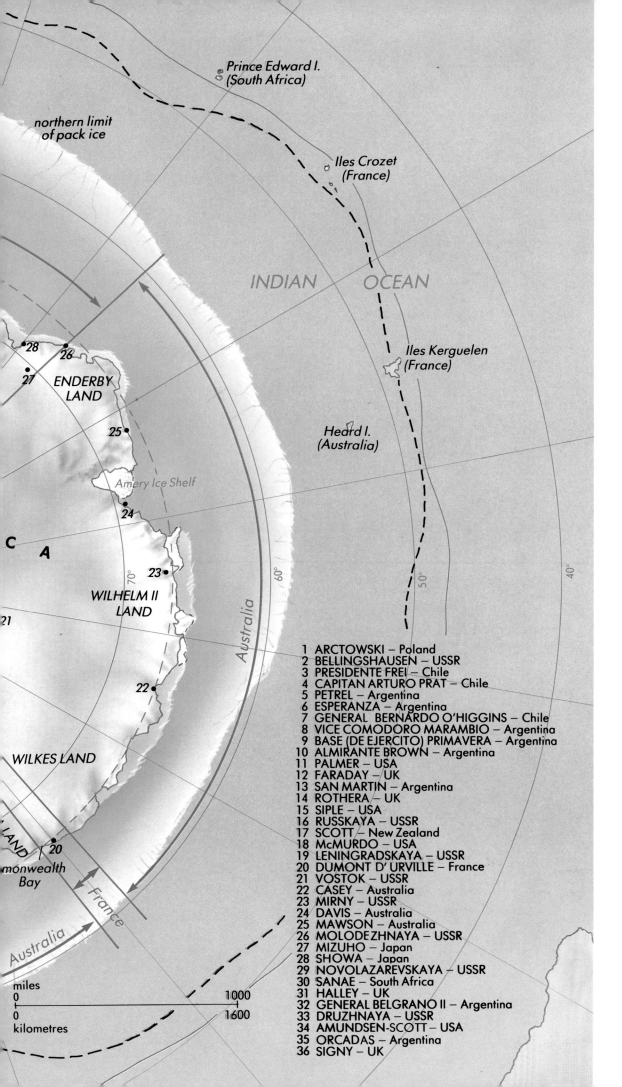

northern limit
of pack ice

Prince Edward I.
(South Africa)

Iles Crozet
(France)

INDIAN   OCEAN

Iles Kerguelen
(France)

28
28

27

ENDERBY
LAND

Heard I.
(Australia)

25

Amery Ice Shelf

24

C

A

23

WILHELM II
LAND

70°

60°

Australia

50°

40°

21

WILKES LAND

20

monwealth
Bay

France

Australia

1 ARCTOWSKI – Poland
2 BELLINGSHAUSEN – USSR
3 PRESIDENTE FREI – Chile
4 CAPITAN ARTURO PRAT – Chile
5 PETREL – Argentina
6 ESPERANZA – Argentina
7 GENERAL BERNARDO O'HIGGINS – Chile
8 VICE COMODORO MARAMBIO – Argentina
9 BASE (DE EJERCITO) PRIMAVERA – Argentina
10 ALMIRANTE BROWN – Argentina
11 PALMER – USA
12 FARADAY – UK
13 SAN MARTIN – Argentina
14 ROTHERA – UK
15 SIPLE – USA
16 RUSSKAYA – USSR
17 SCOTT – New Zealand
18 McMURDO – USA
19 LENINGRADSKAYA – USSR
20 DUMONT D'URVILLE – France
21 VOSTOK – USSR
22 CASEY – Australia
23 MIRNY – USSR
24 DAVIS – Australia
25 MAWSON – Australia
26 MOLODEZHNAYA – USSR
27 MIZUHO – Japan
28 SHOWA – Japan
29 NOVOLAZAREVSKAYA – USSR
30 SANAE – South Africa
31 HALLEY – UK
32 GENERAL BELGRANO II – Argentina
33 DRUZHNAYA – USSR
34 AMUNDSEN-SCOTT – USA
35 ORCADAS – Argentina
36 SIGNY – UK

miles
0   1000
0   1600
kilometres

1

At the Ends of Earth

From space our planet is a sun-lit ball, slowly spinning in a dark sky. The ball turns, blue and fuzzy in its thin veil of atmosphere, and oceans and continents follow each other in endless procession like carrousel horses. Eurasia, the Atlantic, the Americas, the Pacific, Australasia — shapes familiar from schoolroom atlases — swing past. Satellites glimpse them fitfully through swirls of shifting cloud.

Less familiar are the ends of Earth, the centres of rotation at the top and base of the ball. Here the satellites see pale patches, always white, sparkling in summer sunshine and glowing under winter moonlight. These are mantles of permanent ice — sea ice and land ice together, abutting on each other, obscuring coastal boundaries, hiding whole mountain ranges and spreading ragged fringes far over the oceans. The mantles vary with the seasons, growing and shrinking as Earth rolls its way around the sun.

Covering the planet's coldest regions, where water is usually a solid, their whiteness is light reflected from snow and ice. Like hazy mirrors they reflect up to 95 per cent of the sunlight that falls upon them. In winter their areas almost double; in summer they contract but never disappear, for we live in an ice age, and they are its constant witness. Year-round their cold spreads far across the hemispheres. North winds from the Arctic carry chill to New Yorkers and Londoners; southerlies in winter bring polar cold to New Zealand, Australia and South Africa. Even in late summer, when their influence is least, the ice mantles are still a constant presence; both hemispheres, but especially the southern, would be much warmer without them.

From space the two mantles look similar, as though covering similar regions. In fact they overlie regions as different as they could possibly be. The Arctic is centred on an ocean basin almost ringed by land, but the Antarctic is a high continent completely ringed by ocean.

We have known of polar regions for centuries, but for longer than centuries strong palisades of ice have guarded them, setting them apart from the rest of the world. Among the last patches of Earth to be explored, they remained regions of adventure and mystery well into the 20th century, untamed and even unknown. There was a time within human memory when 'polar' meant everything remote from human experience, as well as everything cold and dangerously uncomfortable. Now the palisades are down. For better or worse both polar regions are open as never before to human experience, human understanding and human meddling. Air transport was their final undoing. Virtually every corner is now accessible to anyone with the will and means to go there.

POLAR BOUNDARIES

How big are these curious regions, and where do they start and end? There are no single, definitive boundaries for either Arctic or Antarctic; each starts at its geographical pole and extends an indefinite distance toward the temperate zones. In the south is the continent of Antarctica, and the region of ocean and islands around it is the Antarctic region. In the north a central Arctic Ocean is circled by the northern rims of the great continents and Greenland, and the northern ends of the Atlantic and Pacific oceans, and these together make up the Arctic region. The boundaries of these regions we can draw where we want them to be.

All who need polar boundaries devise their own, and different disciplines use different criteria. Some of the more useful ones appear on the maps in the front of this book.

Geographers often use the polar circles, for they provide two regions exactly equivalent in size and shape, which are useful for comparisons. Lawyers and politicians sometimes prefer other parallels of latitude, closer to or farther from the poles. Biologists look for ecological limits, for example the boundary between tundra and forest, to define polar ecological zones. Oceanographers use boundaries between water masses, and the northern and southern limits of pack ice, to create maritime polar regions. Climatologists use isotherms (lines joining points of equal mean temperatures) to define polar climatic regions.

The polar regions are similar — cold, remote from civilization, difficult for people to live in, and beautiful or dreary, exciting or boring, according to taste. But they are different too, as though a Creator had set out to design two ends for the earth, fundamentally the same but different in as many curious and interesting ways as possible.

The poles themselves are different. At the North Pole a visitor stands on slowly-shifting pack ice close to sea level, probably under an overcast sky. In summer the air temperature will be close to freezing

■ ■ ■

The geodesic dome of
Amundsen-Scott station,
South Pole. Amundsen-
Scott, high on the Antarctic
ice cap and one of the most
inaccessible places in the
world, is maintained by air
shuttles. The Soviet Union
also has an ice-cap station,
almost as difficult and
expensive to maintain,
1300 km (800 miles) away
on the South Polar Plateau.

point, in winter perhaps as low as -30°C (-23°F). A visitor to the South Pole stands on solid ice almost 3000 m (10,000 ft) thick, stretching in every direction to the far horizon and beyond. Winter or summer the sky will probably be clear, but surface air temperatures will range from -30°C (-23°F) in summer to -60°C (-76°F) or lower in winter.

Although colder, the southern visitor stands a better chance of warming up, for at the South Pole is Amundsen-Scott, a permanent US research station with coffee usually on the boil. The North Pole has no station, permanent or temporary. If one were to be built today it would have shifted by tomorrow, for the pack ice is drifting slowly in the direction of Scandinavia. There are several such floating station on 'islands' of more solid ice, drifting with the pack ice and re-supplied by air. Soviet, US or British nuclear submarines occasionally drop by in summer at the North Pole, stopping for a barbecue and a football match on the pack

■ ■ ■

Shifting polar pack ice.
Permanent research stations
are not feasible at the North
Pole, for the pole lies in the
middle of a deep ocean
covered with drifting pack
ice. Research stations
operate from time to time in
the Arctic Ocean basin,
floating on large fragments
of shelf ice (thicker and safer
than pack ice) and drifting
with the currents.

DEFINING THE POLAR REGIONS

Polar circles are parallels of latitude approximately 23°28′ from the poles. The angle is that between the tilted Earth and the ecliptic, the plane on which the Earth circles the sun; it is approximate because the tilt varies slightly from time to time. Polar circles, like the Tropics of Cancer and Capricorn, were defined purely on geometrical grounds by geographers of old; these parallels divide Earth's surface into convenient tropical, temperate and polar zones. On maps the polar circles look meaningful, but on Earth's surface they are less convincing, for there is nothing to show for them. There are no sudden changes when we cross them; they do not separate polar from non-polar climates, or one kind of habitat from another. The circles lie the same distance (2606 km/1,619 miles) from their poles and enclose exactly similar areas (40,333,466 km^2/15,755,260 sq miles), each about 8 per cent of Earth's surface.

Pack ice is a formidable hazard. Even the most powerful modern icebreakers go carefully through heavy ice. Many larger ships use helicopters to spy out easy routes through the ice.

If we live within the circles we can see the midnight sun and experience extended polar days and nights, but there is very little change at the circles themselves. Neither plants nor animals, winds nor ocean currents take a scrap of notice of them. Their main use is in providing a basis for comparison.

The *treeline* is the limit beyond which trees do not grow (a tree for this purpose has to be roughly the height of a man). In the northern hemisphere this is a clearly-defined boundary between tundra and boreal forest, visible in the field and readily plotted on maps. So it has become the most generally accepted ecological limit for the Arctic region. In the southern hemisphere the treeline runs mainly between islands widely separated by ocean and is virtually meaningless as an ecological boundary.

Both polar regions have core-areas of perennial *pack ice* several years old, with outer zones of annual ice which forms each autumn and disperses in spring. As the presence or absence of pack ice has a considerable effect on air temperatures, summer and winter limits of pack ice are ecologically relevant; they are also of critical importance to mariners. They usually appear on maps as mean northern and southern limits of pack ice.

The *Antarctic Convergence* is a boundary at the ocean surface between two well-defined water masses, Antarctic Water to the south and Subtropical Water to the north. Sometimes visible, always detectable by a sudden change in temperature and salinity, it is the most generally accepted boundary defining the Antarctic region. There are similar boundaries between adjacent Arctic water masses, but none so clear-cut or generally useful.

The *10°C/50°F summer isotherm* is a line on the map joining all stations where the mean temperature of the warmest month is 10°C (50°F). In some systems of climate classification this separates polar from sub-polar regions. It is ecologically useful in giving an indication of where warm summers occur, but it says nothing of winter cold and there are not enough climatic stations in either hemisphere to make it truly accurate.

■ ■ ■

Sunshine Glacier, Signy Island, Antarctica. Land ice is an accumulation of snow packed down by wind and consolidated under its own weight until it forms clear ice. In areas where snowfall is high, or where snow and ice fail to melt in summer, huge ice sheets and glaciers form. They may look static, but they are constantly being renewed.

Polar regions are generally colder than the rest of the world, but the Antarctic is much colder than the Arctic. The South Pole, on its ice plateau 2835 m (9,301 ft) above sea level, is chilled both by latitude and by its mountain-top elevation. The North Pole, afloat on the sea, is warmed by the water beneath. Can a polar sea at near-freezing temperature warm anything? Every seal knows that it can, particularly if the air above is much colder. North and south, polar seals dive from ice floes into icy seas to dodge even icier winds.

Year-round ice is a feature of both poles, but again the Antarctic has more than its share. Of all the earth's land ice, 98 per cent is in polar regions, 91 per cent of it on Antarctica, where in places it reaches 4000 m (10,000 ft) thick. In the north, only Greenland and nearby islands have ice caps, overall on a much smaller scale — Greenland has about one tenth the area of Antarctica. Southern sea ice too is about 30 per cent more extensive than northern, adding more to the total area of white that the satellites see each winter.

The ocean at the top of the world and the continent at the bottom generate temperature differences far beyond their own boundaries. Latitude for latitude, most of the southern hemisphere is colder than

the northern hemisphere. Helsinki, a capital city in 60°N, has a mean midsummer air temperature of 17°C (63°F), some 18°C (32°F) higher than midsummer at Signy Island, an Antarctic research station in the equivalent southern latitude. Britain's north Midlands region in 54°N is reasonably habitable, forested and farmed, with snow in winter but no glaciers or permanent ice. South Georgia in similar latitude south is heavily glaciated down to sea level.

In the Antarctic, the lowest temperatures year-round are measured on the polar plateau, not at the pole itself but at the highest point of the icecap some 1300 km (800 miles) away. Lowest summer temperatures in the Arctic occur high on the Greenland ice-cap, lowest winter temperatures in northeastern Siberia, both far from the pole and indeed remote from the polar basin.

From these differences arise many others. Both polar regions have a rugged beauty that has inspired generations of artists and photographers. Despite cold and environmental harshness, both are attractive to wildlife: both have plants and animals of their own, with a surprising range of species and sometimes astonishing abundance. The Arctic and

■   ■   ■   **MIDNIGHT SUN**   ■   ■   ■

The long dark winters and sunlit summers of the polar regions occur because the whole area within each polar circle is tilted away from the sun in winter and toward it in summer. Thus any point north of the Arctic Circle is out of sight of the sun (i.e. the sun does not rise above the horizon) in winter, and in full view of the sun (i.e. the sun does not set) in summer. So the polar circles indicate where we can see that exclusively polar phenomenon, the midnight sun.

Travelling poleward in summer from lower latitudes, the days lengthen; the sun sets later each evening and rises earlier each morning. At the polar circles at midsummer, the sun remains above the horizon throughout the 24 hours. After its noon-time high, the sun rides steadily down the sky as usual during afternoon and evening, though at a very shallow angle. By late evening it is near the horizon; by midnight it is running along the horizon; then it starts to rise again. To see this happening, one has to be at or beyond the polar circles. Similarly at midwinter beyond the circles the sun never rises above the horizon. There is a brightening of the sky during late morning, but even at noon the sun fails to appear. Nearer the poles, the less one sees of day-glow. In 70°N and S, midday at midwinter brings only a twilight glow to the sky; moonlight is often far brighter than day-glow.

Poleward, too, the number of days of summer daylight increases, and for each long summer day, roughly speaking, there is a long winter night to come. On the Arctic Circle itself (66°32') midnight sun is only seen on midsummer day, but only on midwinter day is the sun missing altogether. At Nord Kapp (71°N), the northernmost point of Norway, midnight sun starts on May 16 each year and continues for 72 days; in northern Svalbard (80°N) it starts on April 13 and continues for 137 days. At the North and South Poles, days and seasons merge completely; once risen, the sun spirals steadily around the sky for a day lasting six months, then sets for a six months' night.

Husky teams head for home.
At this latitude, 80°N, the sun
is seen continuously for at
least five months in summer.
As the sun sinks, the snow
hardens, making sledges
easier to pull.

■ ■ ■

A bird's eye view of the South Polar Plateau. The Antarctic ice cap covers mountain ranges that are longer and higher than the European Alps. Mountains emerge from the edges of the plateau, their peaks carved by weathering and erosion. Some, like the rounder mountains in the foreground of this picture, seem to have emerged recently from the ice. Between them flow some of the world's most extensive glaciers.

Antarctic have very few species in common because the plants and animals that have moved in to colonize them come from totally different points of origin. The Arctic has far more of everything living - Greenland alone has over 40 species of flowering plant, while the whole Antarctic continent has only two. And only the Arctic fauna includes resident stocks of that troublesome little animal, man.

Some of the differences can be summed up if, like the old geographers, we define the polar regions as the areas within the polar circles. The circles lie the same distance (2606 km/1,619 miles) from their poles and enclose exactly similar areas containing both land and ocean. The Arctic Circle is mostly land-based, linking the northlands of Scandinavia and Siberia and passing through Alaska, Canada and the bulk of ice-capped Greenland. It crosses from Asia to America just north of the Bering Strait, and between Greenland and Norway just north of Iceland. The Antarctic Circle is mostly oceanic, bisecting the Antarctic Peninsula and passing only along the northernmost coast of the continent; for much of its length it crosses the Ross, Amundsen, Bellingshausen and Weddell Seas.

The Antarctic Circle rings a desert continent without trees, shrubs or continuous ground cover, with transient human populations of only a few hundred scientists and a few hundred more technicians and administrators to support them. By contrast, within the Arctic Circle lie forests, tundra, farmlands and gardens, towns and cities, huge industrial complexes, and a growing human population, both indigenous and immigrant, currently numbering well over 2 million.

■ ■ ■

Broad-leafed willow herb and purple saxifrage make a patch of colour in the Arctic tundra. The thin soils of the Arctic lowlands, accumulated over many years, give a foothold to a wide range of tiny plants. The richer areas support meadows of mosses, grasses and flowering plants. The ground is snow-covered for all but two or three months of the year.

POLAR PEOPLE

How do they live, these polar people? Are they special kinds of humans with remarkable adaptations for living beyond the polar circles?

The Arctic has several different kinds of polar people, including indigenous groups who have lived there for 3000 years or more, and 'outsiders' or settlers of whom many are permanent residents. Up to a few decades ago the total human population remained small. Now the indigenous inhabitants are healthier and more fecund than before and, like the outsiders, are increasing in numbers.

The true people of the Arctic are the Inuit or Eskimos, who inhabit the northernmost plains, rivers and coastlands of North America, Asia and Greenland. Originating from eastern Asia, they are short, solidly-built people, similar in structure and appearance wherever they are found. They form widely dispersed populations with shared ancestry, cultures and languages. In anatomy, physiology, culture and social structure they are superbly adapted to their ancestral life-style, nomadic hunting, gathering and sharing of food.

Until relatively recently these people lived in a timewarp, a late Stone Age all of their own. Moving in small family groups, they owned no more than they could pack onto sledges. Their possessions, like the people themselves, were part of the Arctic, fabricated with skill and astonishing ingenuity from materials that come to hand on Arctic shores – skins,

An Inuit hunter butchers a caribou, Devon Island, Canada. The Inuit have always taken a small toll of the reindeer herds that move north on their annual summer migrations, and some modern Inuit still depend on caribou for food.

bones, furs, shrubs, stones and driftwood. Anything left behind in their nomadic travels was soon reabsorbed into the landscape.

Arctic folk today form settled communities, owning or renting houses like the rest of us. A few are still wholly nomadic, but many combine settled and nomadic living, wage-earning and subsistence hunting in an annual round of activities. From outside they buy in such artifacts of civilization, from motorized sledges to disposable diapers, as they fancy and can afford. Settlement has brought many advantages, but the concentration of human disorder and the influx of new, alien materials have changed the old Arctic for ever.

Their northlands have long been divided politically, so that some Eskimos find themselves American

An Inuit hunter stalks a fat seal on the sea ice. If the seal sees or hears him, it will immediately dive into the breathing hole from which it has just emerged. Hunted by generations of resourceful hunters, inshore seals have become very wary. Most Inuit live by the edge of the sea, hunting on the sea ice in winter, and on the tundra and along rivers in summer.

■ ■ ■

A beacon in the winter darkness. In winter a well-built igloo can last for several weeks. The building blocks, of wind-packed snow, are cut with long knives or saws and built up in spiral fashion, tapering in toward the top. The joints are packed with snow to windproof them. Snow is an excellent insulator — two or three people, with blubber lamps and stoves, can raise the temperature inside an igloo to a comfortable 10°C (50°F).

■ ■ ■

An Inuit woman prepares a mukluk *(traditional boot) sole. Mass-produced rubber boots and windproof parkas are available in most stores, but the old skills have not disappeared.* Mukluks *are made of sealskin which has been softened by chewing; tightly sewn, they are almost completely waterproof. Put on warm and damp in the morning, with a lining of moss, they freeze to the shape of the wearer's feet and remain comfortable all day.*

citizens, others Canadian, Greenlandic or Soviet, yet they remain a distinctive people. Groups of them are seeking common cause with kinfolk in other nations, and a few are planning to re-form a pan-Arctic nation of their own.

On the polar fringe live several diverse stocks of sub-Arctic peoples, including the northern 'Indians' of Canada and Alaska, the Aleuts of Alaska, the Sami (formerly called Lapps) of Scandinavia and European Russia, and several stocks of north Siberian natives including Chukchi, Samoyeds and Yakuts, and the Nenet of the northern forests. Quite distinct from

Inuit, these are hunters, trappers and herders, living in forest, on the tundra and by the rivers. Many in the Old World evolved reindeer-based cultures, including hunting and different kinds of herding, which remain valid to the present day. Those of the New World remained hunters and trappers; reindeer, or caribou, herding was unknown in the New World until formally introduced during the early 20th century. Some of these sub-Arctic groups retain their traditional ways of life today, although all have to some degree been affected by changes introduced by settlers from the south, especially during the past few decades.

■ ■ ■

Summer camp for a family of Greenlanders. Many northern Greenlanders have maintained a more traditional lifestyle, from choice as well as economic necessity. Cotton or nylon tents have replaced huts of skins or turf, and food, clothing and utensils are modern, but the age-old necessity of building up reserves for the winter has not changed. The long summer days are spent hunting and fishing on the tundra to lay in stores for the winter.

■ ■ ■

A Sami (Lapp) herder leads his reindeer to new pastures. Throughout Eurasia reindeer are herded for their meat, skins and milk. Most herders travel with their animals on the equivalent of annual migrations, always moving on to new pastures so that the used ones will not be damaged by overgrazing or trampling. Reindeer feed on lichens and grasses which they dig out of the snow.

Iceland is alone in the north in being a separate sovereign state, founded by Norse settlers 1000 years ago. With a Scandinavian style of living based mainly on fisheries, Icelandics claim the world's oldest democracy and longest-running parliament.

Incomers to the Arctic include representatives of all the countries that border on the northlands — Norway, Denmark, Sweden, Finland, the Union of Soviet Socialist Republics, Canada and the United States of America — and many others who have drifted to the far north and found it to their liking. Incomers are not new; a few from the south have always found the Arctic and sub-Arctic congenial. Among the first were trappers, traders, prospectors, missionaries, soldiers and seamen. More recent waves have included police, administrators, lawyers, hospital staff — all the trades and professions needed to run civilized society in the outback.

In the Arctic, man and the environment grew up together. The several varieties of northern mankind who belong there evolved with the region itself through generations of change. There is no equivalent Antarctic man. As human societies spread from the tropics they reached the southern tips of Africa, Australasia and South America, but never, so far as we know, crossed the Southern Ocean. Both Antarctica and its fringing islands evolved without people. In the far south we are always intruders.

■ ■ ■

The human presence in Antarctica is relatively recent. Here a boatload of tourists pays a close-up visit to grounded icebergs off the west coast of the Antarctic Peninsula, one of Antarctica's most accessible and scenic areas. Tourism in Antarctica is a very recent phenomenon, but operating costs remain high and only the affluent can afford the trip. Several thousand tourists now visit Antarctica each year, despite a generally chilly welcome from scientists and administrators.

Antarctica was first seen by man in about 1820 and first lived on by an over-wintering party in 1899. Visitors of any kind were rare before the start of the 20th century, and only during the 1950s were long-term settlements established, although still with short-term occupants.

Until a few years ago the Antarctic population was almost exclusively male; only recently have a few settlements become civilized to the extent of including women. Now babies have been born on Antarctica, innocent supporters of sovereignty claims. But Antarctica remains a continent to whom people hardly belong. Seven nations claim segments of Antarctica, but no-one claims Antarctic nationality, citizenship or even permanent residence. The first to do so will raise interesting points of international law, for Antarctica is a no-man's-land with a unique political regime.

The early Antarctic explorers discovered pristine islands, an empty continent and an ocean completely void of men and their works. First-comers in the 17th and 18th centuries took nothing and left virtually nothing that we have found. The 19th-century sealers who followed took skins by the thousand and oil by the shipload, leaving rotting carcasses, cauldrons or trypots, tumbledown shelters and a few forlorn

■ ■ ■

Umanak, on the West Greenland coast, is now a small but flourishing fishing port, with good summer harbour facilities for deepwater trawlers and small family fishing boats. A fish-processing factory on the quayside gives employment to a small local community. Growlers and bergy bits (small icebergs) from nearby glaciers fill the fjord and harbour from time to time, but fishermen know how to cope with them. As long as the fishing is good, Umanak will remain prosperous.

■ ■ ■

*An old whaling factory,
Stromness Harbour, South
Georgia. Southern Ocean
whaling flourished from
1904 until the mid-1960s.
Harbours on some of the
southern islands were used by
catching vessels and factory
ships, and a few processing
factories were built ashore.
The last of these ceased
operations in 1965. Now all
are derelict, monuments to
an industry that once
employed thousands of people
and annually slaughtered
tens of thousands
of whales.*

graveyards. Their main legacy, an unfortunate one, was a menagerie of rabbits, mice, rats, cats, pigs, goats, and even cattle on the southern islands. These animals were introduced either purposely as food or accidentally with stores. Many have prospered and spread, so that hardly a Southern Ocean island remains with its natural ecology intact.

Explorers of the early 20th century, mostly on mainland Antarctica, left a handful of huts, cairns and depots. The few artifacts remaining from these famous expeditions are now cherished, some as protected archaeological sites. Whalers in the same period, mostly ship-borne, took millions of whales but left only a few island factories, now derelict. Scientists and their supporters who invaded the continent from the mid-century onward have left many huts and stations, and a litter of rubbish that only now, somewhat sheepishly, their successors are trying to tidy up.

A special kind of nostalgia hangs over places where people have striven and moved on. Both polar regions have a fair share of remote huts, graves, timbers strewn from long-lost ships, century-old cairns, spoons and buttons from half-forgotten expeditions. This nostalgia, extending even to derelict whaling stations in the south and military bases in the north, enhances the polar scene for many who work there, and for many more who visit as tourists. When scenery and reality pall, history and imagination come into their own. Truly, there is something for everyone in polar regions.

2

Polar Cold

One thing known to everyone about the polar regions is that they are cold; together with the tops of a few high mountains, they are the coldest places on earth. Although not strictly true, this in itself worries no one. The world we were brought up in is capped with ice, and we expect polar regions to be cold. But the ice caps are generating worries on a large scale. Soothsayers of modern times warn us constantly that the polar regions are changing, and that polar cold, for one reason or another, has started to behave strangely.

Some scientists are certain that the poles are warming up. Others are no less sure that they are getting colder, or at least that their cold is spreading. If polar regions warm up considerably, they say, the ice caps will melt and we shall all be flooded. If polar regions get colder, weather patterns will change for the worse; the ice caps will spread, and those of us currently living in temperate regions will be frozen out of existence. Flooded or frozen, we can take our choice: one way or another the ice caps are going to change the world we live in.

Some professionals in the worrying game go further: they warn that the destabilization of the poles is due to human activities, in particular to the way in which we have filled the upper atmosphere with carbon dioxide and other gases by burning fossil fuels. What everyone calls 'the greenhouse effect' — enhanced atmospheric warming — the hard-line worriers blame squarely on mankind. The warming, or cooling, or the spreading of cold, is all our fault. Our massive release of fossil energy over two centuries will trigger off one or other of these processes, and may even do so in our lifetimes. A few add tartly that it is just repayment for our greed and irresponsibility in trying to make ourselves comfortable on earth.

Several issues lie scrambled together in these arguments, ranging from good science to questionable near-theology. If we first discover why the polar regions are cold, why they have ice caps and how their cold varies, we shall be better equipped to unscramble them.

WHY POLAR COLD?

Polar cold is legendary and, like many legends, open to doubt and misinterpretation. There is no question that the polar regions on the whole are colder than the rest of the world; or that they include some places that, year-round, are the coldest on earth — dangerously cold places, where anyone in the open is constantly at risk. However, polar regions are huge areas with seasonal ranges and a wide variety of climates, some severe, others tolerable. They do not have a monopoly of cold; non-polar mountain tops and some mid-continental lowlands have very low temperatures indeed in winter.

Why are the poles cold? The earth's surface, both land and ocean, and the atmosphere above it, are warmed almost entirely by the sun. The amount of energy released by the sun varies within narrow limits, giving Earth a mean year-round surface temperature of about 15°C (59°F). The planets that circle closer to the sun (Venus, Mercury) are warmer, and those farther away (Mars, Jupiter and the rest of the family) are cooler. Only Earth is in just the right temperature zone for life to be possible over much of its surface.

Because Earth is a sphere, polar regions receive less heat than tropical regions. There are several reasons for this. One is immediately obvious to anyone who travels to a polar region; the sun, even on midsummer's day, never rises high above the horizon. We are used to the idea that, in any latitude, low sun in early morning and evening is less warming than high sun at midday. For the same reason the polar sun, always low in the sky, is never really hot. Polar sunshine can be strong enough to warm rocks, melt snow and encourage judicious sunbathing; it contains enough ultraviolet radiation to cause sun-tanning, serious sunburn and snow-blindness, but it cannot bring lasting warmth to polar areas.

Second, while the rest of the world receives solar energy virtually every day of the year, polar regions lose the sun for part of the year. Like temperate regions they have summers of long days followed by winters of long nights, but as one approaches the poles, the longer both of these become. At the poles themselves seasons and days merge, summer days six months long alternating with six-month winter nights. Some solar heat is absorbed during the long summer days, but a great deal more is lost during the sunless winter nights.

The third reason, currently very important, is that the ends of the earth wear year-round ice caps. As satellite images show us, their snow and ice surfaces are predominantly white. Instead of absorbing the

HOW IS EARTH WARMED?

Although our planet's molten interior is very hot, little of its heat normally escapes to warm the surface; when it does we notice it as volcanoes, warm springs and other local hot spots. Practically all of Earth's surface heat comes from the sun, which is effectively a nuclear reactor in space. The sun's short-wave radiant energy passes through space and impinges on the planet and atmosphere. A small amount of energy is held in the atmosphere, warming it slightly. A great deal more passes through to Earth's surface. Here some of it is reflected back immediately, giving our planet its bright and cheerful look; the rest is absorbed at the surface, where it is converted to heat.

In retaining some of the sun's energy the atmosphere filters out some wavelengths that would be harmful to life. The atmosphere also acts as a greenhouse or protective blanket, helping to keep in much of the heat generated at Earth's surface that would otherwise escape. Some of this heat warms the atmosphere locally. Both atmosphere and oceans are fluids in constant circulation, carrying heat from one part of the world to another. Much heat is carried toward the poles by winds and ocean currents, with a general effect of temperature levelling. Because of these circulations, the poles are warmer and the tropics cooler than they would otherwise be.

The present level of solar energy output, the fact that the sun is 149 million km (93 million miles) away, and the current composition of Earth's atmosphere combine to give a mean year-round surface temperature of about 15°C (59°F) over Earth as a whole. If the sun's output of radiant energy decreased, if Earth's orbit were wider or its atmosphere a less effective greenhouse, the mean surface temperature would be lower. If solar output increased, Earth's orbit narrowed or the greenhouse effect were enhanced, the mean surface temperature would rise. All these factors have a habit of varying slightly from time to time, enough to account for small variations in climate, and possibly for some major variations. Human activity — the release of gases and combustion particles into the atmosphere — may be altering the greenhouse function of the atmosphere, but it is not entirely clear in which direction the alteration is occurring, i.e. whether it is reducing or enhancing the greenhouse effect.

Noon on an early winter's day, West Greenland. The sun has not risen, but there is enough day-glow to light the fjord entrance and the ships at their moorings. The sea is already covered by a slick of ice and will soon be frozen over for the winter.

■ ■ ■

Midsummer sunshine,
Disko Bay, West Greenland.
Disko Bay, in 69°N off the
West Greenland coast, was
known to Davis Strait whalers
and sealers as a summer
shelter and safe anchorage.
Now it provides a safe haven
for fishing boats. In winter
these waters are ice-covered,
their bergs held fast by
pack ice.

incoming solar energy and converting it to heat, like huge mirrors they reflect most of it back into space. In this way even the meagre warming effect of the polar sun is lost.

One more factor is important. Both the atmosphere and the oceans that cover some 70 per cent of Earth's surface are fluid, and in constant circulation. Both carry heat from one part of the world to another. Much heat in various forms is brought toward the poles by winds and ocean currents, with a general effect of temperature levelling. Because of these circulations, the poles are warmer and the tropics cooler than they would otherwise be. When poleward circulations are strong, polar regions are warmed; when the circulations weaken or are impeded, the poles tend to get colder.

At present, tropical regions bask in mean annual temperatures of 20°C (68°F) or more, while polar regions have annual means near freezing point or below. If the ice caps were absent, mean temperatures both of Earth's surface as a whole and of the tropics in particular would be marginally higher. However, the polar regions would be much warmer, because solar energy would be absorbed locally rather than reflected away. Temperate regions too would be warmer, because they would lose less heat to neighbouring polar regions. The conclusion is that if there were no ice caps, there would normally be no reason for them to form. So why are the polar regions currently cold enough to be ice-capped, and what made the caps form in the first place?

These are questions that nobody would have bothered to ask a few generations ago; the ice caps existed and there did not seem to be any alternative. Now they are very important questions, particularly if the ice caps are in a state of flux, seemingly undecided whether to grow or disappear. What causes ice ages, and what controls them? We need to know, in case we have to try to exercise control over our own ice age.

■ ■ ■

Strange optical effects occur over sea ice at very low temperatures. Here an Inuit hunter, with his dog team, is seen against a mirage that has formed over new sea ice. Behind him, vapour rises from open water and freezes in the cold air, forming 'sea smoke'.

■ ■ ■ MILANKOVITCH CYCLES ■ ■ ■ ■

Earth's orbit around the sun varies in shape from almost circular to elliptical, in a cycle taking 100,000 years. When it is near-circular, Earth's orbit remains almost equidistant from the sun; when the orbit is elliptical, in the course of the year Earth travels farthest from the sun and also comes nearest to it. The angle between Earth's axis of rotation and the ecliptic varies 3°, from 21.5° to 24.5°, in a cycle of just over 40,000 years. When the tilt is greatest, seasonality (the difference between summer and winter) is strongest.

Finally, Earth nods and wobbles on its axis in a cycle of 22,000 years, bringing one or other pole closer to the sun. These three variables, in different combinations, affect very considerably the amount of energy reaching the polar regions at different times. All of these variables can be expressed mathematically (this was the major work of Milutin Milankovitch, a Serbian astronomer) and related to changes during our present ice age. Some scientists feel that they provide a full explanation, to which very little else needs to be added.

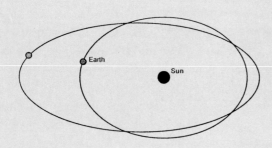

Changes in length of earth's orbital ellipse: 100,000 years

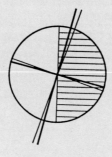

Axis tilt (21.5° – 24.5°): 41,000 year cycle

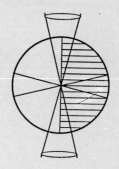

Axis rotation: 22,000 year cycle

ICE AGES

Since the early 19th century, when we first realized that we live in an ice age, it has become apparent that ice ages and ice caps are unusual in world history — mere eye-blinks in a 4.5-billion-year story. Fossils in the geological record assure us that, through most of its existence, Earth has managed without ice caps. During the long capless periods warm-temperate forests have grown beyond the polar circles and warm-temperate seas extended probably as far as the poles themselves.

Our own ice age started 20 to 30 million years ago (some say longer — it depends on one's starting point) and began to intensify three to four million years ago. The ice age before our present one ended over 250 million years ago, so the world had plenty of time in between to warm through.

Ice ages leave unmistakable traces, including moraines and striations (deep scratches) on rocks that were present on the surface at the time. Fossils can also indicate whether polar conditions prevailed at the time they were formed. The last ice age, occurring in Permo-Carboniferous times, seems to have been as extensive as the current one, lasting at least as long. The poles then were in different places relative to the continents, and the ice caps formed over different parts of the world, one of them on an Afro-Indian continent involving what is now part of the Sahara Desert.

THE ICE-AGE CONCEPT

When did we first realize we were living in an ice age? Late 18th-century and early 19th-century discoveries of fossil reptiles and mammals, similar to contemporary ones but in different climatic zones, caused geologists and philosophers to think hard about climatic changes. At the same time, many who lived or worked in alpine or northern regions were uncovering evidence of past glaciations — striations on rocks, erratic boulders far from their parent rocks, ancient moraines similar in form to those made by current glaciers. That major changes had occurred in the world was not denied — the Bible told of a flood, and for as long as possible Noah's flood was made to account for every new discovery. The Swiss scientist Louis Agassiz (later Professor of Zoology at Harvard University) was among the first to marshal arguments that demoted the flood and gave full credit to ice as a geological agent.

In July 1837 Agassiz announced his ideas to a learned society in Neuchâtel, using then or slightly later the term Eiszeit, or ice age (an invention of Karl Schimper, a botanical colleague) to describe the relatively recent period in which ice sheets had spread across Europe. Deeply entrenched opposition developed in Europe and America; it took over 20 years for the ice-age concept to receive full acceptance, and to initiate the whole new field of periglacial studies.

Ice ages occur from time to time because we are in a position of delicate balance relative to the sun and its energy. If the sun's output of radiation were stronger, or if Earth's orbit took us closer to the sun, or perhaps if the atmosphere were marginally more efficient as a greenhouse, the world would always be warmer and there would never be ice ages. If the sun were weaker or further away, or the atmosphere less efficient, Earth would be permanently ice-capped. We are in just the right position, relative to the sun, to be without polar ice for much of the time, but to experience an occasional flip that brings it about. What causes the flip? We do not know, but there are several possible reasons.

Our current ice age began with a long period of slow cooling; some palaeo-glaciologists trace its origins back to as long as 65 million years ago. At that time big changes were occurring in the distribution of continents about Earth's surface, and in the circulation of the oceans. Antarctica, formerly part of the supercontinent of Gondwana, had recently detached itself from Australia. Then a perfectly normal continent of mountains and plains, forests and grasslands (it may even have carried a complement of parrots and ancestral koalas and kangaroos as well), it was drifting slowly southward from temperate latitudes toward its present polar position.

Simultaneously, due to lateral pressures, Antarctica was undergoing a spell of mountain-building. The resulting high land would have been cold

■ ■ ■

*Dog teams returning from a
polar bear hunt. In early and
late winter there is still enough
light for travelling, even
though the sun does not put
in an appearance. Clear skies
often bring intense cold —
earth and sea receive no daily
input of energy, but continue
to radiate their stored heat to
an open sky. Overall, the polar
regions have an annual heat
deficit. Their budgets are
balanced by warm air and
currents flowing in from
temperate regions.*

enough for snow to settle and become permanent, and for glaciers to form. By 15-20 million years ago Antarctica was isolated in a steadily-widening Southern Ocean, and had developed substantial ice sheets. These spread across the continent, giving rise to glaciers that burst through mountain barriers to reach the sea. Thus, in the southern hemisphere, the first polar mirror was formed .

Once the Antarctic had acquired its mirror, the region would lose heat. Circulation in the atmosphere and the ocean would spread the loss around, and the world as a whole would chill. This could have been enough to start the northern glaciation, leading to further reflection and losses of incoming energy. By two to three million years ago, when Antarctica was largely ice-covered, highlands in Alaska, Greenland and Eurasia were in their turn developing glaciers. During the last two million years ice sheets spread widely over lowland areas of the north. Thus, in the north, the second polar mirror was formed .

GLACIAL CHANGES

Having covered the whole southern continent, the ice sheets of Antarctica had little opportunity to vary. The ice could thicken slightly, or retreat. Parts of the ice cap may have disappeared altogether during warmer spells, to re-form later. Any ice that spread far beyond the continental shore would break away to form tabular bergs, as it does today.

By contrast the separate ice caps on southern Patagonia, New Zealand and some of the Southern Ocean islands fluctuated, and so did the ice sheets of the northern hemisphere. The edges of the northern sheets have advanced and retreated at least four times, possibly more, during the last million years. Advances are the mark of 'glacial periods', retreats indicate 'interglacials', although neither is as clear-cut as it sounds. In fact the ice sheets dither, advancing in bursts (called 'stadials') and retreating ('interstadials') several times during each glacial period.

At their maximum the northern sheets spread over Britain as far south as the Severn and Thames estuaries, and across Scandinavia, much of northern Europe, and North America as far as the Great Lakes and New York. In addition, large areas of ocean were vested with both perennial and seasonal pack ice, at times much more so than at present. Ice at the glacial maximum covered some 30 per cent of the earth's surface. Today it covers only about 11 per cent. Continental Antarctica still has 98 per cent coverage, and there are perennial fields of pack ice on both polar oceans. Most of the ice has gone from the Arctic; now there is extensive land ice only on Greenland, Svalbard and a few islands washed by the Arctic Ocean.

We would be wrong to assume that the ice is still in retreat, and that the wasting will continue. The ice sheets are still dithering. Earth is clearly in an interglacial period, but there have been previous interglacials and interstadials just as warm as the present one, and some even warmer, followed by colder spells and the return and spread of the ice. Dithering indicates that the controlling factors are finely balanced, with few feedback mechanisms to stabilize them. Ice sheets can develop quickly when conditions become right for them to do so; it is thought that only a slight drop in mean summer temperature, possibly as little as 2–3°C (4–5°F) would allow seasonal snow fields to persist year-round and develop into ice sheets. Similarly, only a slight rise in mean temperature may be needed for whole areas of continental ice to disperse.

The ice that retreated over much of the northern hemisphere has never entirely left us. It could easily spread again over northern Britain, Eurasia and North America, and we have every reason to believe that one day it will. It could return, as it left, unaided by man. Alternatively, and again without our intervention, it could disappear altogether. Our impact on Earth and its atmosphere, especially our release of 'greenhouse' gases, may be enough to influence the ice, perhaps to trigger early a natural control, perhaps to counteract natural forces. That is one of many things we still have to find out, if possible unbiased by questions of responsibility and guilt.

GLOBAL CHANGES

What causes global fluctuations in temperature? Again we do not know, but can point to several possibilities. The distance of Earth from the sun varies, and so do the angle of earth's axis to the ecliptic and the sun's output of energy, all within narrow limits. The atmosphere changes most of all, from time to time filling with dust, smoke particles or gases from volcanoes that over periods of several years affect both its transparency and its blanketing or greenhouse properties.

But that is not all that is changing. Earth itself continues to evolve; sea floors are still spreading, the continents continue to shift in relation to each other. Some land masses (for example Scandinavia) are still rising, having recently lost a vast overburden of ice. Others (like Britain) are tilting, and others again may still be sinking under the weight of ice they carry. Ocean currents run weaker or stronger, water masses shift their boundaries, climates change as we watch. What ever gave us the idea that nature is static? None of these changes became apparent until we had the wit, the will and the means to take detailed measurements. Now we realize that practically everything we measure in nature has a component of change within it, and that needs careful monitoring too.

Polar ice is certainly changing, and has always done so. Ice caps and glaciers the world over are dynamic, constantly being added to, constantly losing ice by melting, ablation (evaporation) and calving. If they seem changeless, it is because they are roughly in balance. Antarctica is estimated to gain about

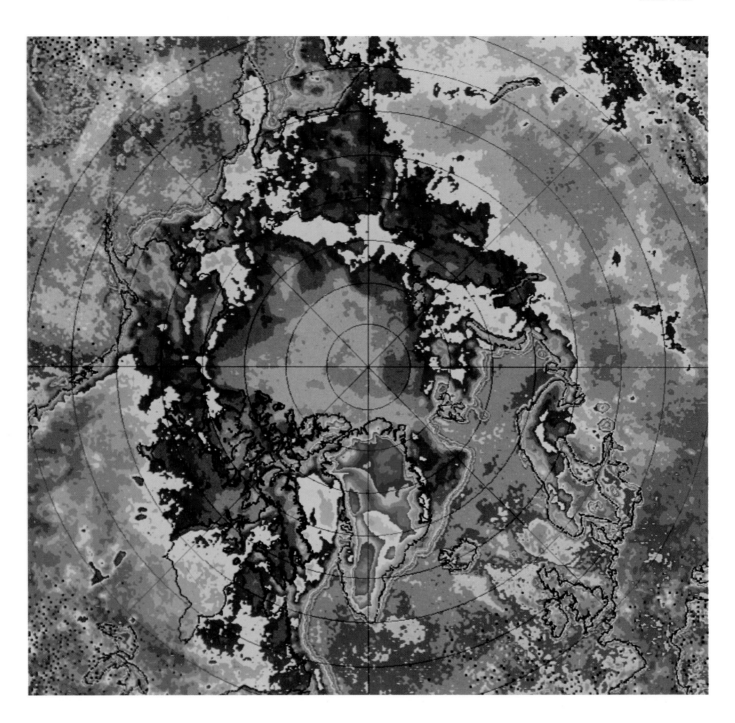

■ ■ ■

Satellite views of the Arctic region in winter (above) and summer (right). These are false colour images compiled from satellites that look through cloud at the Earth's surface. The different colours cannot be interpreted directly as ground or sea temperatures, but the colour masses show the extent of particular temperature related features.

First find the outline of the land masses, then look at the extent of the pack ice in summer and winter. The Greenland ice cap shows up well in both pictures, as does the extent of open water at the northern end of Baffin Bay.

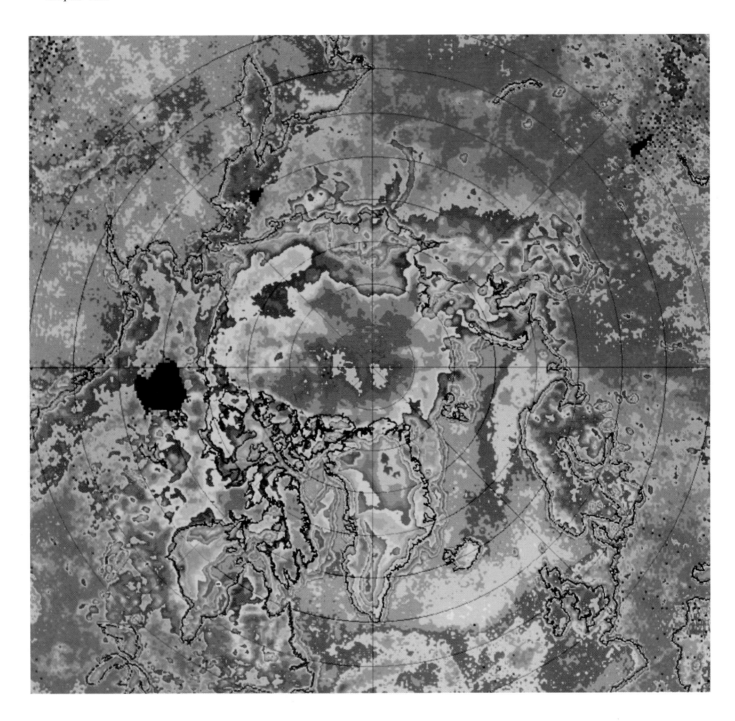

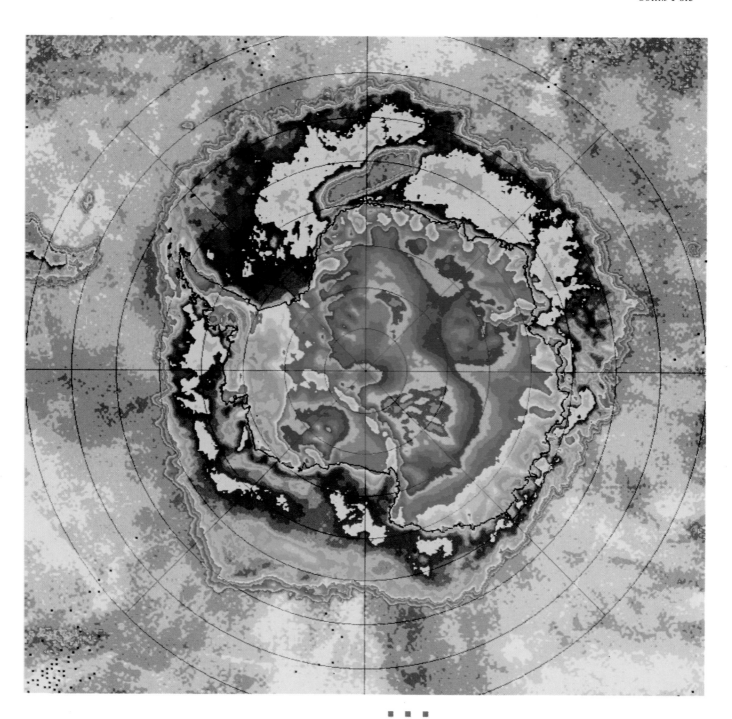

▪ ▪ ▪

These two satellite views show the Antarctic in winter (above) and summer (right). The winter picture shows the extreme cold of the polar ice cap, though the pole itself is not the coldest place. The wide extent of the winter pack ice can be seen, more than doubling the total reflective surface of the region.

In the summer picture, the polar ice cap is still the coldest area. The Weddell Sea remains full of pack ice. By contrast the Ross Sea is almost clear of ice as far south as McMurdo Sound. Huge areas of sea ice persist off the Pacific coast, making approaches by sea extremely difficult.

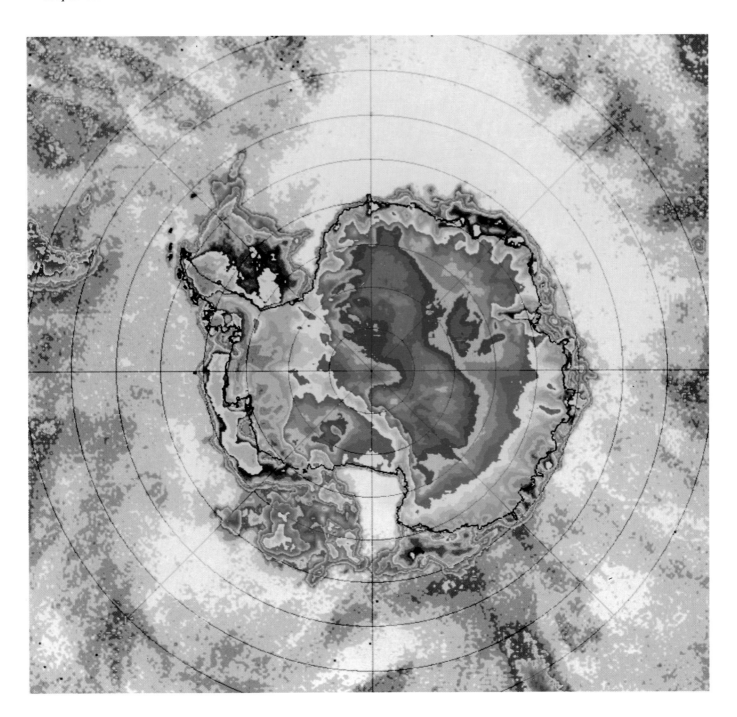

2000 km³ (480 cu miles) of new ice each year, a tiny proportion of its total bulk of 30 million km³ (7.2 million cu miles); currently we believe it to be shedding about the same amount, possibly just a little more. Much of the exchange occurs close to the coast, for that is where most of the new snow falls; turnover inland is very much slower. Greenland has heavier snowfalls and a quicker turnover. Satellite measurements suggest that the Greenland ice sheet is increasing in bulk, possibly by as much as a metre (3.25 ft) every four years.

Similarly the thickness and area of pack ice at the ends of the earth vary from year to year, in ways we do not yet understand. Helped by new technology — in this case nuclear submarines and satellite images — oceanographers have only recently found accurate ways of monitoring the changes.

Geophysicists and glaciologists all over the world are currently working on these problems, trying to discover how ice ages come about, how the ice caps have varied during their history, and the causes underlying the variations. From their work, one point has emerged clearly. The whole system they are trying to understand is dynamic, with natural changes occurring all the time. Measurements are necessary, but long-term measurements are essential, so that they can estimate the rates of change of all the processes involved.

■ ■ ■

An icebreaker tests the thickness of sea ice. At both ends of the world sea ice begins to form in autumn and thickens during the winter. In spring most of it melts, but in some areas it becomes trapped — as in the central Arctic Ocean and the Weddell Sea. Long-term changes in the thickness and density of accumulations of ice are now being monitored as an indication of possible global temperature changes.

■   ■   ■   SOME POLAR WORRIES   ■   ■   ■

Is the climate warming? Almost certainly climates in temperate regions have warmed slightly since the start of the 20th century, but this is what we have come to expect; temperate climates are anything but stable. In the last 7000 years we have passed from the so-called 'climatic optimum', when mean temperatures were 2°C (4°F) higher than today, through several cycles to the 'little ice age' of AD, 1400–1700 when they were almost 2°C (4°F) lower. Between 1880 and 1940 there was an overall rise in the northern hemisphere of about 1°C (2°F), and between then and 1970 a similar fall. The present rate of increase does not seem to be greater than in the historic past, but now for the first time we can monitor the changes accurately, and perhaps discover the cause. They may involve a new factor, for example some man-induced changes in the greenhouse effect, but again they may not. The link has yet to be established.

Are the ice caps melting? Certainly they are; they melt and are being renewed all the time. That is how ice caps work.

Are they melting faster than they are being renewed? In parts yes, in parts no. Greenland's icecap is half the size of Europe, Antarctica's ten times as big, and different parts behave differently from time to time.

Is sea level rising? At present yes, possibly by about 2–3 mm (1/10 inch) per year, or 20–30 cm (8–12 inches) per century. In some places the land may be rising or sinking faster independently of the sea. When air temperatures rise, sea surface temperatures rise too, surface waters expand, and sea level rises.

Is the current rise in sea level the start of a more rapid rise? There is currently no evidence that it is, but if human activities are enhancing the greenhouse effect, and no other factors intervene, it could be. It would be worth considering the implications of a rise of two or three times the current rate, i.e. up to 1m (3.25 ft) per century.

Does warming lead to ice-cap melting? Not necessarily; we cannot infer one from the other. When air temperatures rise, so do sea temperatures. With more water vapour in the air, more rain and snow fall, and the ice caps are likely to increase rather than decrease. That may explain what is currently happening in Greenland. If the temperature rise continues, the surface of the ice caps will soak up much seasonal melt before the ice as a whole starts running away to sea.

Will ice spread across the Arctic again? Almost certainly, if the ice age continues as it seems likely to. There have been four major advances at least, and many minor ones; we would be short-sighted not to expect another, although on current form this is unlikely to happen for thousands of years.

Will the ice caps disappear altogether? Very certainly, but that will take an even longer time.

A glacier descending from Greenland's northern ice cap. Glaciers vary from year to year, advancing, receding, and varying in thickness according to rates of accumulation and dispersal. Glaciologists monitor these changes and try to relate them to climatic trends. Ice caps, made up of many hundreds of annual layers of ice, are an excellent record of past temperature and atmospheric changes.

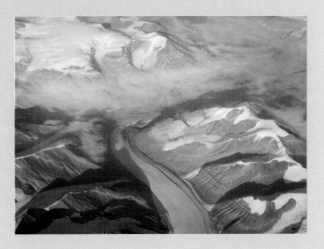

ICE CAPS IN THE FUTURE

We human beings are children of the ice age; we evolved on an ice-capped Earth, and have never yet known our planet without polar ice. If we continue as a species, this is something that our descendants will certainly experience. How long will the current ice age last? We cannot say, but would be very intereseted to find out, for a world without ice caps will be a very different place to live in.

An ice-free world could be quite agreeable for man, a warmth-loving species. With temperate climates extending far toward the poles we would expect to see deciduous forests flourishing again along the Arctic coast, where now there is only tundra and polar desert. There would be new Arctic ports, and exchanges of goods and ideas across a polar Mediterranean. In the south we would have a whole new continent to exploit. There would be minerals of all kinds for the taking. We might even find ourselves farming within a few hundred kilometres of the South Pole itself.

The transition to this happy state will tax our ingenuity, but will not necessarily be catastrophic. As the worriers are constantly reminding us, loss of the ice caps will cause sea levels to rise, and many of our coastal cities will disappear, together with thousands of low-lying islands and huge areas of coastal plains. Some writers, including scientists who should know better, are suggesting that all this will happen in a very short time, at so catastrophic a rate that we shall have great difficulty in coping. This comes close to intellectual bullying. There is at present plenty of evidence that changes are happening, but none to indicate changes more rapid than ones we are used to, and well able to take in our stride.

POLAR CLIMATES

Travellers in polar regions traditionally return with tales of extreme cold, winds, snowfall and blizzard. In Britain these stories go down well; the British climate, a fairly benign mixture of predominantly maritime influences, gives cause for grumbling but seldom for heroics. In North America and other continental regions polar stories had better be good, for they meet more critical audiences. Climatic hardships are far more commonplace. Extreme cold, winds, snowfall and blizzards are everyday occurrences in winter, sometimes fully comparable with the worst that polar regions provide. American expeditions that

Ice on the superstructure of the British Antarctic Survey's research ship RRS Bransfield. *Heavy icing of this kind is always a hazard. A particularly heavy build-up of ice can disable and even capsize a small ship.*

arrive in Antarctica and radio back news of subzero summer temperatures are simply not impressive — it is likely to be colder in New York, and far, far colder in Chicago, Illinois, or Sheridan, Wyoming. In the prairie towns of Canada, children wait for their school buses in temperatures similar to those that defeated Scott on his return from the South Pole.

Climatologists provide their own boundary for polar regions, the 10°C (50°F) summer isotherms. These are useful lines, telling us that at any point on their poleward side mean air temperature of the warmest month remains below 10°C (50°F). Like the polar circles they provide a means of comparison, but in this case the areas enclosed are vastly different. The climatic Arctic so defined covers about 37 million km²

(14.45 million sq miles), slightly less than the polar circle Arctic. The climatic Antarctic covers some 70 million km² (27.34 million sq miles), or nearly twice the area within the polar circle.

With polar regions as large as this, it is misleading to think in terms of a single polar climate. They have not one kind of climate, nor even one each, but a whole range of climates from mild to very severe. Greenland alone ranges from damp and mild in the southwest to very cold and dry in the far north; this is not surprising, for it spans almost 24° of latitude, roughly three times the length of Britain.

Perhaps more surprisingly, stations on the Antarctic plateau vary considerably in climate, depending mainly on their altitude. At Byrd, West

Antarctica (1530 m/5,020 ft), mean summer temperatures in December and January are 13°C (23°F) higher than at Amundsen-Scott (South Pole, 2835 m/9,301 ft) and nearly 18°C (32°F) higher than at Vostok, East Antarctica (3488 m/11,444 ft). They are all cold, but the range is comparable to differences in mean summer temperatures between London, Algiers and central Morocco. Even Antarctic coastal stations show a surprisingly wide range. Winter mean temperatures at Scott Base, McMurdo Sound, and at Mawson, on a milder shore, differ by 16°C (29°F). This is as much as the difference in winter means between northern Norway and Athens.

Latitude is a very approximate guide to temperature in Antarctica. In general, winter and summer

WHERE ARE THE COLDEST REGIONS?

Winter and summer alike, Antarctica is the coldest place on earth. At the South Pole, 2835 m (9,301 ft) above sea level, the mean temperature of the warmest month (December) is -27.7°C (-18.5°F), and of the coldest month (July) -59.9°C (-76°F). This is not the coldest point. A much colder place on the ice cap is Vostok, a permanent Soviet station at 3488 m (11,444 ft): in December the temperature rises to -32.3°C (-27°F), and in August it drops to -68.3°C (-91.5°F). Lowest mean temperatures of all were recorded at Plateau, a US short-term station (now closed) at 3625 m (11,893 ft): here the December temperature is also -32.3°C (-27°F), but the August temperature is -71.4°C (-96.5°F). The high dome of the polar plateau, at over 4000 m (13,000 ft), would be even colder, but nobody has so far built a station there. At Vostok every year in late August the temperature falls below -80°C (-110°F). The meteorologists know when to expect the year's lowest temperatures, and celebrate accordingly. The record low, -88.3°C (-127°F), was read on 24 August 1960.

The Arctic has nothing to compare with these figures. We do not know mean monthly temperatures at the North Pole because there is no station there, but they are likely to be around freezing point in summer and -30°C (-23°F) in winter. The high ridge of Greenland's ice sheet has winter means down to -45°C (-49°F) and summer means of -12°C (-10°F). Lowest winter temperatures in the northern hemisphere occur not in the polar basin but on the continents of North America and Siberia. Coldest in Arctic Canada is Eureka, on Ellesmere Island, with a March mean of -37.6°C (-36°F). Oymakon, in eastern Siberia, has a much lower January mean of -47.2°C (-53°F). Verkhoyansk, a Siberian town on the Yana River, has a slightly higher mid-winter mean of 46.8°C (-52°F), but holds the northern hemisphere extreme cold record of -67.8°C (-90°F). Northern summers are considerably warmer: the midsummer mean in Eureka rises to 5.7°C (42.5°F) and in the Siberian settlements to around 15°C (59°F), comparable with midsummer in Nova Scotia.

■ ■ ■

Deceptive sunshine and blue sky at Vostok, the Soviet Union's permanent research station on the South Polar Plateau. A scattered group of huts half buried in snow and ice, Vostok holds the record for the lowest surface temperatures ever recorded . These occur in late winter, and meteorologists usually know to within a day or two when to expect them. If anyone were to record late winter temperatures at the highest point of the Antarctic ice cap a few hundred kilometres away, they would probably be even lower.

alike, the further south you go the colder it gets. There are several exceptions. On the polar plateau altitude becomes an important factor, and along the coast the presence or absence of sea ice becomes critical. This explains a strange anomaly around the Antarctic Peninsula, where the east side, latitude for latitude, is several degrees colder than the west. Permanent pack ice in the Weddell Sea is mostly to blame.

In the Arctic, cold and warm currents upset the pattern, but winter and summer patterns are quite different. In summer the coldest areas are the pack ice of the ocean basin and the high ridge of the Greenland ice cap. Coldest in winter are the Canadian archipelago and eastern Siberia, the latter coldest of all, with temperatures dipping below -40°C (-41°F).

CLIMATES AND WEATHER SYSTEMS

Weather in the polar regions, as elsewhere, is determined by movements of air masses. These control temperature, wind and moisture, including precipitation. In both polar regions the predominantly cold air sinks centrally, forming stable, dry anticyclonic systems that dominate the coldest areas. Cyclones or depressions containing warm, moist air prowl constantly around the edges, usually in procession from west to east at a rate of 600–1000 km (350–600 miles) per day, bringing winds, precipitation and sudden temperature changes. Weather satellites spot them readily, making weather prediction easier than before, and showing their patterns of movement.

In the north they rarely penetrate the coldest areas of central Canada and Siberia. Instead they swing from the north Pacific over northeastern Asia and Alaska, and from the North Atlantic to Baffin Bay, Greenland and the Norwegian Sea. To these areas they bring relatively mild winters with heavy

■　■　■　LATITUDE AND TEMPERATURE　■　■　■

Latitude is generally a poor guide to temperature in polar regions, although better in the south than the north. Annual isotherms in the Antarctic make a circumpolar zonal pattern, matching the tent-like symmetry of the continent itself. In the north the zonal pattern is disturbed: isotherms are pushed far out of symmetry north or south, mainly by warm or cold sea currents. The North Atlantic Drift, for example, carries heat far into the polar basin, and cold currents flow south along eastern Greenland and Labrador. This provides very different climates along any latitude.

The six settlements listed below all stand close to sea level within a degree or two of 60°N. But their mean monthly and annual air temperatures alone indicate that they have a wide variety of climates. The difference of over 29°C (52°F) in winter means between Bergen, Norway, and Churchill, Canada, is greater than the winter difference between Bergen and Acapulco, Mexico.

Temperatures (°C) at six Arctic stations close to 60°N

	January	April	July	October	Year
Bergen (Norway)	1.5	5.8	15.0	8.3	7.8
Helsinki (Finland)	-5.9	2.7	17.1	5.4	4.6
Okhotsk (USSR)	-22.4	-5.4	11.9	-2.1	-4.6
Anchorage (Alaska)	-10.9	2.1	13.9	-1.7	1.8
Churchill (Canada)	-27.6	-10.1	12.2	-1.4	-7.0
Prins Christian Sund (Greenland)	-4.4	-0.5	7.0	2.4	1.2

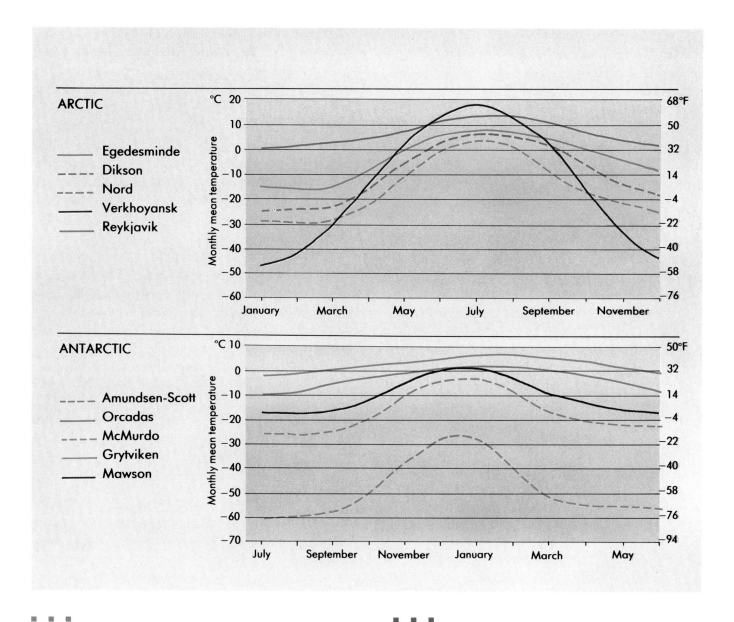

ARCTIC

— Egedesminde
--- Dikson
--- Nord
— Verkhoyansk
— Reykjavik

ANTARCTIC

--- Amundsen-Scott
— Orcadas
--- McMurdo
— Grytviken
— Mawson

▪ ▪ ▪

The Arctic graph (top) shows mean monthly temperatures at five Arctic stations. Reykjavik in Iceland has the most equable year-round temperatures, thanks to the North Atlantic Drift, or Gulf Stream. Egedesminde on the west coast of Greenland, Dikson in western Siberia, and Nord in northern Greenland are all cold in winter because the neighbouring sea is ice-covered. Verkhoyansk in northeastern Siberia has a continental climate of bitterly cold winters and cool summers.

▪ ▪ ▪

The Antarctic graph (below) compares mean monthly temperatures at five Antarctic stations. Grytviken on South Georgia has mild, ice-free winters and cool summers, controlled year-round by sea temperature. Orcadas on the South Orkneys, Mawson on the coast of Antarctica itself, and McMurdo, also on the Antarctic coast but 10° further south, all have very cold winters due to the presence of sea ice; even their summer temperatures are close to freezing point. Amundsen-Scott at the South Pole, 2835 m (9,301 ft) above sea level, is the coldest place of all, all year round.

fall, hence the active glaciers and persistent ice caps of Alaska, Greenland, Svalbard and Scandinavia. Few get up to high latitudes, hence the relative dryness of north Greenland, Siberia and Canada.

In the south they follow in gloomy procession over the islands of the Southern Ocean, piling snow onto the ice caps of Bouvetøya, South Georgia, Heard Island and Iles Kerguelen, and packing it down with strong, persistent westerly winds. Many swing south to the Antarctic coast, providing heavy winter snowfall over the western flank of the Antarctic Peninsula, along Dronning Maud, Enderby and Mac-Robertson Lands, and in other favoured spots. In summer they provide sleet or rain.

So heavy and regular is their snowfall that the resulting ice overruns the coast, creating ice shelves that extend far out to sea. Scientific stations built in these areas have to be renewed every few years, or built on jacks that lift them above snow level, otherwise they disappear and their inhabitants become troglodytes, reaching the surface only through everextending shafts. Also, unless they are specially designed, the weight of overlying snow caves in the roof and makes them unsafe.

■ ■ ■

Arctic tundra in summer. Ponds form as the snow melts, but drainage is poor because the subsoil remains frozen. Many areas of tundra are boggy, with aquatic plants in the hollows and dry-ground plants on the mounds and slopes between them. Most plants form flattish cushions, their low profile ensuring protection from the snow in winter and quick warming when the spring thaw comes.

Other parts of the coast, away from the depression tracks, are relatively snow-free. These are the few areas of Antarctica, totalling only about 2 per cent of the continent, where ice does not accumulate and bare rock appears in summer. 'Oasis' areas of extensive bare rock are found at several points around the coast, occurring where precipitation is minimal. Often they mark areas where former glaciers or ice sheets have disappeared for want of snow. Sadly misnamed, they are usually dry deserts. Few depressions penetrate far inland; heavy snow is rare on the south polar plateau.

Winds tend to blow strongly in the polar regions, mainly because there is little to stop them. Gales following a snowstorm lift the new snow and whirl it about, creating the 'blizzard' conditions that travellers dread. Cold blown snow has the erosive power of sand; it penetrates tents, clothing, ears, eyes, engine cowlings and boxes of stores, making travel difficult or impossible. Some of the strongest polar winds are katabatic or downslope winds blowing off icecaps. Those experienced by Australian explorer Douglas Mawson at Commonwealth Bay, Antarctica, beat all world records for ferocity and relentlessness.

■ ■ ■

Polar bears forage for thin pickings in the early spring sunshine. The tundra is still frozen, yielding little more than a few roots and berries and perhaps the odd carcass. Polar bears are well adapted to the huge differences between summer plenty and winter dearth. In winter and spring they live on fat stores accumulated during the previous summer.

DOWNSLOPE WINDS FROM ICE CAPS

The icecaps of Greenland, Svalbard and Antarctica provide ideal conditions for downslope winds. On gentle slopes they create breezes; on long, steep slopes down to the sea they accelerate under gravity and reach record speeds.

The strongest continuous winds recorded anywhere on earth are the downslope winds of Commonwealth Bay, Antarctica, where the Australasian Antarctic Expedition of 1911–14 had the misfortune to discover what Douglas Mawson, their leader, was to call 'the home of the blizzard'. Winds started up shortly after they arrived, and for the duration of the expedition they found themselves in an almost continuous howling gale. They recorded a mean windspeed of 19.4 m/sec (43.4 mph) for the year, almost always from the south or southeast (i.e. off the long ice slopes behind them). The mean for February, the quietest month, was 11.7 m/sec (26.2 mph); that for July, the stormiest month, was 24.8 m/sec (55.5 mph), and the mean for the stormiest single day was 36 m/sec (80.5 mph). Extreme gusts exceeded 62 m/sec (140 mph), usually breaking the anemometer. In these extraordinary conditions the Australians went about their business, completing full sledging and scientific programmes.

Summers in polar regions can be mild and pleasant. Temperatures near the coast often rise to freezing point and a little above, but where ice or snow are present they seldom rise far above, for melting absorbs much heat and keeps air temperatures low. Wet areas and those with permafrost also tend to remain cool, but in dry tundra uplands and rocky areas, under bright summer sunshine, temperatures can shoot up to well above 10°C (50°F).

High temperatures are not always welcome in polar regions. On sea ice the surface becomes wet and rotten, making sledging difficult and dangerous. Travelling is often best done at night, when the sun is lower and the temperature may have dropped back to below freezing point. Packed snow that supported your weight gives way. What was dry underfoot becomes wet and soggy. Frozen rocks thaw and come loose. Snow slopes avalanche and slump. Villages and settlements that looked clean and neat while the snow was around them suddenly become scruffy and unkempt. Roads turn to slush, roofs and walls leak, floods of dirty water fill the streets.

Damp snow and rain are more difficult to cope with than dry snow. Dry snow brushes readily off clothing and equipment, whereas wetting can cause damage or dangerous chilling. Animals suffer from damp snow and rain almost as much as people. Penguin chicks in down can stand any amount of cold, dry snow, but sleet or rain soak them to the skin and often cause high mortality. In the Arctic, warm weather brings forth hordes of biting insects, driving people to distraction and reindeer berserk.

3

Anatomy of Ice

magine a country about the size of Scandinavia, and in similar latitude, made up of three large islands and many smaller ones. Add mountains of granite, sandstones, limestones and volcanic rocks, with spectacular peaks and crags, rolling uplands and extensive lowland plains. For good measure throw in some of the world's oldest crustal rocks, dating back 3800 million years, and a sprinkling of rich mineral ores. Give this land a maritime climate, like that of British Columbia or Washington in the northwestern United States, tailing away to a drier cool-temperate climate in the far north. Drape it with forests, rich grasslands, upland moors and far-northern tundra, threaded with streams, lakes, rivers and deep estuaries. Stock its waters with fish and aquatic mammals, and its lands with a rich fauna of insects, reptiles, birds of forests, grasslands and wetlands, and a good selection of grazing, browsing and predatory mammals. Exclude people, for all this is happening in the golden age before the meddlesome ape arose.

That is how Greenland must have looked for many millions of years before the onset of the current ice age. On a global time scale this is Greenland's normal condition, from which the white, ice-covered wedge of modern Greenland is a short-term aberration. It is perhaps unfortunate for Greenlanders that, currently, most of their land is buried deep under ice. The three large islands are still there, but it takes ice-penetrating radar to identify them. Forests and moorlands disappeared long ago. The atmosphere above is correspondingly colder. The rivers are stilled, and the surrounding seas are ice-jammed for some or all of the year. All but the fringes of Greenland are deeply entombed in the permanent ice of the world's second-largest ice cap.

It is not difficult to imagine how such changes came about. During its warm phase Greenland would have had mild summers with rainfall, and cooler winters with snowfall — possibly abundant but never lasting through spring. Some three to four million years ago, when global cooling began to bite, summers would gradually have chilled and shortened. Significantly more of the rainfall would have become snow and sleet, and winter snowfields would have enlarged and persisted longer into spring and summer. Land that had previously absorbed solar energy would now reflect it away, accelerating the overall cooling.

Snow hardened to permanent ice, which thickened, spread and began to flow. Ice built on ice, filling the valleys and choking inter-island channels, covering first the uplands, then the inland plains, and finally the mountains themselves. There is some evidence that once this process reached a critical stage, further changes happened quickly, in decades rather than centuries.

During the periods of maximum glaciation, ice covered more of Greenland than at present, blocking coastal fjords and overflowing the land. It cannot have spread far beyond the present coastline, for Greenland has only a narrow submarine shelf, and its surrounding waters are deep. Only in the far northwest are there shallows to support ice. Here the Greenland ice cap was from time to time continuous with the much greater cap covering northern Canada.

During warm interglacial periods the ice retreated, losing both thickness and area, exposing coastlands that, in the south, grew tundra and even forest. The ice sheet may have broken into two or three island caps, though it is unlikely ever to have disappeared altogether. With each hardening of the climate it spread again, scraping the land and bulldozing the dying remnants of vegetation into the cold encircling seas.

WATER AND ICE

The ice that engulfs Greenland and Antarctica is the solid phase of a curious compound formed when two atoms of hydrogen bond themselves to one atom of oxygen. Most familiar of all Earth's substances, so commonplace that it is hard to describe, water is a vital component of our environment, a key compound in life systems. As liquid or solid it covers more than 70 per cent of Earth's surface; as a solvent it makes up some 72 per cent of our own bodies. It is the colourless liquid that we see, pour and handle. It is also a gas, surrounding us constantly in the atmosphere, but invisible so that we are hardly aware of it. Yet only a slight fall in temperature transforms water to a crystalline powder or a bluish-white solid, the form in which it accumulates to engulf islands, mountains and continents.

Ice dominates polar regions in many ways. In summer or winter it comes out of the air, taking on many shapes. In damp climates at sea level it falls like feathers from a bolster, each flake a collection of flat, transparent, hexagonal crystals of extraordinary

∎ ∎ ∎

One of Greenland's many glaciers meets the sea. The long valley it has carved through the coastal mountains terminates in a sea-filled fjord. Two central nunataks (islands in ice) have diverted its flow. At intervals irregular chunks of glacier ice 'calve' into the fjord.

■ ■ ■

*Ice caps grow and shrink.
This Greenland valley, once
filled with ice from the distant
ice cap, is now virtually
empty. Typically U-shaped,
with steep sides and a flat
floor, it shows the immense
scouring power of ice in
motion. In some former time
ice probably smoothed the
tops of the headland in the
forground. More recently, it
flowed slowly and inexorably
down the main valley.*

beauty. Whipped by winds the crystals turn to rounded, stinging pellets, hard enough to polish rocks. In
hailstorms on the polar fringes ice falls like granular
sago. In the cold dry air of the Antarctic plateau it
shimmers in crystalline needles that glisten in the
sunshine as they fall. They gradually accumulate at the
surface, each adding its tiny bulk to the ice cap, which
builds up at a rate of about 5
cm (2 inches) per year.

From fog, ice is precip-
itated as hoar frost, which
gathers in heavy accumu-
lations; its crystalline clusters can be massive
enough to bring down
stays and radio antennae.
Cliffs and buildings are
sheathed with rime, which
thickens as long as the fog
lasts. On aircraft wings,
propellors and rotor
blades, ice forms a dan-
gerous glaze that keeps
wise pilots grounded. On
thin sea ice it produces
clusters of elegant flowers
with crystalline petals; on
windows it draws strange,
feathery pictures. Accum-
ulating on land, it turns first
to coarse sugary crystals,
then compresses under its
own weight, becoming, in
slow stages, a clear, rock-
hard solid. Hard ice is elastic but readily deformable;
under pressure its hexagonal crystals align, then
slide on each other to create the flowing and slumping we associate with
glaciers.

EARTH'S ICE TO WATER RATIO

Water and ice are present on Earth on
an enormous scale. The most widely
used and most consistent unit of
measurement for both is the cubic kilometre
($1 \text{ km}^3 = 0.24$ cu miles). Overall, the surface of
Earth supports about 1500 million km^3 of water
and ice, of which 1400 million make up the
oceans. Of the 100 million units left, some 30
million are currently held in glaciers and ice
fields, and the rest is present as fresh water in
lakes, rivers, streams and the soil, and as water
in the atmosphere. Of the 30 million units of ice,
about 27 million cover Antarctica and possibly
2.5 million cover Greenland. The balance is
scattered as glaciers and ice caps on smaller
Arctic islands and on high land across the world.

Though comparable to land ice in area, sea
ice is very much thinner and relatively trivial in
volume. In the Southern Ocean in summer it
covers about 4 million km^2 (1.6 million sq
miles), expanding to 20 million km^2 (7.8 million
sq miles) in winter. Assuming a mean thickness
of 1.5 m (nearly 5 ft), this implies a maximum
winter volume of only 30,000 units of ice,
compared with the 27 million units on land. The
Arctic Ocean has about 9 million km^2 of sea ice
in summer and 12 million km^2 (4.7 million sq
miles) in winter, implying a maximum volume of
18,000 units for the year.

ing little from year to year, seeming almost as permanent as the rocks they cover. In fact they are more
dynamic than they appear; their substance is constantly changing, and different parts change at different rates. The edges advance and retreat, sometimes
slowly, sometimes in energetic surges that catch
everyone by surprise. Inland they flow majestically
like infinitely slow treacle,
oozing downhill, crossing
plains, slumping wearily to
fill valleys. Pressures from
their own vast bulk drive
them onward. Tensions
tear them apart, opening
wedge-shaped cracks or
crevasses that penetrate
deep, sometimes down to
bedrock,

Every day the ice
sheets lose some of their
bulk by evaporation, and
every summer day sees far
greater losses due to melting. Ice sheets that terminate on land melt
undramatically, their
waters running away in
streams and rivers made
milky with fine sediment.
Those that meet the sea
tumble away in chunks,
forming icebergs and ice
islands that float off on
voyages of their own.

All the time these loss-
es are being replaced by
new snow and hoar frost.
Gains from precipitation
vary over different parts of
the ice sheets. Seaward
edges usually gain most,
for warm maritime air
brings heavy snowfall —
heavy enough to tem-

ICE CAPS TODAY

The ice sheets which cover Antarctica and Greenland
today are mosaics of ice that has fallen as snow and
hoar frost over many centuries. At a casual glance
these great masses of ice are solid and timeless, vary-

porarily bury expedition huts in a matter of hours,
and to build up local ice sheets that spread far over
the coastline. Glaciers, which are relatively fast-moving rivers of ice, usually indicate that there is heavy
local precipitation in their catchment area. Ice sheets

in high-precipitation areas may change very quickly. The Filchner Ice Shelf, in the southern Weddell Sea, moves forward more than 1000 m (0.6 mile) annually; parts of it move twice as fast, resulting in many large tabular icebergs. Where precipitation is lower the ice sheets are more static.

South Greenland, which is subject to a succession of depressions and annual precipitation equivalent to 100 cm (40 inches) of rainfall, has a very rapid turnover of ice. North Greenland, far from the open sea, receives less than a fifth as much precipitation and has a much lower turnover. In the far north the ice cap peters out altogether, starved of replenishing snow. Losses and gains on any permanent ice sheet more or less compensate each other. From time to time there may be spectacular local growth or shrinkage, but the budget overall is roughly in balance.

The thickness of ice sheets varies from time to time. Long-term variations are well recorded; in both Antarctica and Greenland, where mountains rear

This is Greenland's Jakobshavn ice fjord, looking across to Disko Island. In the foreground the jumbled surface of the glacier creeps down from the Greenland ice cap. Beyond are large icebergs, calved from the glacier's seaward edge. In summer these will drift west and south across the Davis Strait, melting steadily as they go.

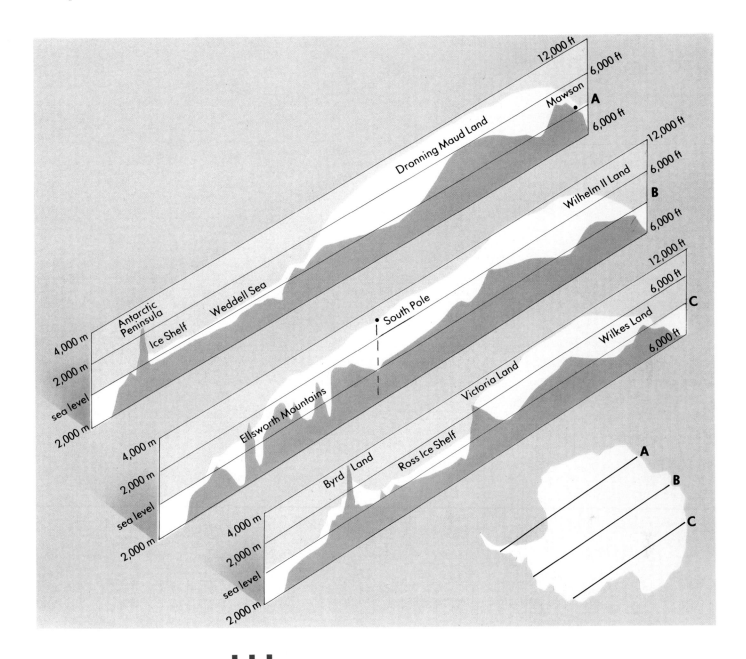

■ ■ ■

The height and overall profile of the Antarctic ice cap have been mapped by airborne radar. These cross sections through the ice cap, in which vertical height is greatly exaggerated, show how Antarctica's continental shelf has been depressed by the weight of overlying ice. If the ice were removed, the continent would rise considerably, just as

Northern Europe has risen since the loss of its ice cap.

Antarctica is really a coalition of two large land masses. The massive eastern block, often called East Antarctica, is geologically similar to Australia and was once attached to it. To the west lies a smaller block of precipitous folded rocks which continue the line of the South American Andes.

A deep valley runs between the two blocks.

The East Antarctic massif (Dronning Maud Land, Wilhelm II Land, Wilkes Land, Victoria Land) is exposed mainly along the coast of Victoria Land, while that of West Antarctica can be seen along the Antarctic Peninsula, in the Ellsworth Mountains, and in Byrd Land.

above the ice sheet, we find many with 'collars' of smooth rock or debris showing that the ice was once much thicker. As measurement techniques improve, we find that the ice is in fact fluctuating rather rapidly, and in interesting ways that are hard to explain.

Ice thickness used to be measured laboriously by a seismic echo-sounding technique. Sledging parties travelling across an ice cap would stop at intervals, set out an array of microphones on the ice, and fire off an explosive charge nearby. The sound waves from the explosion would travel down through the ice, bounce off the bedrock and return to the microphones. The time they took to return was proportional to the thickness of the ice.

Today we can get better results far more quickly.

■ ■ ■

A post-glacial landscape of ice-polished rocks. A few thousand years ago it probably had a capping of ice. Since then, thin soils have accumulated in cracks and crevices and on sandy gravels left by the melting glaciers, allowing tundra vegetation to gain a foothold. Lakes fill deep hollows in a shallow ice-cut channel.

■ ■ ■

The heavily-crevassed surface of Lamplugh Glacier, Alaska. The dark 'tramlines' which follow the sinuous course of the glacier are rock debris fed in from mountainsides higher up – they are a clear indication of the direction of movement of the ice. The glacier surface, almost bare of fresh snow, is deeply fissured due to the combined forces of sunshine, gravity and pressure.

Aircraft overflying the ice cap at carefully controlled heights transmit radar impulses that penetrate the ice and bounce off the bedrock — they are also reflected from the surface of the ice and from internal layers and discontinuities. The echoes are picked up by receivers in the aircraft, and recorded for subsequent analysis. Many hundreds of signals can be sent and received in a single flight, allowing almost continuous mapping of the altitude both of the ice cap and of the land beneath. The intermediate echoes also yield valuable information about the layering within the ice.

Satellites are currently plotting the surface contours of our polar ice sheets far more quickly and precisely than could ever be achieved from the ground. Their monitoring detects small changes in ice thickness, of the order of a few centimetres, which can be recorded at frequent intervals to disclose any long-term changes.

THE ICE RECORD

The ice of long-standing ice sheets, formed from seasonally deposited snow, contains a remarkable record of past events. Snow absorbs gases from the air as it falls, and often brings down with it tiny fragments of dust from the atmosphere. On landing, snowflakes trap air between them which, under pressure from overlying layers, forms bubbles within the ice. Later compression reduces these bubbles to almost nothing, but the gases remain entombed, awaiting liberation.

Glaciologists used to dig pits in ice sheets, then count, measure and sample the layers of ice exposed. Summer and winter precipitation could usually be distinguished, so that almost every ice sheet yielded a record of annual snowfall going back a few decades or, in some instances, a few centuries. Short-term trends in summer temperatures or precipitation could be deduced from variations in the thickness of the annual layers. However, the method was laborious, and the results had to be read and interpreted directly on the spot.

Then a few years ago a whole new research field of ice chemistry came into being. It required uncontaminated samples, obtained by drilling down into the ice sheets and removing intact cores of ice. Such cores have now been drilled from several sites in Greenland, Antarctica and lesser ice sheets, and their analysis is yielding remarkable details of past events. Cores several centimetres in diameter are extracted, going down to whatever depth is possible. At Camp Century, northwestern Greenland, cores more than 1500 m (nearly 1 mile) long have been taken, believed to represent over 120,000 years of precipitation. Cores of similar value have been taken at Dye 3, a radar defence station high on the south Greenland ice cap, and from several locations on the Antarctic ice sheet.

No longer need glaciologists be content simply to count layers. They pass sections of core to geochemists, who analyse the oxygen isotope ratios of the ice, and the chemistry of the air bubbles, from various levels. The results provide estimates of the age of the ice, and the mean temperature that prevailed when it was being formed. Fine chemical analysis reveals levels of atmospheric contamination by lead, radioactive compounds and similar airborne pollutants, indicating when these substances first entered the atmosphere and whether their incidence has increased. Microscopic examination shows the presence of significant layers of clay, salt deposits, and volcanic and other dusts, all evidence of the conditions prevailing when the ice formed. These records can often be related to known events, for example to particular volcanic eruptions, atomic bomb tests, or nuclear catastrophes like Chernobyl.

ICEBERGS

Icebergs are land ice at sea. Often large, even massive, they have broken free from glaciers or ice shelves and drifted off on their own. There is no standard rating for bergs, although small ones (cottage-sized) are called 'growlers' and lesser fragments 'bergy bits'. Some of the largest northern bergs, breaking away from the ice sheets of north

◾ ANALYSIS OF ICE CORES ◾

Cores recovered from ice sheets can be boxed up, refrigerated and sent to laboratories all over the world. So long as they remain frozen, their record is safe indefinitely. This is just as well, for analysis of ice cores is a slow and painstaking business. Samples of ice and of the air bubbles within them are treated in many different ways.

For samples up to a few thousand years old the ratio of the heavy oxygen isotope O^{18} to lighter O^{16} gives a useful measure of prevailing temperature. High O^{18}, indicating that the temperature of evaporation at the ocean surface was relatively high, tells of summer snows and warmer interglacial conditions; thin bands of alternating high and low temperatures indicate annual cycles of snowfall. For older samples, radioisotopes of such elements as beryllium, carbon or chlorine may give a better measure of age.

In the shorter term, layers of volcanic dust or high acidity can often be matched with known volcanic events. The eruption of the Indonesian volcano Tambora in 1815, for example, left recognizable traces of sulphuric acid in both the Greenland and the Antarctic ice sheets. Atmospheric lead recorded in Greenland increased from almost zero in the 18th century to low values in the 19th and early 20th centuries, then doubled and redoubled in the late 20th century with the advent of leaded petrol. Sulphate and nitrate concentrations too have increased in Greenland snows throughout the present century, probably due to emissions from factory chimneys.

Northern atmospheric nuclear tests in 1954 and 1962 provided sharply defined layers with high levels of radioactive caesium (Cs^{137}) and strontium (Sr^{90}). In Antarctica the layers occur one to two years later than in Greenland, showing the time taken for the pollutants to travel from one hemisphere to the other in the atmosphere. Data from ice cores can be matched against similar data contained in sea bed sediments, usually showing excellent correlation.

❄

Greenland or from islands in the Canadian archipel-ago, form ice islands a few kilometres long and wide. These are strong enough for heavy aircraft to land on, and for semi-permanent scientific camps to be established safely. The camps drift slowly with the rest of ice pack, while the scientists work in comfort on oceanography, climate, ice movements and marine biology.

Greenland produces most of the Arctic bergs, mainly from glaciers along its eastern and western flanks. It releases some 15,000 sizeable bergs each year, of which two-thirds fragment and melt away fairly quickly. The rest make their way south, melting and shedding bergy bits as they go. Only a few travel far enough south to menace shipping lanes.

Very much larger bergs, including all the world's largest, are generated from the broad, fast-changing ice shelves of Antarctica. Flat-topped, slab-sided,

■ ■ ■

This iceberg — a small one as southern tabular bergs go — was once part of the ice cliffs of Coats Land on the Weddell Sea. If it continues to drift north into warmer waters, it will probably take 10-20 years to disintegrate. Antarctic bergs, calved from the orderly ice shelves that barricade more than 90 per cent of the Antarctic coast, tend to be flat-topped and slab-sided. Arctic icebergs, calved from turbulent, heavily crevassed glaciers, tend to be irregular, turreted and relatively small.

■ ■ ■

The smooth lemon meringue contours of this iceberg were created by underwater melting when only the peak of the berg stood above the water. Since then the berg has become top-heavy and rolled over, probably in two stages. Now firmly aground, its waterline shows the effects of wave action and its peaks are rapidly melting.

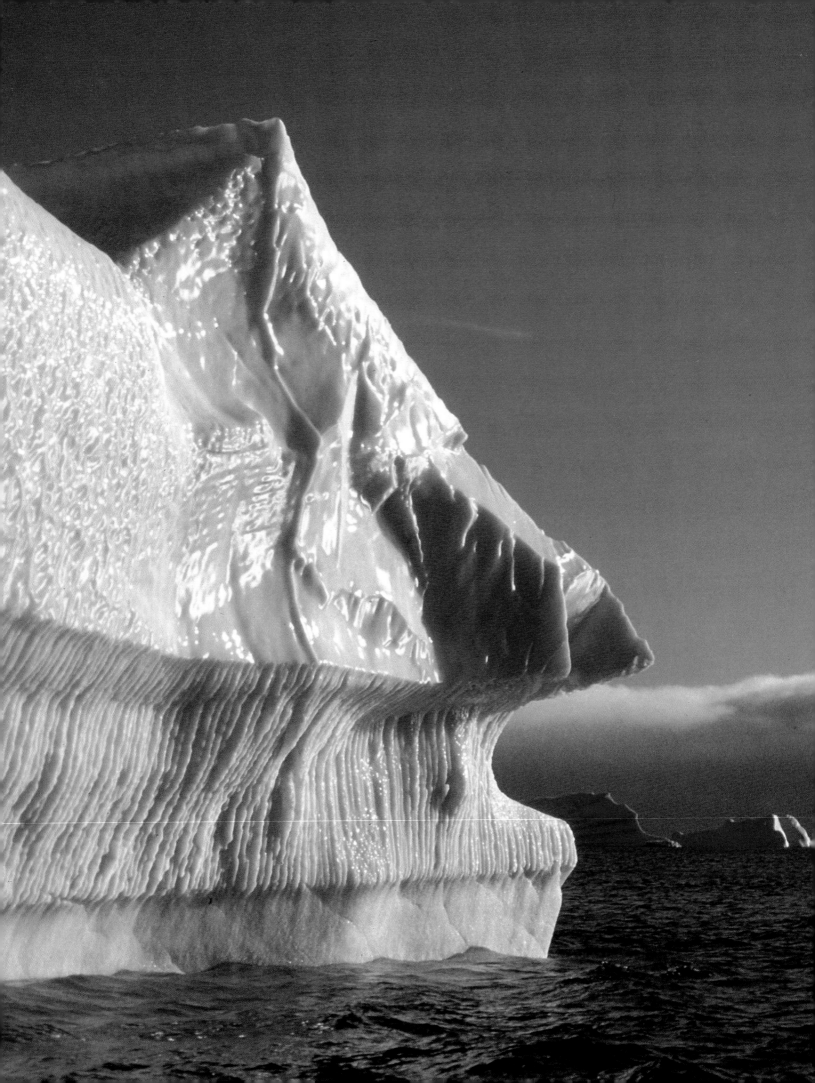

■ ■ ■

*Another berg with a history.
Smoothed by underwater
melting, the upper half of this
berg has acquired a beaten-
pewter finish from facing the
warm sun. The horizontal
ridge half way up is an old
waterline, showing that it
has recently risen out of the
water, possibly due to loss of
bulk by sudden fragmen-
tation. A new waterline is
forming below. As more and
more melting occurs, the
berg will steadily rise.
Millions of gallons of fresh,
pure water are released from
icebergs every day.*

standing 20–30 m (60–100 ft) above the waterline, southern tabular bergs can measure 100 km (60 miles) or more in length and width. The movements of such massive lumps of ice are of great interest to many people. Some are big enough to be seen and monitored by satellite; smaller ones can be fitted with radio transmitters and monitored whenever a satellite passes over. Several glaciologists around the world are studying the day-to-day movements of icebergs and their ultimate fate

Bergs are driven by ocean currents and winds, but as more than 80 per cent of their bulk lies below the waterline, currents are often the main motive force. In the north, long-term ice patrols by air and sea have established where most bergs are to be found, and where they are likely to travel. Along the east coast of Greenland, for example, convoys of them drift south every year; along the southwest coast they drift north, cross Baffin Bay, then start a long south-ward drift that carries their remnants past Labrador and Newfoundland into the North Atlantic.

The huge keels of larger bergs keep them out of shallow water but strand them on shoals. Two or three bergs grounded across a harbour mouth can be a considerable nuisance — there they stay, virtually immovable, until winds, tides and currents combine to send them on their way. Oil companies take them seriously; small bergs advancing on drilling ships anchored in shallow water have to be diverted by tugs, adding substantially to operational costs. Any future oil operations in the Southern Ocean will need to take into account the very much larger tabular bergs that are found there, unmanageable by even the largest tugs afloat.

Satellite monitoring in July 1986 revealed, for example, three enormous bergs totalling 11,500 km^2 (4,300 sq miles) — over half the area of Wales — that had broken away from the Filchner Ice Shelf in the southeast corner of the Weddell Sea. Later an air-borne monitoring survey established that they were at least 500 m (1,600 ft) thick. One carried with it the Argentine station Belgrano (established by US scientists in 1957 but now completely buried except for the top of its radio mast), and also the more recent Soviet scientific station Druzhnaya, unmanned at the time but maintained for summer research. These bergs drifted north, coming to rest on shoals near their point of origin. There they are likely to stay until some of their bulk melts away, then Druzhnaya will become a floating station. Helped by winds and currents, the bergs will make their way west and north in the clockwise-moving Weddell Sea gyre, to emerge in a few year's time off the tip of the Antarctic Peninsula.

Small bergs melt within two or three years, but bigger ones take many years to melt, and travel far while doing so, often drifting into shipping lanes. The largest are visible by day and show up clearly on a ship's radar. Smaller ones, which merge into storms or fog and get lost in the clutter on a radar scope, are more dangerous and can be massive enough to rip a ship's plates on impact. The stability of large bergs, even in relatively warm seas, has led many entrepreneurs to consider towing them to drought areas where their pure, fresh water would be greatly appreciated. Two or three anchored off southern Australia or California, or moored in the Persian Gulf, would be worth a considerable fortune, but the difficulties of harnessing and shifting large bergs have so far proved insuperable.

▪ ▪ ▪

Alternating layers of dense (dark blue) and more porous (white) ice formed this berg in Paradise Harbour, Antarctic Peninsula. Formed in an area of heavy snowfall, where glaciers have a rapid turnover, this is probably a much younger berg than those pictured on previous pages. Eroded under water, then tilted and lit from behind, it gives the impression of a pillared Grecian temple.

FRESHWATER ICE

Polar regions tend to be dry, and the colder they are the drier they are likely to be, for cold air carries little moisture. In the far north, and over much of Antarctica, desert conditions prevail. If there are streams, they flow only for a few days each year; if there are lakes, they thaw only around their edges, and seldom for more than a week or two in late summer. On the Arctic tundra and on sub-Antarctic islands, rivers and streams flow seasonally; ponds and lakes thaw reluctantly in spring and are quick to freeze over in autumn. Soils too freeze solid for much of the year, their contained ice expanding and causing them to heave and contort.

No large rivers start in either polar region, but some of the world's largest flow from central Asia through Arctic Siberia and into the Arctic Ocean. The Ob-Irtysh, Yenisey, Lena, Indigirka and Kolyma, all huge river systems with wide, sluggish estuaries and deltas on the Arctic Ocean, freeze over to a depth of several metres each autumn. Their flows continue beneath the ice throughout winter, but at much reduced rates. At this time of year these large northern rivers become important highways for transporting goods locally by sledge. In spring the ice cover breaks up within a cataclysmic few hours, releasing massive flows of water which wash away banks and realign navigation channels. The Lena, bringing over 500 km³ (120 cu miles) of water annually to the ocean, delivers less than 1 per cent of it in each of the cold months of January, February and March, but over 35 per cent in the warm month of June.

The fresh water and heat that these rivers bring northward in spring help to shift ice from inshore waters of the Arctic Ocean, opening them for navigation. A few years ago Soviet planners seriously considered the possibility of diverting some of the large rivers south, to give badly needed irrigation to some of the arid southern republics. Climatologists of many nations were horrified at possible changes to the Arctic Ocean, which in their view could have a far from healthy effect on world climate. Major plans affecting the Lena and Ob-Irtysh seem to have been shelved, but comparatively minor schemes for altering two lesser rivers, the North Dvina and Pechora, may go ahead toward the turn of the century. Neither scientists in the Soviet Union nor in the West expect serious consequences from this comparatively mild experiment.

SEA ICE

Sea ice starts to form in autumn when the air is still and the water surface chills below freezing point. First comes a porridge of fine crystals, then a layer of soft fudge that thickens in hours and hardens to brittle toffee. Wind at this stage breaks the layer into pancakes — tiny floes that rub themselves circular with the movement of the sea. Continuous hard frost causes further freezing and thickening. After 24 hours at low temperatures the ice may be 20 cm (8 inches) thick, and strong enough to walk on. After a week it may be twice as thick, and strong enough to take a sledge.

Heavy swells at this stage can break the ice sheet into floes, and strong winds or currents shift the floes bodily. However, by early winter it is usually cold enough for the floes to consolidate again quickly, and for the freezing to continue. Sea ice usually reaches a thickness of 1–2 m (3–6 ft) by midwinter or shortly after. Snow accumulating on it weighs it down in the water and causes the surface to flood; this too freezes, adding further thickness as the year goes on.

● ● ● POLYNYAS ● ● ●

These are 'lakes' or patches of open water occurring in anomalous places, for example off cold polar coasts where ice is constantly forming, or in the middle of a wide expanse of sea ice. Coastal polynyas are usually due to strong offshore winds, which break up the ice as fast as it forms and push it away from the land; some may also be due to strong currents between islands. Those occurring in mid-ocean ice sheets are thought to form because of upwellings of warm water. Satellites often pick them out because the open sea is much warmer than the surrounding ice.

Ecologically, polynyas may be extremely rich, for the absence of sea ice allows early spring penetration of sunshine, wind-stirring of water to bring nutrients to the surface, and high productivity early in the season. In Antarctica polynyas allow penguins and other seabirds to breed much further south than they would otherwise be able to. In the Arctic they open up channels and bays, attracting fish and other prey species, and becoming the haunt of whales, seals and seabirds.

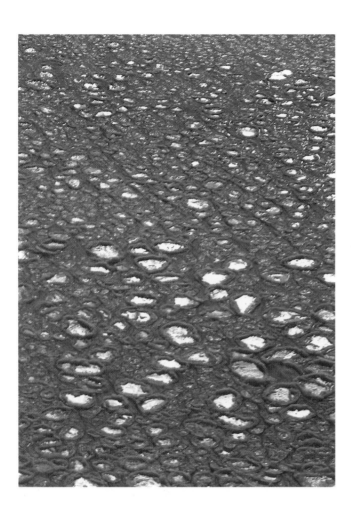

■ ■ ■

'Pancake' ice, an early stage in the formation of sea ice. When the sea starts to freeze, ice crystals float to the surface to form a thick mush, which then congeals to a solid layer a few centimetres thick. If slightly disturbed by wind or swell, this solid surface breaks into fragments which rub together, forming rounded plaques of ice with raised edges. If the air is cold enough, the plaques freeze solid to form the basis of annual sea ice.

■ ▪ ▪ **PROPERTIES OF WATER** ▪ ▪ ▪

If we suddenly met water for the first time it would take us by surprise, for it has many strange properties. Physicists tell us that at normal temperatures it should be a gas, but weak hydrogen bonds hold its molecules together and make it a liquid. As a liquid it is more viscous than might be expected, and has a higher surface tension; these are the properties that make it 'wet'. Much heat is required to convert it from solid to liquid form and from liquid to gas, and it has remarkable powers of dissolving other substances.

When a solution is cooled and ice starts to form, the ice crystals separate themselves from the dissolved materials. So the pack ice that forms on the sea is frozen pure water, although often contaminated with brine.

On cooling, water molecules pack down together. This causes the density of the water to increase, but only as far as 4°C (38.5°F). Between 4°C and freezing point its density decreases slightly. One important consequence of this is that, on ponds in winter, cold water sinks from the surface to the bottom, but the coldest layer of all forms on the top.

At 0°C (32°F) the molecules arrange themselves in layers to form ice crystals, but stay far enough away from each other to ensure that ice is less dense than water. So ice forms on the surface of a pond, not at depth, and for same reason pack ice forms on the surface of the sea, not on the sea bed.

There are many forms of ice, depending on temperature and pressure. Normally a hard, fairly elastic solid, ice flows under pressure, producing those splendid monuments to gravity called glaciers. Ice passes readily from solid to gas - clothes on a line continue to dry even when they are frozen stiff. Similarly, glaciers and ice sheets lose substance by ablation (evaporation) even when it is too cold for them to melt.

■ ■ ■

*New ice forming on a calm
evening in a coastal polynya
in the eastern Weddell Sea;
the air temperature is -25°C
(-13°F). Calm seas that are
about to freeze develop an
'oily' appearance, as ice
crystals form a thin,
coherent slick at the surface.
Undisturbed, the slick
thickens to form immense
glossy sheets of ice spreading
as far as the eye can see.
Usually there is a enough
disturbance and pressure
from outside to cause these
fragile sheets to break up. The
fragments, just a few
centimetres thick, override
each other like panes of
cloudy glass, interdigitating
in fantastic patterns.*

Most sea ice breaks up in spring, melting, moving away from the land and ultimately dispersing, but ice fields formed in deep bays and those trapped in gyres by wind or currents may stay around for many years, reaching thicknesses of several metres. The central Arctic Ocean and the Weddell Sea in Antarctica have multi-year ice of this kind.

Annual sea ice has many consequences. Ecologically it forms a boundary between the sea and the atmosphere, reducing gaseous exchanges and penetration of solar energy, and therefore productivity. Whales and diving birds and mammals must be wary of it, working only where there are breathing holes available. Yet polar species of whales work happily among the pack ice each year, and many seals and seabirds use it as an agreeable extension of land. Several species of seal breed on it, and so does one species of penguin (see Chapter 4). The thin ice of polynyas, or open stretches of water within pack ice, acts as a growth substrate for algae and serves as a winter feeding ground for krill, one of the most important animals in the ecology of Antarctic seas.

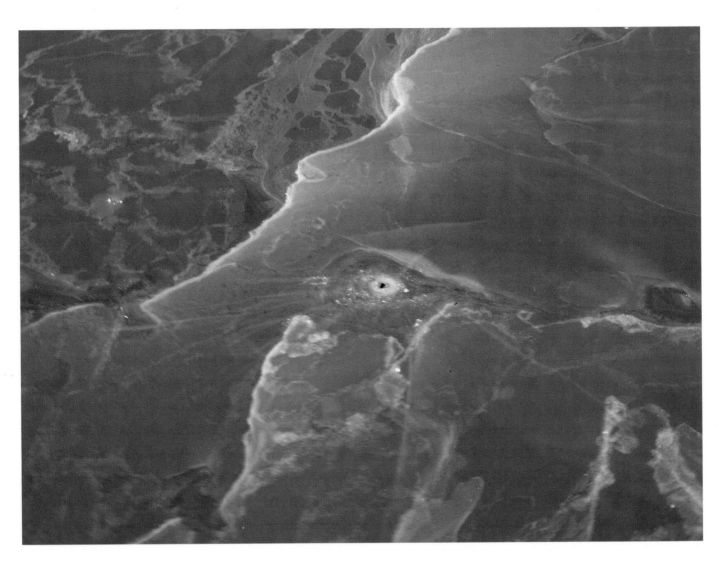

■ ■ ■

This thin layer of sea ice formed overnight over a wide area of polynya (open water surrounded by sea ice). In the middle of it is a breathing hole punched by a Weddell seal (seals drive upward with their noses to make breathing holes, then keep their edges well nibbled to prevent them icing over) The ice is too thin to bear the weight of a seal, but tracks show that several emperor penguins have already used the hole to escape from the sea and rest up for a few hours.

Fast ice (i.e. sea ice growing close to land) and drifting pack ice keep the warmth of the sea away from land. Islands and coasts within the winter ice zone experience much longer and colder winters than those that are ice-free. Among Southern Ocean islands tussock grass and other flowering plants grow only on those that are warmed by the sea in winter, and the whole ecology of ice-free islands is accordingly richer.

To navigators and economists sea ice is an unrelieved nuisance and a hazard. Where previously it inhibited or stopped exploration, now it necessitates expensive icebreakers, ice-strengthened cargo and passenger ships, expensive marine insurance and high levels of navigational skill to make use of polar waters. Ports that would otherwise be useful all the year round, for example those of northern Siberia, lie dead for half the year. Whole stretches of coast with good economic potential remain undeveloped. Sea ice and icebergs add substantially to the cost of

exploring for oil, and even more to the cost of bringing it from wellhead to market. Overland pipelines
would not have been considered for Alaskan or
Siberian oil had seaways been safer for tankers.
Similarly, fisheries are restricted, and voyages of all
kinds are endangered by floating ice.

There is no remedy, but the detection and monitoring of sea ice distribution by satellites has
improved greatly within the last few years, and new
polar satellites give promise of far better monitoring
in the future. Marine engineers are considering the
possibility of carrying goods under the ice, rather
than through it. Experienced submariners, if no one
else, are convinced that when sea ice is present, the
waters beneath it are much safer than those on the
surface. We may yet see cargo submarines and trains
of submarine tankers plying under sea ice, opening
up seaways that are currently closed to us.

■ ■ ■

For seals and other polar
animals, sea ice is a
convenient and useful
extension of land. This
illustration is based on a
story told by Midshipman
Clements Markham RN,
member of an Arctic
expedition in 1850-51. In a
letter to his father he wrote:
'I saw a bear swimming
across a lane of water and
pushing a large piece of ice
before him. Landing on a
floe he advanced stealthily
toward a couple of seals
which were basking in the
sun at some little distance,
still holding the ice in front
to hide his black muzzle.'

4

Life in Polar Seas

Old-time polar expeditions travelled traditionally by sea — the long sea voyage was an essential part of the exercise, and sea-going and polar traditions became inextricably mixed. Although often supported by navies, or sponsored in some other way by governments, the early expeditions were usually starved of funds. Whether official expeditions or private, northward bound or southward, they faced similar problems, and the opening chapters of their narratives have an engaging sameness.

They sailed in ships far too small for the purpose, under-crewed to save berths, under-insured to save expedition funds, but overloaded beyond legal limits and well past the point of danger. In holds, on deck, wherever there was space, they stowed prefabricated huts, timbers, two or three years' supplies of food and fuel.... In corners of the deck, makeshift shelters housed sledge-dogs, ponies or mules with their mountains of fodder, and sometimes live pigs or sheep for fresh meat on the voyage. Crew, shore parties and scientists fitted as best they could into cabins, saloons, tween-decks and crow's nests. Leaving their final port of civilization, usually with hangovers from a round of parties and civic receptions, they staggered off into the unknown, facing weeks of tribulation in the world's coldest and stormiest oceans.

It was traditional for the landlubber members of these expeditions, green but game, to help with the sails, heave coal in mid-ocean, feed and water the unfortunate animals, and man the hand-pumps to keep afloat. The scientists began their programmes as soon as they left port, recording the weather (in early spring, usually horrible), and pausing occasionally to trawl, dredge and take soundings in deep waters. The first sight of floating ice raised three hearty cheers, and entering the pack ice was a blessed relief — at last the ship would stop heaving. By the end of a five- or six-week voyage everyone had 'shaken down' and come to know their colleagues in adversity, and all on board had passed their first test, coming to terms with the polar ocean.

There are still oceanographic expeditions, resupply ships and tourist liners that give the adventurous a taste of crossing a polar ocean. For many Antarctic expeditions it remains part of the game, although voyages tend to be shorter today. Scientists' time is precious, and senior expeditioners usually fly as far south as they can — perhaps to the tip of South America or South Africa — before taking ship. Those working with US expeditions can fly all the way south, through Christchurch, New Zealand, to McMurdo Sound, Antarctica. Others fly in from South America to Teniente Marsh, a Chilean airstrip on King George Island, in the South Shetlands group. More expeditions will be seeking to do the same as more Antarctic airstrips are created.

For most Arctic expeditioners a sea voyage is no longer an option. Those travelling to continental destinations, to Iceland, Greenland or Svalbard, usually go by air. Many thank heaven for the comfort and speed of air travel; but just a few regret the passing of the preliminary cruise, with its slow, measured introduction to polar life and its spirit of adventure and fun.

POLAR VOYAGING

For marine biologists and oceanographers no two stretches of ocean are quite alike. Of all expedition scientists, they in particular valued the voyage, especially on a slow ship. Purists preferred to be under sail, for that meant a slower and often a more stable passage, with no engine noise to frighten whales and seals. Fast ships cut through the sea, slow ones travel with it. The slower the pace, the more chances there are to study the ocean — to watch and measure the changes from tropical to temperate waters, from temperate to sub-polar, from open sea to pack ice, from offshore to inshore conditions.

The changes are striking, and often a clue to what is going on in the waters themselves. Inshore waters are usually muddy, bedraggled with debris from the land. Offshore waters are clearer and greener, deepening in colour as the depth increases. Whereas tropical waters are usually a hard, blue-rinse or azure blue, mirroring the dark blue sky, temperate and colder waters tend to be steely blue-grey, reflecting the clouds above them. Pack ice is silver-grey when it first forms, whitening as it thickens and gathers a covering of snow and hoar frost. Maturing, rafting and folding under pressure, it brings vivid white, blues and greens to the palette. When the sun is low it reflects lilac and rose-pink.

All ocean waters contain microscopic, drifting surface-living plants (plant plankton or phytoplankton) and animals (animal plankton or zooplankton).

Polar and sub-polar seas, stirred by strong, continuous winds, are among the world's roughest, but also among the richest in the ecological sense. Oceans between latitudes 40° and 50°S (the 'roaring forties'), driven constantly by westerly winds, have some of the longest and highest waves. On weather (western) shores they break into massive, destructive surf. This is why many sub-polar islands have towering, inaccessible western cliffs, which are a death-trap to ships.

Phytoplankton is the equivalent of trees and grass on land — the ocean's major means of trapping solar energy by photosynthesis. Zooplankton browse and graze on the phytoplankton — they are roughly the equivalent of grasshoppers, caterpillars, sheep and other land herbivores. On the health and abundance of plant and animal plankton depends ultimately the success of all other life in the oceans, from the great whales to the sponges of the deep.

Rich patches of polar ocean sometimes show an abundance of plankton. Areas of water several hectares across may be tinted green, brown or reddish with algae, sometimes pink from shoals of shrimp-like krill or whale-feed, sometimes flashing silver with larval fish. Whaling skippers in polar waters often judged where to hunt their prey from the colour of the sea. North or south, pink indicates shoals of swarming crustaceans, and crustaceans attract rorquals, the filter-feeding whales that were once the bulk of the catch. The most knowledgeable Antarctic skippers claimed they could tell one kind of krill-patch from another, and knew the whales' preferences at different periods of the summer hunting season.

Convergences, or boundaries between adjacent water masses, are most readily detected by sudden shifts in temperature, usually of the order of 2–3°C (4–6°F). On most ships today water temperature is measured by a thermometer in the coolant-water intake (where sea water is pumped inboard to cool the engines) and routinely entered in the log. A more sophisticated way is to net samples of plankton; biologists know which species of crustacean or diatom to expect on either side of the boundary, and are seldom wrong.

In calm weather the boundaries sometimes appear quite clearly at the surface. From the bridge one sees a zone of discoloured water flecked with oil and foam, the oil originating from micro-organisms killed by the differences in temperature and salinity between adjacent water masses. The Antarctic Convergence has a reputation for showing up in this almost magical way, especially in the Southern Atlantic sector where it seems to form a particularly sharp boundary.

Seabirds too are a good guide. They know all about such boundaries and their lethal effects on plankton. Huge flocks of birds feed at the Antarctic Convergence, far more than on either side of it. In calm weather the Convergence can be marked by mist, for the temperature shift in the waters is reflected

Emperor penguins on sea ice at the southern end of the Weddell Sea, Antarctica. Emperors breed in colonies numbering several thousand birds, and occur further south than any other species of penguin. The males alone incubate the single eggs, huddling together for warmth on the sea ice in the coldest eight or nine weeks of winter. The chicks will be ready to go to sea by November or December. These chicks are six to eight weeks old.

in the air masses above them, and warm air adjacent to cold air creates local condensation. Shipborne passengers note the change too; polar air has a sharp, cold nip, while sub-polar air feels relatively damp and bland.

Young pack ice is a floating home for microscopic plants, which discolour the undersides and edges of the floes and in summer fill the waters between them. Older pack is less attractive to plant life, too thick to allow light to shine through it, and deeper in the water than many species seem to prefer. The outer edge of the pack is a feeding ground for birds

and seals — they loaf about on the floes between meals and dive over the side for dinner.

Melting pack ice in summer is especially profitable, for the retreating floes leave algae and browsing organisms loose in the water for seabirds to scavenge. A few species of seal and seabird spend most of their lives on pack ice or fast ice (i.e. sea ice that grows out from the land). The seals breed there, while the birds mostly come ashore to nest, although one species of penguin, the emperor, contrives to breed on the Antarctic inshore ice, making itself virtually independent of land.

■ ■ ■
A colony of king penguins on South Georgia. Like emperors, their closest kin, king penguins have an unusual breeding pattern, keeping their chicks through the winter. Eggs are laid between November and March, and the chicks take just over a year to achieve independence. This picture shows two groups of courting and incubating birds (black) among hundreds of chicks (brown).

OCEAN PRODUCTIVITY

By world standards the Arctic Ocean is tiny, deep in the centre and shallow around its edges, like a wide-lipped basin. Almost all of it lies within the Arctic Circle, and none of its surface waters rise far above freezing point throughout the year. Almost half of it is permanently ice-covered.

The Southern Ocean, also relatively small by world standards, is very much larger. Ring-shaped, much of it lies outside the Antarctic Circle. Since it spans warmer latitudes than the Arctic Ocean, it is on the whole a much warmer ocean. Although its southern shores are near-frozen even at the height of sum-mer, its northern boundary extends into cool-temperate regions. Only 2.6 per cent of it is ice-covered.

Polar seas have the reputation of being biologically very rich, in general much richer than tropical seas. This is only partly true; seas the world over are patchy, and both polar and tropical seas have rich and poor patches. Tropical seas, warm and placid, tend to form layers which remain unmixed; in the open ocean this leads to a chronic dearth of the nutrient salts and gases which plants and animals need for photosynthesis and respiration. In consequence there are few microscopic plants (mostly diatoms and algae), which are the basis of all other life in the sea.

■ ■ ■ ■   POLAR OCEANS: SOME COMPARISONS   ■ ■ ■ ■

The Arctic Ocean, which includes the Barents and Greenland Seas, Baffin and Hudson Bays, and the many small seas close to the coasts of Canada, Alaska and Siberia, is a relatively tiny ocean of 14.5 million km^2 (5.66 million sq miles). The Southern Ocean, which includes all the 'inshore' seas close to the continent and extends out to the Convergence, is about twice as big — 28 million km^2 (11 million sq miles). For comparison the Atlantic Ocean is nearly four times the size of the Southern Ocean, and the Pacific Ocean over six times as big.

The Arctic Ocean is a deep basin with a wide, shallow continental shelf. The central deep, a rectangular depression 2500 km (1,550 miles) long and 1500 km (930 miles) wide, surrounds the North Pole, aligned at a right angle to Greenland. Three parallel submarine ridges cross the depression, the central Lomonosov Ridge, a mountain chain rising from 4000 m to 1000 m (13,100 ft to 3,300 ft) below sea level, dividing it unevenly into two basins. The smaller Eurasian Basin descends to a depth of 4500 m (14,700 ft) off northeastern Greenland; the larger but shallower Amerasian Basin lies between the Canadian archipelago, Alaska and Siberia. The continental shelf, only 200 km (125 miles) wide on the Canadian and American side, broadens to 500–1000 km (300–600 miles) off eastern Siberia.

The Southern Ocean has a narrower but deeper continental shelf, mostly less than 100 km (60 miles) wide but 400–600 m (1,300–2,000 ft) deep, a consequence of the ice load that constantly weighs down Antarctica. The continental slope falls steeply to wide abyssal plains 3000–5000 m (10,000–16,500 ft) deep, with a steep-sided trench descending to 8000 m (26,250 ft) off the eastern flank of the South Sandwich Islands. A submarine mountain chain links the Antarctic Peninsula with the South Shetland, South Orkney and South Sandwich Islands, and ultimately with South Georgia and Patagonia. South of the Indian Ocean, Iles Crozet and the Prince Edward Islands stand on one submarine plateau, Iles Kerguelen and Heard Island on another.

The Arctic Ocean extends from 90°N to about 70°N but the Southern Ocean is nowhere closer to the South Pole than 78°S. The sea ice that covers both oceans is reduced to a core in summer but spreads massively in winter. In summer Arctic pack ice covers 6.6 million km^2 (2.58 million sq miles), about 45 per cent of the ocean; this is a field of thick, heavily-ridged ice several years old, most of it within the polar basin. Each winter new ice extends to cover more than 12.5 million km^2 (4.88 million sq miles), or 85 per cent of the total. Antarctic pack ice in summer covers a meagre 2.5 km^2 (0.98 million sq miles), less than 3 per cent of the total ocean area. This too is heavy, multi-year ice, the bulk of it circulating endlessly in the Weddell Sea. In winter new ice spreads to cover 22 million km^2 (8.59 sq miles) or 60 per cent of the total ocean.

There are correspondingly few microscopic animals drifting at the surface, and therefore scanty numbers of fish, seabirds and sea mammals. Exceptions occur in areas of upwelling, for example off the coasts of Peru and southwestern Africa, where surface waters are displaced by offshore winds and cold, nutrient-rich waters well up from deep water. This is where some of the richest warm-water fisheries in the world are found.

Generally speaking, polar waters are richer than tropical waters, although not uniformly so. Those that are permanently ice-covered remain unmixed and biologically poor — there are enough nutrients in the water to support a brief spring bloom of diatoms, but no more. In the central Arctic Ocean, for example, ice-cover persists throughout the year and the spring bloom lasts a meagre two months. Peripheral waters with seasonal ice receive enough wind-stirring to allow a longer spring flush of plant life. But the fringing Arctic seas, ice-free in summer, have a bloom lasting four months or more, and are seasonally among the richest in the world. Once upon a time hunters came from all over the northern hemisphere to take whales, walruses and fish in the peripheral Arctic waters. Today their spring and summer wealth is closely monitored and fished, mainly by those living close to them — rightly so, for they are the only resource available to support the prosperity of Iceland and Greenland, and many Arctic and sub-Arctic communities of Scandinavia, USSR, Canada and Alaska depend heavily on fishing.

■ HOW RICH IS SEA WATER? ■

The biological richness of sea water is measured by the number or weight of organisms present in a sample of known volume. However, a simpler test in oceanic water (where there are no suspended sediments from land) is to lower a white disc the size of a large dinner plate into the ocean on a cord, and see how far down it can be lowered and still be visible. In waters with few organisms, the disc (called a Secchi disc after its inventor) remains visible for many metres; where there are plant cells and small animals present it disappears into a greenish haze within a few metres of the surface. In tropical waters, which are generally poor in species and low in productivity, a Secchi disc may remain visible at depths of 40–50 m (130–165 ft).

The world's clearest sea water was recorded in the Weddell Sea, Antarctica, in early spring, when a Secchi disc was seen at a depth of 79 m (259 ft). This was in water covered by sea ice, that had lost all its plant cells of the previous summer and remained virtually unstirred throughout the winter. Close to the transparency of distilled water, this record may be matched elsewhere, but it is unlikely to be surpassed by more than a metre or two.

■ ■ ■

Kerguelen cormorants breed only on the cliffs of Iles Kerguelen. Similar and related species breed on other Southern Ocean islands and far south along the Antarctic Peninsula, feeding locally, diving to the sea bed offshore for fish, and polychaete worms and other invertebrates. They lay four to five eggs. Their brilliant feathers become waterlogged when they dive and have to be dried out afterwards.

Upwelling areas are especially rich in fauna and flora. Several are known in the Arctic, for example among the channels of the Canadian Arctic archipelago and in the Barents Sea, and they are a particular feature of the Southern Ocean, due to strong surface currents generated by westerly winds. The seas east of South Georgia, the South Sandwich chain, Iles Kerguelen and other Southern Ocean islands are some of the world's richest and most productive. The stirring is continuous and the season lasts several months each year.

An unfailing indication of biological richness is the number of seabirds present. In the tropics, as in ice-bound polar regions, there are very few species of bird, and very few individuals — a week's observation may yield no more than a few dozen birds, flying singly or in small flocks. Temperate and ice-free polar waters show a greater variety of species and much greater numbers of birds. In the north, auks, puffins, kittiwakes and fulmars are predominant; in the south, the huge mixed flocks of feeding birds include albatrosses, several kinds of mollymawk, diving and storm petrels, prions, skuas and penguins. Each species feeds in a slightly different way, at different depths or taking different kinds of prey, so there is little competition between them.

Whales, seals and fish are also good indicators of plenty, although not always easy to spot. It is no accident that commercial sealing and whaling have always been most successful in temperate and subpolar regions, or that today's largest commercial fisheries are cold-water operations.

POLAR WATER MASSES

Oceans in every part of the world give an impression of uniformity and homogeneity. This is misleading. To oceanographers, oceans consist of distinct water masses, with discrete boundaries, salinities, temperatures and histories, fitting together like a giant three-dimensional puzzle cube. Tell an oceanographer the temperature and salt content of the sea close at hand, and he or she will almost certainly identify the water mass you are in and be able to say, with fair accuracy, where you are.

Plants and animals also perceive the ocean in this way. Some, such as whales and seals, are cosmopolitan — they seem not to worry about what kind of water they are in, crossing boundaries and isotherms without problems during their long migratory journeys. Many tinier forms are much more sensitive and therefore more restricted. Some show a strong preference for particular water masses, and sicken or die if they find themselves in water of different salinity or temperature. Hence the dead and dying at the Antarctic Convergence.

Arctic water masses, like the Arctic Ocean itself, tend to be static. The upper layer of ocean, constantly encumbered with ice, receives very little mixing and has low productivity. Diluted by summer floods from the great Siberian rivers and driven clockwise by winds, it circulates around the Arctic basin, discharging ice floes into the North Atlantic Ocean. Beneath this upper water lies a thin layer of richer water that pours off the Siberian continental shelf, and beneath that a deep layer of slightly warmer water that is thrust in constantly from the Atlantic Ocean, circulating counter-clockwise. The deepest parts of the Arctic basin, below about 800 m (2,200 ft), are filled with a reservoir of cold, very static water. These layers tend to keep to themselves. As the surface waters are nutrient-poor and receive little from the richer layers beneath, the central Arctic basin as a whole has little life of any kind.

■ ■ ■

An Antarctic 'ice fish', a species that feeds on or close to the sea bed in Antarctic offshore waters. These fish have little or no red pigment in their blood—apparently Antarctic waters contain enough oxygen for them to manage without. The blood of many species of polar fish contains anti-freeze agents.

Peripheral waters receive more stirring and mixing, especially in summer when the seasonal ice has dispersed. Some patches of the Barents Sea, some areas among the channels of the Canadian archipelago, and other locations where, for one reason or another, nutrient-rich water wells up from below, have very high productivity indeed, yielding plankton on which hordes of fish, birds and aquatic mammals feed throughout summer. Some of these northern 'oases' have been known for centuries to local hunters. Generations of outside fishermen have also been aware of them, for they were once rich whaling, sealing and fishing grounds. Some continue to support substantial commercial fisheries. Others — the Barents Sea, for example — have recently been heavily overfished, and are currently of little use to human communities or to the seals and seabirds that once thrived on their bounty. They need a long rest from hunting, and a chance for overtaxed stocks to recover.

The Southern Ocean is a more lively collection of water masses. Close inshore, prevailing winds blow from the east, so the coldest surface waters circulate westward and slightly toward the land. Prolonged freezing every winter forms surface ice that, because it is frozen fresh water, leaves behind a cold, more salty residue of sea water. This sinks to the continental shelf, pours down the continental slope and creeps northward across the ocean floor, where it forms a layer several hundreds of metres thick, extending over the southern hemisphere and beyond. This is referred to as Antarctic Bottom Water. Antarctic Bottom Water formed in the Weddell Sea can be detected in the Atlantic Ocean well north of the equator.

Further out to sea the prevailing winds are westerlies, driving surface waters east and slightly north. The zone where the two wind-blown currents diverge, called the Antarctic Divergence, is one of upwelling, for new water is brought up constantly from below. The offshore water, called Antarctic Surface Water, continues out across the width of the Southern Ocean to meet warmer subpolar surface waters. At the boundary where they meet, the Antarctic Convergence, the slightly colder and denser southern waters sink below the warmer waters from the north, continuing their northward journey some hundreds of metres below the surface.

The northward flows of Antarctic Bottom Water and Antarctic Surface Water are balanced by a poleward flow of warmer water, called Circumpolar Deep Water, at intermediate depth. This water mass, pulled upward to the surface at the Divergence, contains the secret of the Southern Ocean's wealth. Unused by plankton during its many years away from the ocean surface, it is rich in phosphates, nitrates and other nutrient salts. Returning to the surface, continually renewed, stirred by wave action and lit for more than 12 hours a day in summer, it supports dense populations of planktonic diatoms and algae, on which all other organisms depend.

The full potential of Southern Ocean surface waters, realized in the disturbed zones downwind of islands, is quite remarkable. Some of the highest oceanic productivity in the world has been recorded from these areas in summer, comparable with the productivity of good temperate pastureland ashore. However, these are small areas compared with the huge expanse of the Southern Ocean. Overall, Antarctic marine productivity is not much higher than that of temperate seas, and winter productivity is poor — little better than on land.

FOOD WEBS

Visiting polar seas in summer gives an impression of plenty. Plant plankton clouds the surface of the sea and tints the waterline of ice floes. Towing a nylon net for a few minutes yields catches of copepods, euphausiid shrimps, fish larvae and other tiny creatures. Fat seals drowse on ice floes, whales plough lazily through the waters, flocks of seabirds dip, dive and fill the skies with their wings. How these creatures fit together into the polar jigsaw puzzle is the everyday business of marine ecologists.

Sea ice is a polar world of its own. Both fast ice and pack ice are usually cracked and fissured, effectively becoming extensions of land far out at sea. Thin ice is a haven for plankton; the green cells of plant plankton settle on its spongy undersurface, and crustaceans and other herbivorous invertebrates dodge among them, browsing like inverted sheep. Surface-living fish eat the invertebrates, and seabirds and seals feed impartially on both. To seals, whales and dolphins, sea ice can be dangerous, for they are air-breathing mammals and drown if they cannot find holes to breathe through. Nevertheless some species

North Pole ■

South Pole ■

live far into the pack ice throughout the winter. In spring the retreating ice edge becomes a favourite hunting ground. Rorquals, the large plankton-feeding whales that migrate to polar regions each summer, are especially attracted to ice edges, for the melting ice releases plankton in shoals thick enough for them to feed on.

In the open water food webs are much the same. Here sea temperatures rise several degrees in summer. Once again clouds of free-living plant plankton provide sustenance for shoals of animal plankton, and these in turn sustain the top predators.

ARCTIC PREDATORS

Many species of surface-living fish, including salmon, char, capelin and Arctic cod, feed in the colder Arctic waters, while warmer sub-Arctic waters support northern cod, skate, haddock and coalfish. These same species are fished, both locally and commercially for southern markets.

Some 50 species of Arctic seabird gather about the richest areas. These include 14 species of auk, guillemot and razorbill, ten species of gull and skua, terns, fulmars and cormorants, all of which breed in June and July, often in huge cliff colonies. They feed

■   ■   ■   WHO EATS WHO?   ■   ■   ■

In polar and non-polar regions alike marine plants and animals form interlinking webs of dependency. Plants — mostly microscopic, single-celled diatoms and algae — require energy from sunlight and nutrients from surface waters in order to grow, reproduce and build up their numbers. The tiny animals that browse on them prosper whenever and wherever the algae prosper. So, in their turn, do the larger animals that feed on the tiny ones, and the still larger animals, sometimes called the 'top predators', that complete the food chains. Waste products from animals and dead organisms of all kinds are decomposed by bacteria, and their chemical components are returned to the nutrient pool for recycling.

Food webs — collections of food chains which are a rough guide to who-eats-who in the sea — can be drawn to express all these relationships. Though some of the species may differ, the pattern of relationships is the same for both the Arctic and the Antarctic Oceans, and indeed for most of the world's oceans. Plant plankton of varying sizes, which are the primary energy fixers and the basic food, appear at the top of the web. They live only in the upper few metres of the sea, and are eaten by animal plankton — mostly very small crustaceans and juvenile forms of other animals, including fish. The animal plankton are consumed mainly by fish and seabirds, and also by baleen whales, those with filters of 'whalebone' in their mouths that strain the plankton from the water. The fish are eaten by other fish, larger seabirds, dolphins and toothed whales — and human beings are the top predators of all. Debris of all kinds descends from the upper waters of the sea to the sea bed, to nourish sponges, worms, molluscs, starfish, tunicates, bottom-living fish and other creatures of the deep.

Two brown skuas feed on the carcass of a recently-dead southern fur seal, watched and scolded by a gentoo penguin. Skuas often prey on penguin colonies, taking unguarded eggs and chicks. The seal, an old male, died of exhaustion and battle wounds toward the end of the mating season. Note the thickness of the fur and the insulating blubber.

at sea, sometimes travelling far from their nesting grounds. Sub-Arctic storm petrels and long-distance migrants such as sooty shearwaters and skuas from the southern hemisphere meet them at the feeding grounds. The breeding birds provide food for native hunters, who takes eggs, fat juveniles and adults from their colonies.

Polar bears, almost diagnostic of the Arctic, wander between tundra and offshore ice, the males tending to travel alone, the females with one or two cubs at heel. Their white fur, affording superb insulation at sea or on land, traps the sunlight like a custom-made greenhouse. Polar bears mate in early spring and spend the summer hunting seals on the pack ice. In autumn they find a den on land or inshore sea ice. In winter they sleep — their body temperature falls slightly, but they can resume activity quickly in emergency. Tiny cubs born in January or February feed on the milk of their still-sleeping mother, emerging with her in March or April. Cubs stay with their mothers for two years, learning to feed on roots, shoots, berries, birds, eggs, small mammals, river fish or seals caught from the sea ice. Formerly endangered by hunting, polar bears are now protected by international convention throughout the Arctic and sub-Arctic.

Six species of seal live in the coldest Arctic waters among the sea ice, and two more on the Arctic fringes. Walruses, the largest of the northern seals, live in eastern Siberia and Alaska, with a separate group in eastern Canada, Greenland and Arctic Europe. Large males grow over 4 m (13 ft) long. Shallow-water feeders, they use tusks and sensory whiskers to find clams in the mud. They winter inshore and disperse northward in small groups in spring. Pups are born on the pack ice in May, and family groups spend the summer hunting beneath the ice.

Ribbon and grey seals are found only on the Arctic fringes, respectively in Pacific and Atlantic waters. Bearded and ringed seals breed inshore in the Arctic basin. Hooded and harp seals live in large groups on the offshore pack ice near Labrador and Jan Mayen Island — harp seals also occur in the White Sea. These species have long been hunted for their pelts, especially the fine pelts of pups and yearlings.

Northern fur seals breed on the beaches of the Pribilov Islands and other islands in the Bering Sea. Managed successfully for most of this century by an international commission, they provided a sustained yield of pelts, mainly from non-breeding males, that supported an extensive industry. The US Government discontinued its involvement in the 1980s and the future of the Pribilof fur seal herds is currently uncertain.

The Bering Sea and cold waters from eastern Canada to Svalbard support several species of whale and dolphin. White whales and belugas have always been traditional prey to the Inuit. Early commercial hunters took bowheads, bottlenoses and northern beaked whales, and later operations have concentrated on the larger grey, humpback, sperm, blue, fin, sei and minke whales. Stocks of all species are currently low, but should recover now that commercial whaling is finished. Inuit communities retain rights to hunt a few whales each year for food.

■ ■ ■

*Walruses sunbathing,
Round Island, Alaska.
Among the largest members
of the seal family, walruses
dive deep for their food,
scraping the mud of the sea
bed for clams with their
long tusks. Sensory bristles
grow from their bulbous
noses and may help them
to locate clams — their eyes
are small and probably
ineffective in muddy water.
Walruses were once hunted
for their hides and fine
ivory tusks, and the Inuit
still take them for food.
Now that restrictions have
been imposed on trading in
elephant ivory, the value of
walrus tusks has increased,
and there are well-founded
fears in the north that
walruses are again at risk
from poaching.*

■ ■ ■

*Silver-coated crabeater seals
under Antarctic sea ice.
Seals climb onto land or pack
ice to sleep, mate, and
produce and nurse their
pups. On land they drag and
hump their heavy bodies like
weary, over-fat caterpillars.
In the water they become
totally different creatures.
Crabeaters feed mostly
on krill.*

■   ■   ■   KEEPING WARM IN POLAR SEAS   ■   ■   ■

Plants, invertebrates and fish which live in polar seas take their body temperature from the cold water surrounding them. As this seldom varies more than 2–3°C (4–6°F) in the course of the year, theirs is a cold but constant environment. Seabirds, seals and whales are homeotherms, i.e. warm-blooded, maintaining body temperatures of 38–39°C (100–102°F). Penguins spend days at a time in the water, whales spend all their lives there. So how do warm-blooded creatures manage to maintain their body temperature in near-freezing waters?

Like all other homeotherms they generate heat by muscular activity and retain it by insulation. Fur and feathers are good insulation on land and in shallow water, but of no use in deep water. Their efficiency depends on the layer of insulating air they hold close to the skin, and at depth that layer of air is compressed, allowing heat to leak away. All swimming birds and mammals have a thick skin and a layer of fat — called blubber — under the skin. Blubber is both a food store and additional insulation. It does not need an extensive blood supply, so can be maintained at a lower temperature than the rest of the body. The blood supply to the skin, which passes through it, can be varied according to the animal's needs.

When a warm-blooded animal is swimming actively and generating a lot of heat in its muscles, blood supply to skin and blubber increases and the skin sheds excess heat to the sea like a radiator. Penguins emerging from the sea after a hard swim show this clearly; the undersides of their flippers are bright pink with engorged blood, paling to white as they cool down. In an animal resting at the surface, the blood supply to the skin is reduced; now skin and blubber cool almost to sea temperature and become effective insulation, conserving body heat.

Harp seals, so called because of a harp-shaped brown patch on their backs, are fish-eating seals of the northern sea ice. Ranging widely over the North Atlantic and neighbouring Arctic seas, they breed in three distinct stocks off Newfoundland and Jan Mayen Island and in the White Sea. Theirs are the snow-white pups with appealing black eyes that sealers are licensed to take in tens of thousands each year. Conservation-ists intent on banning the killing of harp seals may be missing a point: the species as a whole is probably far more at risk from fishermen taking more than their share of capelin and other important food species.

■ ■ ■

A polar bear examines his reflection in the clear ice of a lake. With their white coats and huge paws, polar bears are the most characteristic of Arctic mammals. They are nomadic, roaming the tundra and sea ice in a constant search for food. Males are usually solitary, but females often have one, two or three cubs at heel. They swim well. Their dense white fur sheds water and ice, and traps sunlight deep down, helping to warm them close to the skin.

■ ■ ■

Northern fur seals at a breeding colony on St Paul's Island, Pribilof Islands. Here one large male (top centre) tends a group of about 30 females, many of them with small black pups. A second male looks on (top right), ready to move in and round up some of the females should the opportunity arise. Pribilof Island stocks of this species have been managed successfully for many years; most of those culled for the fur trade are young males.

■ ■ ■

Steller's sea lions relax on a buoy in Prince William Sound, Alaska. Sea lions lack the dense underfur that makes fur seal pelts valuable; Aleuts use their tough skins for covering boats.

ANTARCTIC PREDATORS

The Southern Ocean holds huge stocks of fish, both surface-living and deepwater. Unrelated to northern species and not especially welcome to northern palates, they are caught commercially on a large scale, mostly in offshore waters around the ice-free southern islands, for deep-freezing and processing into meal.

Antarctica and islands within the Convergence support some 40 breeding species of bird, including four species of albatross, 20 species of smaller petrel, seven species of penguin, and a miscellany of gulls, terns, skuas, sheathbills and cormorants. The penguins and petrels nest in large colonies and fly or swim to distant feeding areas. With no land predators to worry about, they nest in tens or hundreds of thousands on beaches, coastal flats and cliffs, mostly from October onward. Petrels lay single eggs, most other species two or three. The ocean-feeders form large mixed flocks, but each species fishes in its own way. Some dip for fish or squid at the surface, others take krill and tiny fish; snow petrels feed almost entirely among pack ice, hovering and dodging precariously between the floes; prions filter surface waters for zooplankton; penguins feed below the surface, the larger ones at considerable depth.

Six species of seal live within the Convergence. Southern elephant seals are the largest — up to 6 m (20 ft) long. They breed on the southern islands, taking squid and fish in the deep waters nearby.

■ ■ ■

A group of killer whales, the ultimate predators of all the world's oceans. Killer whales hunt in packs of up to a dozen, unmistakable in their livery of black and white. They are usually led by a large male, up to 10 m (33 ft) long, with a sail-like dorsal fin. Although found in tropical and temperate seas, they seem just as happy among pack ice — one will occasionally rise out of the water and rest its chin thoughtfully on a floe, while having a good look around. They are often found where emperor and other penguins congregate (although it would take many penguins to make a square meal for a killer), and are reported to capsize floes that have seals sleeping on them.

■ ■ ■

Humpback whales gained their name from their habit of arching their backs and waving their tail flukes just before diving. Each animal has a distinctive black and white pattern on its tail, as individual as a signature. Whale-watchers have gathered files of hundreds of tail patterns, enabling them to trace the long migratory movements of these huge, gentle creatures.

■ ■ ■

Rockhopper penguins, Iles Kerguelen. Smallest of the polar and sub-polar penguins, rockhoppers breed in colonies of a few dozen to a few thousand pairs, usually where there are steep rock staircases to climb from the sea. Their nests are piles of pebbles, which they defend vigorously against neighbours. They lay one large and one smaller egg, usually kicking the smaller one out of the nest.

ANTARCTIC PENGUINS

■ ■ ■ ■ ■ ■

Penguins are flightless seabirds that walk, swim and dive. Wings have evolved into narrow flippers which propel them through the water; feet and tail have become rudders when swimming. In cold waters penguins are kept warm by dense plumage with an underlayer of down and subdermal fat. The largest species dive deepest, some to 500 m (1,600 ft) or more.

Penguins are southern hemisphere birds, mostly of temperate or cool seas, but seven species live in or close to the Antarctic region. Emperor penguins live only on coastal Antarctica. The largest of living penguins, weighing over 40 kg (90 lbs) in full fat and standing almost a metre (3.25 ft) tall, they breed in May or June on sea ice. They do not make nests, and only the males incubate, standing with the single egg on their feet for nine weeks during the coldest period of winter. Females spend the winter at sea, returning in July and August at hatching time. The chicks, fed by both parents from food carried in the crop, grow slowly at first, then rapidly, reaching independence in January. Adelie penguins also breed in Antarctica, but they nest in summer, producing two eggs. Chinstrap penguins breed only on the Antarctic Peninsula and nearby islands. Gentoo and crested macaroni penguins range widely throughout the southern islands, north and south of the pack ice. Rockhopper and king penguins breed only on warmer islands near the Convergence. Emperor and king penguins, the two largest species, feed on fish and squid at intermediate depths, and also on krill and surface fish. The smaller species feed mainly on surface-living fish and krill.

Like rockhopper penguins (above), macaroni penguins lay two eggs of different sizes but rear only the larger one — an unusual form of family planning. Their golden crests are colourful all year round, but especially flamboyant during courtship. Male and female stand on the nest, braying at each other and waving their heads violently, like noisy chrysanthemums. A hillside colony of 20,000 pairs, all in full courtship, is a memorable sight.

Their thick, oil-yielding blubber made them the prey of 19th-century sealers — seal oil, like whale oil, was good for lighting and lubrication. Ross seals and crabeaters live almost entirely on the pack ice, feeding respectively on squid and krill. Weddell seals live on the inshore sea ice surrounding Antarctica, diving deep for fish and squid. Leopard seals, slender creatures with wide jaws, live all over the region, feeding on fish, seabirds and smaller seals. Often they patrol off penguin colonies, catching birds as they return from sea. Southern fur seals were hunted almost to extermination at their island breeding grounds throughout the 19th century. Now protected, they are again plentiful on South Georgia and stocks are returning to other Southern Ocean islands.

Small groups of southern bottlenose, minke and killer whales live year-round among the Antarctic pack ice. Polynyas and cracks provide the open water they need for surfacing. Male sperm whales, together with humpback, blue, fin, sei and minke whales, migrate from warmer waters each summer to feed in the Southern Ocean. Sperm whales dive deep for fish and squid, while humpbacks and rorquals take mainly small fish and animal plankton in surface waters. From 1904 onward the migrant species were hunted commercially every summer by whalers of several nations, and processed at shore stations or on factory ships moored off the southern islands. Later, fleets of ocean-going catchers and factory ships worked the rich waters along the receding edge of the pack ice. The industry produced whale oil and a range of by-products, including meat-meal and fertilizers. During the 1960s the industry collapsed. Whale stocks in the Southern Ocean remain low, but some are beginning to show signs of recovery.

■ ■ ■

Survivors of a turbulent past, these two young elephant seals would once have been prime targets for sealing gangs. Largest of all living seals, male elephant seals reach lengths of 5 m (16 ft) and weigh well over 3 tonnes. They dive deep for their food, eating mainly fish and squid. In whaling times they were a useful source of oil — their blubber is many centimetres thick. Stocks on all the southern islands, once almost wiped out, have now recovered.

■ ■ ■

Weddell seals are a species of the high Antarctic, breeding mostly on inshore sea ice around the continent and on the South Orkney and South Shetland Islands. Huge breeding colonies numbering thousands have only recently been discovered along the Weddell Sea coast — Antarctica keeps its secrets well. They dive deep for their food, which is mainly fish and squid, using sonar trills to hunt in the inky darkness. In McMurdo Sound in winter Weddells use their teeth to keep breathing holes open; many have worn, broken and abcessed teeth as a result.

5

Land Animals and Plants

Reared in warmer climes and more generous environments, most of us expect life in polar regions to be sparse. We marvel that living creatures of any kind tolerate the polar cold. The terms we use to describe polar ecosystems illustrate this attitude. 'Tundra', our name for the most widespread kind of polar vegetation, means 'treeless' — absence of the familiar company of trees is what first strikes us about polar plant communities. 'Polar desert', the term we use to refer to tundra's poorer relation, suggests a dominance of rocks, ice and snowdrifts, an environment indifferent to life, where living creatures are present only on sufferance.

These are useful terms, but negative, limited, and remarkably unappreciative. If we can celebrate the annual miracle of daffodils and lambs in a temperate spring, surely we can appreciate the achievement of a sparrow-sized snow bunting, alert and cheerful at -30°C (-24°C), or a tuft of lichen alive and in business on a frozen island in the North Polar basin.

The Inuit and Indians who live in the Arctic see things differently, and on the whole more positively. Knowing nothing of more complex environments, they concentrate on what they have. In their languages, which are primarily spoken rather than written, they have a host of terms that describe different forms of snow, qualities of vegetation and animals, and relationships between snow, rocks and plant and animal species. Underlying their perceptions is the concept that the minutiae of the environment are important, and that every creature is successful in its own way, and doing its best for its own welfare, and for the welfare of those who must hunt it in order to survive.

This makes better sense and far better ecology than our own grudging acceptance of polar ecosystems. Plants and animals do not live in conditions to which they are unsuited. Natural selection would quickly destroy any that did. Living creatures in polar regions are there because they have found plenty of what they need — at least as much as in temperate regions, and possibly more. They have adapted to the stringent conditions, accepted the challenge of cold and wind and months of twilight, and won. It is the business of the polar ecologist not to marvel that they are there but to discover how they manage to be there, and what compromises they have made for the sake of survival.

RESIDENTS AND VISITORS

In winter the Arctic tundra seems empty and all but dead, but nowhere in the world is the onset of spring more striking. Once the snow starts to melt, the land yawns and stretches and everything springs to life, all within a miraculous two or three days. Arctic plants are few and small, and there is less variety of species than in warmer climates. But in favoured spots they carpet the ground, creating gardens glowing with flowers and rich in earthy scents. Small birds and mammals appear — snow buntings, ptarmigan, ravens, busy lemmings, weasels, hares, foxes — creatures that spend winter under the snow or in white camouflage against it.

One of the earliest signs of Arctic spring is a whirring of wings, bringing in migrant ducks, geese, swans, shorebirds and warblers from the south, to fill the tundra with cackle and song. They fly in from as far away as New Zealand and southern Africa and from Antarctic coastal waters, risking long flights over forest and ocean. Some are terrestrial species, others marine, but most are wetland birds, come to breed on the ponds, streams and soggy grasslands of the tundra. Of some 150 species of Arctic breeding bird, all but eight species are summer migrants.

Summer sees the tundra shift from pale green to dark green. The soil thaws and becomes waterlogged. The ice of thousands of lakes, ponds and streams suddenly becomes water. Insects become plentiful — Arctic bees, beetles, moths, butterflies, mosquitoes and sandflies swarm in plague populations from early summer onward. These are closely followed by the rabbits, mice and other small creatures that leave the forest edge for the tundra, and the reindeer and caribou that journey northward on their annual tundra-wide migrations.

If summer is colourful, autumn is vivid. Berries and leaves turn red, then golden-brown for just a week or two of brilliance before the first winter snows. The migrants, fattening after their labours on the last of the summer bonanza, start to move south, their numbers augmented by young. Resident birds and mammals change into winter dress and disappear into the gathering snow. Twilight falls, and then the long winter darkness. Tundra life is over quickly, but it is spectacular while it lasts.

Antarctica is always colder than the Arctic, and its terrestrial life is harder to find. Heavily ice-covered, with persistent snows in winter and summer, at first

■ ■ ■

Summer in West Greenland. Here is tundra at its best — a mature stream basin, with good soils developed on well-drained river gravels, supporting a relatively rich and varied flora. No wonder the early Viking colonists, fresh from the valleys of southern Norway, felt at home in the country they called Greenland.

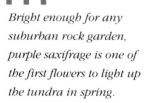

Bright enough for any suburban rock garden, purple saxifrage is one of the first flowers to light up the tundra in spring.

■ ■ ■

Like mountain moorlands in temperate climates, Arctic tundra has many small shrubs that flower in early spring, then quickly produce autumn berries. Here a cranberry bush, only a hand's breadth *across and hugging the ground, packs all its surplus energy into a dozen bright berries. The Inuit, tundra birds and even polar bears love them.*

glance it seems an unlikely place for plants of any kind. Neither the continent itself nor its warmer peninsula support true tundra. There are no summer migrants, no small mammals or birds, and compared with the Arctic, far fewer plant species. Nevertheless, Antarctica is far from dead. Biologists delight in its improbabilities — tiny moss clumps in crevices that are damp for a few hours each day, lichens clinging to rock walls, tufts of hardy grasses flourishing in tiny ice-greenhouses under the snow, millimetre-long mites and insects....

Islands within the pack ice fringing Antarctica support similar vegetation. Those beyond the limit of the pack ice support much richer fell-field or moor-land ecosystems, with more terrestrial invertebrates and even a few species of indigenous land bird. All the Antarctic islands, and the continent itself, are breeding grounds for enormous populations of seabirds and seals.

CONTRASTING POLAR VEGETATION

Though the land ecology of the two polar regions is basically similar, there are interesting differences between them. Within the ecological boundary of the treeline, Arctic lands support three major communities or biomes; from south to north these are forest-tundra, tundra, and polar desert. Neither forest-tundra nor tundra itself, the Arctic's most characteristic biomes, have any equivalent in the Antarctic. Only polar desert, the northernmost and poorest Arctic biome, comes anywhere near the poverty of Antarctica. However, the most meagre Arctic version of polar desert is more complex than anything Antarctica has to offer .

There are several reasons for these differences. The south has no equivalent of the northern conifer-ous forests, no treeline, and only oceans in the regions where Antarctic tundra would grow. What land there is in the far south lies close to the ice cap,

■ ■ ■

Tiny Arctic willows and dwarf birches dominate this patch of northern tundra, where nothing grows more than ankle-high. Tundra plants benefit by staying close to the ground — although the air is cold, the sun warms soil, shoots and roots, and the wind is tempered by ground friction. Perennial plants grow slowly — willow stems no thicker than a pencil may be decades or even centuries old.

ARCTIC TUNDRA VERSUS ANTARCTIC POLAR DESERT

Devon Island, in 75°N, is a northern outpost of Canadian Arctic tundra, on the boundary between tundra and polar desert. On its lowlands, representing the poorest kind of northern tundra, botanists have found 132 species of moss, 30 species of liverwort, nine species of fern, and no fewer than 90 species of flowering plant, all within a few hectares. In the Soviet Arctic, on some of the coldest and remotest islands north of Siberia, it is still possible to find as many as 60 species of flowering plant, with miniature poppies, saxifrages and grasses among the hardiest.

For the whole Antarctic continent, including the relatively warm Antarctic Peninsula, surveys have shown only 45 species of moss, five species of liverwort, no species of fern and only two species of flowering plant. South Georgia (54°S) and other comparatively mild Southern Ocean islands within the 10°C (50°F) summer isotherm have richer floras, though still very restricted in numbers of species. South Georgia has more mosses and liverworts than Devon Island, almost as many ferns, but still only a third as many flowering plants.

■ ■ ■

Banks of polar snow close to the sea often turn vivid green or red in summer. The colour is due to minute algae, which grow on snow contaminated by salt spray. In Antarctica the colours are densest close to penguin *colonies, where nitrates and phosphates from the birds' droppings help to create a growth medium. Here on Petermann Island, in 65°S, patches of red and green alternate across the melting snow banks.*

equivalent in climate to the most northerly reaches of the Arctic. Arctic tundra has had time to acquire deep, relatively mature soils. Plants grow for longer each year, there is more moisture for them, and the vegetation itself modifies the ground, providing cover and shelter for new plants to become established. Antarctica's ice-free fringes seem but newly emerged from the ice; both their soils and plant communities are comparatively new and immature — they have not yet had time to do better.

'Recruiting' too is different. Flora and fauna from the Arctic fringe are constantly trying to establish themselves further north, and many succeed. Most of the indigenous Arctic flora and fauna are closely related to temperate species, showing clearly where their ancestors came from. The Antarctic has no such reservoirs to draw on. Much Arctic recruitment seems to have happened during the last two million years of the current ice age, as tundra and forest fluctuated

north and south before the ice sheets. The Antarctic ice sheets have advanced to the edges of the continent, but their retreats have scarcely left room even for proto-tundra on the periphery.

NORTHERN TUNDRA AND POLAR DESERT

The word 'tundra' is used rather confusingly to describe both a kind of vegetation and the place where it grows. Typically it is a low-standing mixture of shrubs, flowering plants (including grasses and reeds), mosses, liverworts, lichens and algae. Intermittently along its southern edge grows forest-tundra, a transitional zone of tundra with a scattering of trees and tall shrubs. In places forest tundra replaces a more sharply-defined tree line. Along its northern edge tundra grades into polar desert, a similar mix but thinner and much reduced in species, including only the toughest and most stunted plants.

A biologist examines filaments of green algae growing in a small stream in the polar desert conditions of Signy Island, South Orkney Islands.

The treeline — where the northernmost trees, of whatever species, never quite achieve full proportions — follows fairly closely the 10°C (50°F) summer isotherm, suggesting that trees at their ecological limit will grow only where summer mean temperatures are above that figure. However, ground moisture, winter snow levels, the length of the growing season, wind and permafrost, and several other factors help to decide where trees will grow. One issue of vital importance is the survival of seedlings. Even if trees at their northern limit produce seeds often, the ground may be inhospitable to them, and their seedlings have great difficulty in growing. There may be no recruitment to the forest edge for several years on end.

Contrasting with the three-dimensional forest, tundra is two-dimensional, bare and flat. Few of its plants reach waist height. Many stand knee-high or prostrate themselves along the ground, as though trying to avoid the tundra winds. Snow-covered in winter and frozen solid for eight months of the year, tundra becomes waterlogged during the spring thaw. Melt-water cannot escape through the permanently frozen subsoil or evaporate into the cold, saturated air. Nor does it drain naturally from the surface, which until recently was glaciated and lacks drainage channels. Boggy tundra supports many species of marshy, water-tolerant plants. Drier, better drained

■ MORE ARCTIC/ANTARCTIC COMPARISONS ■

Since the Arctic first became cold, plants and animals have always moved north to try their luck. Plenty must have failed to make good, but the richness of the northern tundra and even of the northern polar desert show how many were successful. By contrast, Antarctica has long been separated from other continents, and most of the Southern Ocean islands have never been linked to any other land mass, so the chances of 'recruitment' have been fewer. Very few land plants or animals from the southern temperate zone have crossed the ocean to colonize them. Some temperate species introduced by man have been wildly successful, demonstrating that only the opportunity for cross-sea transport has been lacking.

Arctic plants in a variety of habitats support over a dozen major groups of invertebrates; among the insects alone, for example, there are butterflies, bees, beetles, hover-flies, mosquitoes, biting simuliid flies and many others. Antarctica and the fringing islands have relatively poor soils, very little fresh water and few plants; the land fauna is correspondingly restricted to a few micro-organisms, insects and mites. Antarctica's largest land animal is a wingless mosquito-like fly that breeds in tidal pools.

Arctic tundra supports eight species of non-migrant land bird, about 150 species of summer migrant bird, and over 40 species of land mammal, ranging in size from mice to musk oxen. Antarctica has no land birds, and only its warmer fringing islands support a few resident species between them. Nor does the Antarctic possess any land-living migrants or native land mammals, though several of the warmer islands support rats, rabbits, reindeer and other introduced mammals.

❄

patches support xerophytic (drought-tolerant) plants, sometimes growing in circular or hexagonal patterns. These result from soil movements caused by cycles of freezing and thawing. Tundra soils tend to be immature and unstable, readily lifted by strong winds. Their patchiness makes the vegetation patchy, a mosaic of plant communities and open ground.

The deepest soils, the richest assemblages of plant species and the most complete ground cover occur on the southern tundra, where metre-high thickets of shrubs alternate with mosses, grasses, heathers and other flowering plants. Early summer, shortly after the thaw, sees the tundra at its best and most colourful, with dwarf lupins, buttercups, windflowers, gentians and a host of other flowers making a spectacular carpet. From July onward grasses and shrubs begin to redden, and berries all too quickly colour the autumn scene. Summer walking on the southern tundra demands strong boots and insect repellants, for voracious mosquitoes and simuliid flies constantly seek a meal of blood to enhance their egg-laying. Birds and mammals are their usual victims, but human beings do just as well.

North of the 6°C (42°F) summer isotherm, on the northernmost mainland coasts and islands, tundra becomes a thinner and more threadbare carpet. Mature soils are rare and the vegetation is more stunt-ed, seldom more than 20 cm (8 inches) high. Tiny willows, heathers, avens, rushes, mosses and grasses create an incomplete cover. In many species, a few thin stems emerge from an elaborate network of roots — much of the plant body is underground, where it is safer from browsing animals and wind-nip. Others adopt a cushion form — dozens of short stems grow from a central point, creating a small, compact plant body which defies wind and cold. Temperatures within these compact cushions rise several degrees above air temperature, so that the plant creates its own greenhouse.

■ ■ ■

Soils, permafrost, the length of the growing season and many other factors determine the position of the treeline in the North American and Eurasian Arctic. Close to the treeline spruce and other conifers grow in patchy, irregular fashion, clustering together for mutual support. They are often stunted and misshapen, sometimes showing intense wind-sculpturing and browsing by mammals. There are usually few seedlings, for germination is often difficult and early growth poor.

■ ■ ■

A dog lichen growing in a mixed community of mosses, grasses and shrubs on the West Greenland tundra. Lichens are tough, leathery plants, a cross between algae and fungi, and often the first plants to colonize rocky terrain. Rootless, relatively insensitive to drying out and strong winds, they are ideal plants for harsh conditions.

■ ■ ■

Willow catkins growing not on trees but on tiny shrubs just above ground level. These are female catkins of the dwarf species Salix arctophila. *Each plant will bear just a few catkins and may not be able to produce a crop every year. The white furry growth catches the sun, warming the seeds.*

■ ■ ■

Graceful campanulas — tundra harebells — grow in clusters among the tundra grasses. The blue, semi-transparent flowers are a signpost for pollinating insects. They also attract the sun, warming the developing seeds at the base of the petals.

■ ■ ■
Brown club-mosses, lichens
and true mosses make up a
dense mat at the tundra-
forest edge. Dead-looking
though these mats may be,
they often contain fungi,
nematodes, insects, mites,
spiders and other creatures
living in predatory
relationships to each other,
all depending ultimately on
the energy that their host
plants trap from sunlight.

In this cooler zone, sometimes described as fell-field, less than half the surface of the ground is covered with vegetation. Flowers appear spasmodically, and the rich variety of the southern tundra is lacking. These features are a response to shorter summers and more particularly to harsher winters. Where there is little winter snow to protect them, plants suffer severely from dryness and abrasive winds.

Further north, beyond the 2°C (37°F) summer isotherm, the vegetation thins to less than 20 per cent cover. Polar desert vegetation occurs on the coldest shores of the Arctic Ocean, on both mainland and islands. All the less hardy species have disappeared, leaving only the toughest lichens, mosses, algae, and tiny flowering plants in thin, scattered mats among the bare rocks and shingle. They grow best in snow-melt runnels or damp patches of soil, indicating that lack of water, not cold, is the limiting factor in their growth. The polar desert zone can be surprisingly colourful, lit by the brilliant reds, oranges, greens and blacks of encrusting lichens.

ARCTIC TUNDRA BIRDS AND MAMMALS

Arctic tundra in winter provides poor pickings for birds and mammals. Of the eight species of resident bird, four — Lapland buntings, snow buntings, Arctic and common redpolls, all eaters of seeds and small insects — move southward to the warmer edges for winter. Only the larger rock and willow ptarmigan,

ravens and snowy owls spend the coldest months on the tundra. Ptarmigan, digging through the snow with feathered feet for shoots and seeds, have white winter plumage, an obvious adaptation for polar living. Ravens and owls patrol the tundra year-round for insects, birds, small mammals, offal, or anything else good to eat. All the resident birds breed in May and June, when food may be plentiful and 24 hour-long summer days afford ample daylight for foraging.

Tundra food is sometimes abundant, sometimes scarce, depending on local conditions. An unseasonable overnight fall of snow or a few days of hard frost after a thaw can make a big difference to food supplies. Breeding success fluctuates widely from season to season. In years when lemmings and voles are plentiful snowy owls may raise clutches of seven or eight chicks. In poor years they may raise none at all, and only survive by moving to other areas.

From April onward the migrant birds crowd in, hungry after their flights. Swans, geese, ducks and waders (shorebirds) take long-distance cross-continental routes, using recognized flyways and stopover points. Gulls, terns, divers and smaller waterfowl migrate shorter distances from temperate wintering grounds, perhaps only from the coast. Migration allows them to take advantage of the seasonal abundance of food and relative dearth of predators in the Arctic, but there are problems too. Limited by time, they must begin breeding immediately. Most are already paired when they arrive, and take up territories familiar to them from previous years. They have to forage and start nesting and laying within hours of their arrival. If the thaw is late, or if there are a few days of bad weather, their breeding cycle may be delayed and end in disaster.

Most of the migrants feed on buds, growing shoots, freshwater algae, insect larvae, crustaceans, beetles, crane flies and other invertebrates of soil, pond and stream. The predators among them, including skuas, gulls and hawks, live on smaller birds, eggs, nestlings and small mammals. Late April and May are incubation time. During June and July, tundra foods should be at their peak of availability, so that hungry, rapidly growing chicks can be fed to capacity. If all goes well, by early August most juveniles have fledged and left the breeding grounds; their parents undergo a post-nuptial moult and follow their young before winter sets in. In a poor season with a delayed start and scanty food, chick mortality can be high; many nests are abandoned at the end of the season to give the parents a chance to survive to breed another year.

About a dozen species of mammals reside year-round on the tundra, ranging in size from musk oxen and caribou to lemmings, voles and shrews. The large mammals live out in the open, relying on their insulating pelts, body fat and their habit of communal huddling to keep them warm in the hardest weather. The smaller ones live under the snow, close to the ground and well sheltered from the worst weather. No Arctic birds or mammals hibernate (i.e. allow their body temperature to fall and enter a state of suspended animation). All the overwinterers remain active, except polar bears, which dig themselves into snow dens and become torpid at the time of cubbing. Their body temperature remains high, so they are ready for quick action if disturbed.

Musk oxen, caribou and reindeer were traditionally hunted by native people, and later fell easy prey to trappers and whalers with rifles. Musk oxen suffered especially, for they were easy targets and their meat was highly palatable. Once found grazing all over the tundra, they now survive naturally only in north Greenland and the Canadian archipelago.

CARIBOU IN CONFLICT

Caribou herds number anything up to 300,000 animals and range over enormous areas. The 'Arctic' herd, one of thirteen designated herds in Alaska, is thought to contain a quarter of a million animals, ranging over 360,000 km^2 (140,000 sq miles) of tundra. These huge grazing areas are needed because tundra regenerates slowly after grazing. Attempts to constrain the caribou or restrict their movements are likely to cause local over-grazing and long-term damage.

Natives of Alaska have the right to hunt caribou for their own subsistence. They do not herd the animals, but fiercely defend their grazing lands against alternative uses. Pipelines, roads, oil-drilling sites and camps they regarded with suspicion, arguing that any disturbance of the tundra which alters or restricts herd movements can only have damaging effects on the caribou. The issue is complicated because some herds are 'international'. Many animals of the Porcupine herd of northern Alaska, for example, winter across the border in Canada's Yukon Territory, but spend their summers in US territory on the oil-rich North Slope of Alaska. Some 75 per cent of the herd calve in a designated refuge area flanking the Beaufort Sea, which oilmen want to explore and perhaps exploit. Both Canadian and US natives have hunting rights over this herd, and both governments feel responsibility toward it.

Spokesmen for oil interests usually contend that, to maintain prosperity in the north, oil-rich lands must be exploited, but that their operations can be managed to avoid serious damage to the tundra or the herds. They point to their success in designing the trans-Alaska petroleum pipeline to avoid problems with wildlife: caribou quickly got used to its presence, and the most careful research has failed to show any deleterious effects on their welfare.

The debate continues. Very similar arguments are taking place in eastern Canada over caribou grazing lands, and in Scandinavia and Siberia over reindeer pastures. Conflicts are likely wherever alternative uses are suggested for the enormous areas of seemingly empty tundra that hunters and herders claim for grazing.

▪ ▪ ▪

This male bar-tailed godwit, about to re-settle on its well hidden eggs, is one of about 50 species of wader (shorebird) that breed on the Arctic coastal tundra each summer. Birdwatchers of temperate shores know bar-tailed godwits as winter passage-migrants.

▪ ▪ ▪

Willow ptarmigan are year-round residents on the North America and Eurasian tundra. They concentrate in areas of low scrub that provide them with their main food—buds and young shoots, supplemented in spring and summer by insects.

▪ ▪ ▪

Greater and lesser snow geese breed on the high tundra of North America, Greenland and Siberia. Wetlands along the tundra coast, when they feed on young emergent vegetation, seem especially to their liking.

▪ ▪ ▪

Familiar throughout the Arctic as year-round residents, snowy owls penetrate farther north than almost any other species of bird. Although owls are traditionally night predators, snowy owls hunt by daylight in summer.

■ ■ ■

Woolly musk oxen, with characteristics of both sheep and cattle, survive in some of the coldest areas of the tundra. About the size of ponies, solidly muscled, with manes of fine matted fur, they move in groups of a dozen or more, usually with calves trotting at heel. When threatened by predators they form a solid circle with horns pointing outward. This is a good defence against wolves, but not against men with guns — at one time they were shot for meat all over the Arctic. Now the species is better protected, and stocks are being reintroduced in some areas. Musk oxen respond well to domestication, and are being farmed experimentally in Siberia.

■ ■ ■

Caribou grazing along the shores of Bathurst Inlet, Northwest Territories, Canada. Caribou, like reindeer, spend most of their time in herds. In summer they spread over the tundra to feed, keeping alert to each other's presence and bunching together if danger threatens. Their main predators are wolves and men. A lone adult caribou in good trim is usually a match for any lone wolf, although two or three wolves together can often outwit or outrun a caribou, or take what they want from a small herd.

ARCTIC FOXES

Smaller and silkier than the common red fox, with rounded ears and a bottle-brush tail, Arctic foxes live year-round on tundra throughout the Arctic region. Grey-brown in summer, they blend well with tundra rocks and vegetation; blue-grey or white in winter, they blend into the snow. Arctic foxes prey mainly on hares, birds and tundra rodents. Breeding in April and producing litters of up to five or six, in good seasons they may rear all the cubs of a first litter and go on to raise a second before the end of summer.

Arctic foxes live by their wits, foraging singly or in pairs and taking a wide variety of foods. Birds and their nests, voles, mice or lemmings dug from the snow, soil beetles, worms and carrion are all acceptable. On the coast they scramble on bird cliffs, eat seal droppings and placentae, and patrol the shores for whatever the sea washes in, from plankton to dead fish. They scavenge after larger predators, especially polar bears and wolves, picking over the carcasses they have left and storing away surplus food for later sustenance. Readily caught on trap lines baited with carrion, Arctic foxes are the prey of native trappers all over the north and prized for their white winter pelts. So valuable is their fur that Greenlanders and others have attempted to farm them, but the species does not take readily to domestication.

An Arctic fox in white winter fur. The face is more weasel-like than that of the common red fox. The species is an extremely persistent and fearless predator.

■ ■ ■

The Arctic sea is a wide table with space for plenty of diners, but space on land may be more restricted — only certain places are suitable for nesting birds, hence the very high densities of some breeding colonies. A stretch of water alone is no defence against maurauding foxes, wolves or bears when the sea freezes over for several months every year and predators can walk in over the ice. Only the most inaccessible cliffs will serve, like this cliff in Greenland, used by nesting kittiwakes. Once discovered, a cliff quickly becomes crowded with birds. Undisturbed, it may be used for centuries.

Standing 1–1.5 m (3.25–5 ft) at the shoulder and weighing up to 300 kg (660 lbs), musk oxen live in herds of a dozen or more. Their long matted fur is waterproof, windproof and very warm. In summer they graze widely on the tundra, in winter moving to high ground where forage can be dug from the thin snow. July to early October is the rutting season, and calves are born from April onward. The species' only serious predator is the wolf. Stocks recently reintroduced to Siberia, Svalbard, Alaska and northern Norway have prospered. Since musk oxen are amenable to management and their meat is acceptable, they seem likely candidates for tundra farming.

Caribou of North America and reindeer of Eurasia are deer of the same or closely-related species. Large bucks stand 1–1.5 m (3.25–5 ft) at the shoulder; the biggest weigh up to 250 kg (550 lbs). The fur is dense — individual hairs are hollow and tightly packed together, making the pelt light but very warm. Caribou winter in small groups in the forest or southern tundra, feeding on the young shoots of trees, grass and lichens. Woodland caribou are non-migratory or make only short annual movements. Those of the forest edge and tundra migrate north from April onward, browsing as they go on the new growth of grass and lichens. Their calves, born during the migration, run with the herds. By July, northern stocks are well established on coastal plains. Starting in August, they begin to return south. Rutting occurs in September, and by the first snows all have returned to their winter feeding grounds. Wolves often accompany the migrations, and man is a major predator — both Indians and Inuit value caribou for their fur, meat, antlers, sinews and bones.

Reindeer in Eurasia followed similar migrations, but for thousands of years native peoples have lived with them in a range of nomadic relationships, from hunting to herding. Hunters lived along the migration routes or travelled with the herds. Herders managed the deer in various ways, which have now been modifed to suit modern times. Reindeer herding provides a reasonable living for the Sami (Lapps) of Scandinavia and many different peoples in Siberia. Both reindeer and herders have been imported to the New World — several large herds are currently being managed successfully in Canada and Alaska.

Tundra predators include grizzly and polar bears. Though fierce if accosted, both species spend much of their time scavenging and feeding peacefully on carrion. Grey wolves are more active predators, taking reindeer, caribou, musk oxen and smaller prey. Arctic foxes and short-tailed weasels are the smaller-scale predators, hunting small mammals and birds. Winter residents, they change from grey-brown to white when the snow comes and their winter furs are much prized by trappers. Coyotes, otters, lynxes, porcupines, wolverines, red foxes, muskrats and snowshoe hares commute between winter forest and summer tundra. Alaska and varying hares are residents, wintering in some of the coldest, most exposed parts of the northern tundra. Eight species of shrew, nine species of vole and three species of lemming occur on the tundra, but only the lemmings and two species of vole winter in colder regions. From time to time lemming populations fluctuate wildly, giving rise to legendary 'lemming years' .

■ LEMMING CYCLES ■

Lemmings, which are herbivores the size of small rats, seem especially well adapted to tundra life. Wintering in the warmth and protection of snow burrows, in favourable conditions they breed almost continuously, producing four or five litters per year, each of up to six young. Two or three years of such fecundity over a large area can cause a population explosion.

Predators such as snowy owls, skuas and foxes move in and gorge themselves on lemmings. Eventually, when the lemmings have eaten out their local food supply, the population rapidly collapses. A few migrate successfully, but most die of stress, starvation or disease. Lemming populations tend to fluctuate locally in cycles of about four years. Larger mammals, for example Arctic hares, fluctuate for similar reasons, but with cycles of up to 11 years.

A Greenland collared lemming, an inhabitant of the tundra of northwest Greenland, northern Canada and Alaska. Lemmings feed on vegetation of all kinds — no other tundra mammal so adeptly and quickly turns vegetable debris into meat to feed foxes, weasels, skuas and owls.

■ ■ ■

These are lesser sheathbills, year-round residents of Iles Kerguelen and other Indian Ocean islands. To many visitors sheathbills look like pigeons, but they are in fact nearer to gulls. They make their living by scavenging along the shoreline in winter and on penguin colonies in summer. These two have a nest in the moss-covered cliff just behind, but are more interested in the photographer's bag, which they are hoping to raid for sandwiches.

■ ■ ■

This is a white-chinned petrel, a resident of various sub-Antarctic islands. White-chinned petrels nest in burrows which they dig deep into the peaty turf. Sealers used to call them 'shoemakers', perhaps because they sit at the mouths of their burrows in the evening, tapping with their bills. They tend to leave the islands at daybreak and return at dusk, seldom appearing above ground in daylight.

■ ■ ■

Skuas are predatory brown gulls, with white wing-bars and a distinctive combination of webbed feet and curved, talon-like claws. Antarctica has two closely related species, the south polar or Maccormick skua and the brown skua. Southern skuas feed at sea on krill and fish, scavenge carcasses of seals and whales,and harass penguin colonies.

■ ■ ■

Albatrosses, the largest members of the petrel family, sweep the southern oceans on long, tapering wings. Here two small albatrosses, black-browed mollymawks, contemplate each other on a bluff on Bird Island, South Georgia.

■ ■ ■

Antarctic islands have no tundra and no colourful flowers. What colour there is along the shore comes from lichens. These tough, rootless plants need no soil, but cling to rocks and challenge wind and waves to dislodge them. Here several species combine to make a brave showing in a sunny, sheltered corner of the South Shetland Islands.

LIFE ON ANTARCTICA AND THE SOUTHERN ISLANDS

South of latitude 50°S only Antarctica and a few scattered islands in the Southern Ocean provide a toehold for vegetation. Some of the islands — the Snares, Auckland Islands and Staten Island, for example — are forested, but most are not. Their isolation and the prevailing maritime climate have produced on them plant communities that only superficially resemble the forests and tundra of the north. Hence the absence of a southern treeline or southern tundra.

The Antarctic Convergence and the northern limit of the pack ice, though marine boundaries, are surprisingly relevant to land communities, for both reflect air temperatures, and small islands take their air temperatures mainly from the surface waters surrounding them. For example, South Georgia and the Falkland Islands lie in similar latitudes, but on opposite sides of the Antarctic Convergence. Both are fringed at sea level with tall tussock grass, but the Falklands, by far the warmer of the two, support a moorland vegetation of ferns and grasses, with over 40 species of flowering plant. There are also over 60 species of breeding bird, of which two-thirds feed on land. There are also pastures which support flourishing herds of cattle and sheep. South Georgia has no moorland, a few ferns and only 16 species of flowering plant; only two of its 25 species of breeding bird, a pintail and a pipit, are land birds. Though introduced reindeer flourish, there are no sheep, and the richest vegetation is best described as patchy fell-field.

■ ■ ■

King penguins incubating among tussock grass, the typical coastal vegetation of South Georgia. Kings, like emperors, make no nest but hold the single large egg on their feet, under a fold of feathered skin that forms a brood pouch. The parents take turns incubating through rain, snow and blizzards.

On the colder southern islands, invested every winter by pack ice, there is no tussock grass. At sea level the richest vegetation is a fell-field much less varied than South Georgia's. Mosses and lichens predominate; there are no ferns and only one or two species of flowering plant. Snowfields close to the sea that persist into late summer often develop striking patches of green and red, due to algae that proliferate on the snow surface. These cold southern islands have no land birds — vagrant waders, swans, ducks and other water birds blow in each summer from South America, but none survive to breed.

None of the southern islands has been connected to a continent during the time in which mammals have evolved, so none has a land mammal population of its own. Up until the mid-19th century the Falkland Islands had a species of small feral dog, which may have been a human import from South America; it killed sheep, so was not allowed to survive. Geologically the Falklands belong to South Africa rather than South America, though their vegetation and 40 or more species of land bird are mostly of Patagonian origin.

South America is also clearly the original home of many terrestrial species on South Georgia and other islands in its lee. Iles Kerguelen support indigenous species of duck and rail; islands south of New Zealand have acquired parrots and passerines which are presumed to have originated from southern Australia.

The sealers and whalers who explored the southern oceans from the late 18th century onward brought rats and mice with their stores, and landed rabbits, sheep, goats, cattle, pigs and other mammals to provide food for land-based or shipwrecked crews. Some of these mammals died out fairly quickly, but others flourished, to the detriment of the native vegetation and fauna. Feral cattle still graze among sea lions on the Auckland Islands, and rabbits and wild sheep continue to devastate much of Iles Kerguelen. Brown rats sport innocently in the tussock grass of South Georgia, feeding on roots and shoots; they may be responsible for deaths among the breeding seabird communities. Feral cats have certainly done great damage to seabird colonies on some of the southern islands.

Sheep and horses introduced on South Georgia in the early 20th-century whaling days did not survive, but small stocks of reindeer brought in from Norway during the 1920s for sport have flourished. Botanical distinctions between Norwegian tundra and South Georgian fell-field did not deter them; they found the upland forage to their taste and quickly spread. For a time they were controlled by the whalers, who kept track of the small herds and culled them for meat, but when whaling came to an end in the mid-1960s they were left to themselves. Originally contained between icefields that came down from the island's main ice cap to sea level, they have recently been released; retreat of the glaciers in the last two or three decades has allowed them to spread to new areas. Now the population has burgeoned and South Georgia's reindeer are numbered in thousands. The herds range over several peninsulas on the northern shores of the island, presenting a management dilemma to those who claim custody of South Georgia and responsibility for its flora and fauna.

Continental Antarctica itself has no semblance of tundra. On the 2 per cent of land surface that is ice-free, soils are poor and undeveloped. The whole continent supports only thin, widely-scattered polar desert communities, of which the richest are found in damp areas close to sea level around the warmer coasts. Richest of all are the islands along the western coast of the Antarctic Peninsula, where maritime climates prevail in summer. Together with the South Shetland and South Orkney Islands, these have the greatest variety of mosses, lichens and algae, and Antarctica's two species of flowering plants, a grass and a pink, which have not yet been found on the continental mainland.

The moss clumps contain collembola (springtails), tiny primitive insects, which appear to browse on fungi within the clumps. There are also mites, presumed to be predatory on the collembola, and wingless mosquitoes whose larvae feed on the algae which grow in brackish tide pools.

The continental coasts, ice-invested in winter, are colder and often more windswept, with correspondingly meagre flora and fauna. Wherever rocks emerge from the ice of the interior, individual clumps of algae, lichens and moss are likely to be found; summer trickles of snow melt-water encourage them, indicating again that dryness is as important a limiting factor as cold. Lichens appear at altitudes of 2000–3000 m (6,500–10,000 ft), even to within 5°(550 km/340 miles) of the South Pole.

■   ■   ■   ## REINDEER HERDING   ■   ■   ■

Reindeer under herding are mostly semi-wild deer following instinctive patterns of migration and feeding. Herders understand the social structure and annual needs of their herds, working with them as much as possible, handling them when necessary and taking what they want, but otherwise leaving them alone. The Norwegian Sami run some sixteen herds ranging in size from a few hundred to almost 20,000; herds are tending to increase in size, with fewer herders involved. Siberian herds too have a wide size range.

Herding practices vary. Some of the smaller herders treat their animals almost like domestic cattle, while those with larger groups domesticate some but leave the rest wild, mustering them from time to time for culling or management. Domesticated reindeer are widely used for transport, carrying goods and people on their backs and hauling sledges.

Cows may be domesticated for milking, though there has been little or no selection of animals for milk production and yields are low. Milch herds are now rare in Scandinavia. Milking and the production of butter, cheese and yoghurt are still widespread east of the Yenisey River in Siberia, especially toward the south. The Soviet authorities collectivized reindeer husbandry in an attempt to reduce nomadism, and made several efforts to create a reindeer dairying industry, but these ideas now seem to have been abandoned, though successful herding continues throughout eastern Siberia.

Reindeer follow traditional paths well known to their herders, breaking into smaller bands for foraging but always rejoining the main herd. Herders identify individuals, especially leaders, and domesticate a number of animals that run with the herds and help to keep them under control. They guide the herds between known feeding areas, especially during the six months or more when there is snow on the ground, keeping predators away, keeping the herds together, and avoiding overgrazing and pasture damage. On summer pastures the animals are left to wander freely.

Some herders move with their animals on long north-south migrations. Others shift the herds in wide circuits around permanent settlements, living in temporary camps en route, and mustering and moving on from time to time. Soviet herders working under collectivization are no longer nomadic in the old sense, but work from temporary camps, leaving their families in central villages. The most successful operations remain those in which the reindeer continue to set the pattern of movement, and the herders follow.

POLAR AGRICULTURE

Though none of the native populations of polar regions aspires to agriculture, farming has often been attempted by incomers. Traditional agricultural methods require soil of reasonable maturity, suitable weather, a long-enough growing season, and crops for which there is, or can be guaranteed, an accessible market. Meeting all these requirements in the same place has proved difficult, and few attempts at polar agriculture have so far proved successful.

Iceland and southwest Greenland, colonized originally by Scandinavian crofters, have had the longest record of success. The original settlers raised crops, cattle and sheep in the warm valleys during a period when the climate was especially favourable. A later downturn in climate may have left them hungry, perhaps unable to grow fodder to keep their stock during the long unproductive winters, and may have forced them to leave. Today conditions seem favourable again. South Greenland supports husbandry at a crofting (subsistence) level; sheep-farmers produce a small surplus of meat, much depending on spring weather for lambing and successful summer hay crops. Iceland has a strong farming community, raising sheep, cattle, poultry and vegetables both in the open and under glass for local consumption.

The isolated communities of the Scandinavian north have a long tradition of crofting for self-support. Even so, farming is barely viable unless combined with fishing, forestry or other profit-making activities. Short-season fodder crops, growing quickly in the long summer days, make it possible to maintain cattle and sheep well north of the Arctic Circle. Reindeer herding is by far the most appropriate agricultural activity, widely practised in Sami areas.

Soviet agronomists, in early post-revolutionary attempts to make their northlands self-sufficient, were prominent during the 1920s and '30s in developing early-ripening cereals and other short-season crops. Their efforts succeeded, but Arctic crop-raising did not develop as expected. Perhaps the necessary development capital was never made available. Whatever the reason, only a small proportion of the total cereal and vegetable requirements of the large Soviet Arctic population is grown within the region. Cattle and horses are raised for dairying and meat on Siberian collective farms, and reindeer herding, for meat, milk and cheese, is conspicuously successful throughout Siberia.

Canadian agriculture extends far north toward the sub-Arctic, and is practised in many areas where, though summers are warm, winters are brutally cold. In Labrador, Quebec, Yukon Territory and parts of the Northwest Territory, pioneers attempted cropping and cattle-raising to provide fresh meat and vegetables for growing local communities. Similarly, climatically-favoured valleys of Alaska - the Tanana, Matanuska and Susitna, for example - have been farmed, making use of warm summers to grow vegetables, root crops and fodder for wintering cattle. Truck-farming and hothouse crops for local consumption have been attempted successfully, and both Alaska and Canada run reindeer herds which have now passed well beyond the experimental stage.

In all these areas farming has been shown to be possible, occasionally yielding memorable crops and outsized vegetables. However, seasonal reliability is low, production costs are high (boosted by high wages), and local markets are limited. Almost anything, from milk to cereals and salad crops, can be produced more cheaply and more reliably in the south and freighted in. The more efficient transport links become, the less chance Arctic agriculture has to develop.

There have been several optimistic attempts to farm various islands in the Southern Ocean. Iles Kerguelen, Campbell Island, the Auckland Islands and several others have from time to time received parties of settlers, but isolation, bad weather and development costs sooner or later defeated their efforts. One of the earliest and most ambitious attempts was an agricultural colony of 300 British settlers led by Charles Enderby, who descended on Port Ross, Auckland Islands, from Australia and New Zealand in 1850. The colonists cleared an area of rata (hardwood) forest and built a small settlement, hoping to grow crops and vegetables, raise stock, and repair and maintain ships of the whaling and sealing fleets then operating around the islands. None of these ventures succeeded, and the colony left after two miserable years.

6

Early Explorers

Man began as a tropical animal, a product of the rain forests like the anthropoid apes of today. Tens of millions of years ago our forebears made the small, vital switch from tree-swinging to walking, from anthropoid to hominoid, the step that liberated them from the forests and opened the world to their ingenuity. They spread from tropical forests to grassland, into the warm temperate zones and beyond. Long-limbed, virtually hairless, poorly insulated, they were — as we still are — the wrong shape to live for long in a cold climate.

What forced them onward? Like ourselves, our ancestors probably had a capacity, unusual among mammals, for year-round breeding. A growing intellect would have given them adaptability and a high rate of survival. Then as now, this combination must have produced a rapidly growing population and the need for geographical expansion. The world itself was changing. In all but the tropics, mean temperatures were falling as the ice age advanced, posing new problems and offering new opportunities for every plant and animal species. Their newly acquired skills of introspection and putting two and two together must have helped the hominoids to adapt at this critical time, and to seize the opportunities offered. Armed with conscious thought and intelligence, using fire and stealing the skins of other animals to keep warm, they pressed on into the cool-temperate fringes of the world.

NOMADIC HUNTERS

Perhaps as long as 300,000 years ago, with the world already chilled into its current ice age, hominoids inhabited the central Eurasian mainland. As hunters and gatherers of the northern steppes and forests, they would certainly have experienced cold, the winter cold of a mid-continental climate.

Twenty to thirty thousand years ago, during the decline of the Würm–Wisconsin glacial period, ice covered the Arctic Ocean and permanent ice sheets spread over much of Britain, Scandinavia and northern Canada. Semi-Arctic conditions prevailed over wide areas of what is now the north temperate region. It was probably at about this time that the first hunters wandered north to the Arctic coast. Their movements would not have been purposeful but rather the opportunist expansions of hunters who found conditions favourable, wandering far afield perhaps to avoid competition with each other. Families of hunters and fisherfolk living beside the great Asian rivers may have moved northward along them during warm climatic spells. Those who travelled eastward into the Chukchi (Chukotskiy) region discovered Beringia, a lowland of temperate forest and grassland, and used it as a stepping stone from Asia to North America.

Although they did not know it, the first Eurasians to cross Beringia became the first Americans. In North America they found a continent similar to the one they had left behind, perhaps slightly warmer,

---

■ CROSSING BERINGIA ■

Beringia formed an intermittent bridge across the Bering Strait, linking Asia and North America, and owed its existence to the vagaries of the northern ice sheets. Huge accumulations of ice on land have the effect of reducing the amount of water in the sea; that is why, at the height of glaciation, sea level all over the world was some 100 m (300 ft) lower than it is at present. Offshore islands became peninsulas, coastal plains became wider, southern Britain was joined to Europe, and in the far north of the Pacific Ocean a wide corridor of land stretched invitingly between Asia and America. From time to time, when warmer conditions melted the ice, the sea level rose, and the corridor that was Beringia became marshland, eventually narrowing and disappearing under the waves of the Bering Strait. This transition happened several times. It is not happening at present because much of the land ice has disappeared from the northern hemisphere and sea level remains high.

Beringia was a bridge for many mammals. At least 20 species, including musk oxen, moose, bison, caribou, Arctic hares and foxes, lemmings and ground squirrels, took advantage of it to cross to America. Several species now extinct, including woolly mammoths, deer and and forest musk oxen, also made the crossing, but they were heavily hunted and probably destroyed by man.

THE SPREAD AND RETREAT OF ARCTIC ICE

Two to three million years ago permanent ice began forming in the northern hemisphere. *One to two million years ago* the Greenland ice cap was complete, and ice was gathering on high ground acrosss the northern hemisphere. *During the last million years* there have been *four major glacial periods*, in which increasing cold has caused ice sheets to spread widely across lowlands in the north, and *three major interglacial periods* in which warming has caused the continental ice sheets to retreat to high ground.

The four glacial periods just mentioned have been identified from evidence in the central European Alps and North America, and the last three have been matched in Scandinavia. Somewhat confusingly, each group of scientists working on them has given them different names. Some of the warmer and colder spells (called stadials and interstadials)

alternating with these glacial periods can be correlated across the different regions, others not. An approximate chronology is shown below.

Ice on land reached its southernmost extent during the Mindel–Kansan glacial period, the time at which human beings first appeared in Europe. The Riss–Illinoian period provided the longest spell of intense cold in the north, bringing truly Arctic conditions to the whole area for the first time. During the following interglacial Neanderthal communities spread across Europe and Asia. The second interstadial of the Würm–Wisconsin glacial period brought warmer-than-present conditions to parts of the Arctic; it was during this time that many species of mammal, including man, crossed Beringia from Siberia to the Americas. Ice during this glacial period reached its farthest spread just over 20,000 years ago, almost disappearing by 10,000 years ago.

Glacial Periods			Date of onset	Duration	Areas affected
Alpine name	**American name**	**Scandinavian name**			
Günz	Nebraskan		750,000–800,000 years ago	50,000 years	North America and Alps ice-covered, Northern Europe and Arctic Ocean relatively ice-free. Two stadials.
Mindel	Kansan	Elster	620,000 years ago	60,000 years	Extensive ice over Northern and Central Europe and North America; ice on Arctic Ocean. Two stadials. First human beings in Europe.
Riss	Saale	Illinoian	350,000 years ago	150,000 years	Extensive ice cover over northlands and Arctic Ocean. Neanderthal man in Europe.
Würm	Warthe–Weischel	Wisconsin	110,000 years ago	100,000 years	Extensive ice cover, mostly disappearing during warm interstadial. Three stadials. Human and animal migration from Asia to North America.

■ ■ ■
*The old Inuit were nomadic,
always ready to pack their
few belongings onto sledges
and move to new hunting
grounds. Using winter sea
ice as an extension of land,
they hunted fish and seals.
In summer they paddled
their kayaks among the pack
ice, harpooning seals and
even whales. Their impact
on the environment was
slight.*

and without other tribes or families already in posses-sion. The grasslands and forests harboured game, also spreading eastward across Beringia. The species they hunted included woolly mammoths and woolly rhinoceros, now long extinct, as well as birds and mammals that would be quite at home on the north-ern tundra today.

SETTLEMENT IN THE NORTH

Soon after these human incursions into the far north the climate began to cool again. The world was entering what we now think of as the third and most recent stadial (cool period) of the Würm–Wisconsin glaciation. As they spread eastward into North America the newcomers would quickly have encoun-tered the edges of the Canadian ice sheets. Persistent winter snows, merging with the existing ice sheets, would have urged them slowly south through present-day Alaska and British Columbia, bringing them eventually to the North American plains.

We know little of these migrants, for they left no artefacts, no legends, no written records of their adventure. Culturally they probably matched the Neanderthals of Europe, living in caves and tempo-rary shelters. What little they left behind in their trav-els we may never find. Like their modern Arctic descendants, they probably lived mainly on coasts and river banks. Post-glacial warming and rises in sea level must have washed away their camps and settle-ments long ago. Their lasting legacy is the rich variety of indigenous peoples who today populate the Americas from Labrador to southern Chile.

These were not the first Eskimos, and did not give rise to them, although they were probably the ances-tors of the Indians of the northern forests. Millennia after the first invasions, possibly a mere 3,000 years ago, much of the major Arctic ice sheet had gone and Beringia had long disappeared under the sea. A new wave of maritime folk from the Chukchi area of east-ern Asia, with a ready-developed Arctic culture, spread eastward across the Bering Strait and estab-lished themselves in Alaska. Later they extended in successive waves to eastern Canada and Greenland. From these peoples arose the several different groups whom today we call Eskimos or Inuit.

While various groups of hunters and gatherers were spreading across Beringia, others were pressing into northwestern Asia and northern Europe, hunting where tundra and forest were replacing the remnant ice sheets. Successive waves of nomads moved north from forest to tundra, following reindeer herds, or trapping and hunting by the edges of rivers and lakes. Like the new North Americans, these Eurasian folk were small and hardy, but their origins and the hunting and herding cultures they developed were quite distinct.

At about this time, some 12,000 years ago, warm temperate environments further south were encour-aging human populations to exchange hunting and

THE FIRST NORTH AMERICANS

The people of the Canadian and American northlands are divided anthropologically into three main groups, based on language. In the western sub-Arctic are the Dene, formerly identified as Athapaskan Indians, in the eastern sub-Arctic are the Innu or Algonquian Indians, and in the Arctic are the Inuit, formerly and to some degree still called Eskimos. Dene and Innu are traditionally forest and tundra dwellers. Inuit are traditionally inhabitants of coastal tundra. All were semi-nomadic, living in widely scattered bands or communities, supporting themselves in family groups by hunting and gathering techniques that changed little over the centuries.

The Dene and Innu are part of the great North American Indian family, whose forebears roamed the northern plains 25,000 or more years ago. The Inuit and closely related Aleuts of the Bering Sea are quite separate, probably descended from stocks of East Siberian Chukchis who crossed the Bering Strait by boat and lived on either side of it, perhaps 6,000–10,000 years ago. The Aleuts remained in the west while the Inuit spread eastward along the northern American coast, through the Canadian archipelago to northern Labrador, and eventually into Greenland. Several cultural waves can be identified archaeologically, the earliest dating from about 4,500 years ago, the latest (to which modern Inuit are closely akin) from less than 1,000 years ago.

The Inuit distinguish themselves by their methods of hunting and travelling by sea, using individual and family boats made from skins stretched over frameworks of wood or bone. Travel on land or between land and sea ice was done using dog sledges. Like the Dene and Innu, they traditionally dressed in hand-stitched clothing of caribou, reindeer or bear skin, with reindeer leggings and sealskin boots. The clothing was serviceable but elegant, trimmed with fur both functionally and for decoration.

The Inuit moved in small family groups, living in tents, sod huts or snow houses according to season and need. Their year was ruled by the seasons. In winter they hunted seals, walruses and polar bears along the coast and on the sea ice. In summer they combed the tundra for birds, small mammals and berries, fished along rivers and coasts, and hunted seals and whales from kayaks. Some of the Inuit of Keewatin and Hudson Bay moved away from the sea and developed other hunting and trapping skills, making particular use, like the Indians, of migratory herds of caribou. Music, songs, stories and religion played important roles in their lives.

Elements of aboriginal skills and beliefs are still to be seen in Dene, Innu and Inuit life, handed on from parents to children and fostered in schools and at social gatherings. Although many of these North American peoples are now settled in villages or towns, they still rely on hunting and travelling skills to secure part of their food, income and traditional clothing.

Inuit hunters in traditional dress wait by a seal breathing hole. Their harpoons are steel-tipped and secured with seal-hide traces. The ice is thin, only a few days' old, and covered with crystalline 'ice flowers'.

gathering for more static pursuits — cultivation, the establishment of settled communities, manufacture, trading, and ultimately leisure and the pursuit of learning. These were scarcely options for the north, for the dry steppes and far northern forests and tundra were, and are, relatively tough, intractable environments, yielding little leisure for anyone. The steppes supported nomadic pastoralism based on camels, sheep and horses. The northlands encouraged only hunting, fishing and food-gathering in simple patterns that have continued almost unchanged to the present day.

As the southern civilizations prospered, their need for raw materials increased. One after another they spread their influence, sending prospectors, traders, missionaries, armies and navies to search and extend the boundaries of the known world. As yet, this was mostly the subtropical and warm-temperate world, for the northern forests and the cold regions beyond them had little to offer and were troublesome to exploit. The Roman Empire, spreading further north than any of its predecessors, reached a practical limit in the northern European forests, finally stabilizing along the Rhine and the Danube.

THE ARCTIC UNVEILED

Among the pioneers of world discovery we remember first the great explorers of the Renaissance — Vasco da Gama, Ferdinand Magellan and Christopher Columbus, for example — who between them revealed the extent of the world's oceans. Theirs are well-documented voyages, yielding stirring stories of adventure and persistence rewarded, and we rightly honour them. Yet they were not the first explorers, or even the first European explorers. There were many earlier European voyages no less adventurous and enterprising, some pre-dating the Renaissance by five centuries or more. Among these were the earliest recorded voyages to the Arctic.

Nor was the non-European world uninhabited before Europeans spread across it. Did Columbus discover America? Not really. By the time he arrived several million good Americans (although he mistook them for Indians) were already calling it home. Did Magellan discover Tierra del Fuego? Only if we discount the Alacaluf Indians who had lived for generations on either side of it, tending the fires that gave the island its name. By the time the earliest

■ AGRICULTURE AND CITIES: ■ A TEMPERATE OPTION

The first steps from nomadism to civilization seem to have been taken in sub-tropical climates. 10,000–12,000 years ago, more or less as the last glacial period was ending. Almost simultaneously in a wide zone across the world, in the Mediterranean basin, the Near and Far East and Central America, hunting and the gathering of wild crops gave way to cereal cultivation and animal husbandry. Nomadic bands settled to crop-raising, and villages, towns and cities developed around the cultivated fields. New techniques of pottery, metal smelting and weaving began to enhance the quality of life. About 7,000 years ago farming spread to temperate regions as the forests were cleared, and hunting and gathering communities were inevitably ousted by crops and grazing animals.

The first cities arose 5,000–6,000 years ago, in fertile, sub-tropical river valleys as far apart as Egypt, Mesopotamia, northern India and central China. These centres of civilization, attracting raw materials and creating surplus goods, were the focal points along tenuous trade routes, eventually linking with each other across miles of land and water. Civilization gave some citizens leisure to think, and scope for exploration and the accumulation of learning; these too were initially the product of warmer climates.

Europeans discovered the Arctic, non-European Inuit had already lived there for two or three thousand years.

The first Europeans to find the Arctic were northern mariners, probably monks or missionaries of the 8th or 9th centuries AD. But the first to seek the polar regions in an intellectual sense, to be aware of them and consider them seriously, were the Greek and Roman geographers of the 5th and 4th centuries BC, working in Athens and other centres of learning around the eastern Mediterranean. Knowing nothing of eastward migrations to the Americas, and little of the lands that lay to the north of them, they possessed speculative but surprisingly accurate information. Much of this disappeared with the fall of the classical civilizations, to be rediscovered and often vindicated by Renaissance explorers.

During the 4th century BC popular concepts of geography reflected earlier Babylonian ideas. Earth was a disc, centred on the Mediterranean Sea, and possibly supported by elephants. That is the picture that comes across from Homer's epic *Odyssey*. Earth's outer boundary was formed by the Streams of Ocean, which flowed just beyond the Pillars of Hercules, known today as the Strait of Gibraltar. What lay beyond that, nobody knew.

However Aristotle and some of his colleagues came up with a new idea. Without travelling far from home and using only their wits and a minimum of experiment, they convinced themselves that the earth was a sphere. If this were true, they reasoned, a cold polar zone must exist far away to the north, complemented by a hotter zone to the south. So the Athenians can be said to have invented the polar regions, literally.

Their ideas were not entirely novel, for Pythagoras and his students, two centuries earlier, had suspected that Earth was a sphere; Aristotle re-examined and built on their concept. Only spheres, he argued, could have formed when matter condensed out of space. The sun and moon were spheres, so why not Earth and the other planets? Only a sphere would invariably cast a crescentic shadow across the moon during an eclipse. Only the surface of a sphere could provide the kind of horizon familiar to us, one that allows landmarks to rise above and sink below it, in whatever direction we travel.

And polar cold? Aristotelian geographers understood that a spherical earth warmed by sunlight would be hotter at the equator than at the poles, for reasons we still hold valid today. Contemporary astronomers could tell them why; far to the north, the sun would rise only to a limited angle above the horizon, giving about the same amount of warmth as the early-morning sunshine in Greece, and in the winter it would disappear from the sky altogether, leaving the earth unwarmed for several consecutive months.

From their own discussions with travellers, the Greek geographers would have known that the further one walked or sailed in the direction of the prominent pole star, Polaris, the colder both air and land become. The pole star, standing in the northern sky, was well known in Athenian times. The familiar constellation of Arctos, the she-bear, rotates about it, with Arcturus, the bear's-tail star, tagging along behind. Everyone knew that Arctic or 'boreal' winds (Boreas was the North Wind himself) in winter could bring ice and snow even to sunny Greece. So the zone of intense cold under Arctos, later to be called the Arctic, became known to Mediterranean philosophers long before anyone sailed north to discover it.

Similarly, travellers and winds from the south brought tidings of warmth. A broad equatorial zone

■   MEASURING THE EARTH   ■

Eratosthenes, working in Egypt, based his calculation of the circumference of the earth on the observation that in Syene (present-day Aswan) at noon in midsummer, the sun's rays shone vertically down a well, i.e. the sun was overhead. At the same time in El Iskandariya (Alexandria), some distance to the north, vertical buildings cast shadows which indicated that the sun's rays were striking them at an angle of about 7.2°, one-fiftieth of a complete circle (360°). Assuming the sun to be far enough away for its rays to be parallel, Eratosthenes concluded that the circumference of the great circle (the Earth) on which the two cities stood must be equal in length to 50 times the distance between them. This distance he estimated at 5000 stadia (926 km/580 miles), probably basing it on the time it took to travel from one to the other. The resulting value for the circumference, 250,000 stadia (46,300 km/29,000 miles), is an overestimate by about 15 per cent.

Eratosthenes' measurement of the shadow angles was probably fairly accurate. Had he known the correct distance between Aswan and El Iskandariya (840 km/522 miles), his estimate would have been 42,000 km/26,250 miles, i.e. within 5 per cent of the true circumference. His calculation was important in that it showed how small a proportion of the world's surface was occupied by the 'known' world (the Mediterranean and its immediate environs) and what vast areas remained for other climatic regimes.

of intense heat lay in the heart of the African desert, directly under the sun's path, a wasteland as hot as the north was cold. In about 250 BC Eratosthenes, an astronomer and mathematician working in Egypt, measured some of the distances involved. He estimated Earth's circumference by measuring the lengths of shadows at Aswan and Alexandria, close to and further from the equator, and a known distance apart . His calculation gave a result of 46,300 km (28,900 miles), some 15 per cent longer than we now know it to be, although surprisingly accurate for its time.

This measure implied that the known, inhabited world of the Mediterranean basin occupied only a small fraction of the earth as a whole. To north, south, east and west there were spaces vast enough to accommodate completely different kinds of environment. There could be a vast land of ice and snow in the Arctic, a vast desert covering the whole equatorial region, and symmetry demanded a southern hemisphere polar region (much later to be called the Antarctic) as extensive and frigid as the Arctic.

Ancient geographers who accepted this model of a spherical earth with graded climatic zones had little hope of exploring it. The equatorial zone would probably prove too hot to be traversed by land or even by sea; and what lay beyond the torrid zone could never be known. It was at least a thousand years before voyagers began to test these far-sighted, improbable hypotheses.

THE FIRST VOYAGES TO THE ARCTIC

Europe's first overseas explorers were probably Irish monks of the 7th and 8th centuries, who set sail from Britain in tiny ox-hide curraghs in search of solitude. St Brendan's miraculous voyages from Ireland by a northern route to America are recorded in the Navigatio manuscripts, a curious blend of fact and imagination concocted between the 5th and 10th centuries AD. The manuscripts describe, among many other wonders, a far northern floating crystal pillar in a silver mesh harder than marble. Is this the first-ever description of an iceberg in pack ice? Several of the monks seem to have settled and founded small communities as far north as the Faroe Islands and Iceland, living on fish and farm produce. Scholars in the monastic communities may well have read of cold lands to the north, perhaps as long-forgotten myths or theories that carried little weight.

The monks were quickly followed by the Vikings, a rumbustious people of Scandinavian origin who explored and colonized the North Atlantic Ocean from the late 8th century onward. Farmers with a flair for sailing, restless and opportunist, they left their firesides in southern Scandinavia and roistered far afield, raiding, trading, conquering or parleying according to circumstances. The Vikings began as inshore sailors with small, shallow-draft ships, handy in bays and rivers. Later they built larger ships with high prows, and sailed them in deeper waters. In their 10th-century heyday they dominated huge territories from the Caspian Sea to the coast of Spain.

■ ■ ■

This is the prow of the 9th-century Gokstad ship, the archetypal Viking longship — lean, fast and predatory.

A view of the world by Johannes of Armssheim, dated 1482 and based on the writings of Claudius Ptolemaeus (Ptolemy), the famous geographer of Alexandria who died c. AD 150. Europe is recognizable, with a northern extension to accommodate a 'mare glaciale' or icy sea. North Africa, the Mediterranean Sea, the Black and Caspian Seas, and Arabia are clearly delineated, as are fragments of India and Southeast Asia. The Indian Ocean, already well known to navigators, was still thought to terminate in a large land mass in the south.

THE VIKINGS IN THE ARCTIC

Farmers and burghers of southern Scandinavia, the Vikings lived in family communities under autocratic chieftains. Some were inshore seamen — fishermen and traders with remarkable boats, open, high-prowed and shallow-drafted, that could be sailed or rowed on any body of water from rivers to rough inshore seas. Fleets of these maritime Vikings set sail from their homelands in Denmark, southern Sweden and Norway during the 9th and 10th centuries AD, taking with them many outlaws, landless second sons, and others with little to lose. For two centuries and more they plundered and destroyed coastal and riverine settlements all over Europe. Although popularly regarded as pirates and reprobates, the Vikings were also traders, quickly reverting to settling and farming when they had seized good land. Many of their agricultural settlements and trading posts developed into townships and centres of colonization.

In fact three separate groups of Vikings made their presence felt across the northern world. An eastern group from Sweden, the Varangians, spread east and south across Europe and Russia, following the Volga south to the Caspian Sea and Baghdad, and the Dnieper to the Black Sea and Constantinople. From raiding they graduated to slaving and trading in furs and oriental spices, founding several European city states, including Kiev and Novgorod.

Vikings from Norway and Denmark explored the coasts of Germany, the Low Countries, Britain, France and Iberia, entering the Mediterranean and exploring eastward. Successive waves of them raided and settled the coastlands, sailing their shallow-bottomed ships into estuaries and up rivers to loot far inland. Territory won in mainland Britain and Normandy allowed many of these Vikings to settle to farming and trade.

Hardiest of all were the deep-sea Vikings, mostly of Norwegian stock, who in larger longships sailed and rowed their way north and west in search of furs, walrus ivory and land. They explored their own coasts north to the White Sea, raided northern Britain and colonized the Faroe Islands. In about AD 860 they established a permanent colony in southern Iceland, the direct antecedent of the present state. In 984 a group under Eirik the Red sailed westward to establish settlements in Greenland. A few years later expeditions under Eirik's son, Leif Eiriksson, explored even further west and reached the eastern seabord of America, naming it Vinland. Here they established small temporary settlements, perhaps summer camps for timber-cutting and hunting. There is evidence of a semi-permanent colony at L'Anse aux Meadows, in northern Newfoundland, which may have lasted for several years.

Part of the excavated remains of a Norse village of about AD 1200, at Brattalid in southwest Greenland. Established in 985 by Eirik the Red in the sheltered harbour of Eriksfjord, and known as 'the eastern colony', the settlement has several large family buildings and many smaller ones.

■ ■ ■
This woodcut from Historia de Gentibus Septentrionalibus, published in Antwerp in 1562, is of a sperm whale. Clearly the artist had never seen one.

We know of Viking wanderings from the folklore of the countries that they ravaged, and from their own sagas or narrative poems. Fragmentary, obscure, often contradictory, the sagas still provide vivid accounts of an extraordinary people who navigated ice-bound waters in open boats, penetrated the Arctic Ocean, colonized Iceland and Greenland, and explored the coast of North America far beyond the Arctic Circle.

Vikings were the first Europeans to encounter the Inuit, who by this time were established as the true people of the far north. Inuit lived around the Bering Strait, between North America and Asia, and in small groups scattered along the northern shores of North America as far as Greenland, more or less where their descendants are found today. Penetrating north along the West Greenland coast, the Vikings met some of the easternmost Inuit communities, then spreading south into the milder sectors of Greenland. They may also have met them on the Labrador coast, and on some of the far northern islands. Vikings certainly met Indians further south in 'Vinland', a stretch of eastern North America south of the St Lawrence estuary that they visited but did not colonize. It may have been Indian hostility that prevented them from settling this coast, the warmest, the most fertile and surely the most desirable of all their western discoveries.

From the 14th century onward a new brand of European explorer appeared along these same Arctic coasts. Whale hunters from Western Europe began to make summer voyages northward in sturdy, well-equipped sailing ships. The first were probably Basques from the Bay of Biscay region. Traditionally they hunted sperm whales and slow-moving right whales during their annual migrations along the European coast. Now they took to following their prey into Arctic waters, rediscovering Newfoundland and penetrating northward along the foggy coast of Labrador.

Soon they were followed by Dutch and British whalers. As demand increased in Western Europe for whale oil and springy 'whalebone' (baleen), the whalers spread far into the Arctic in a constant search for new whaling grounds. Their voyages clearly established that to the north of Western Europe there were seas which were open in summer, although they were always limited by pack ice edging in from the north.

This information became highly relevant during the next phase of world discovery, when the most knowledgeable navigators of several nations set out to find sea routes to the Orient. Their quest was for routes eastward and westward, but the mariners involved found themselves inevitably forced both north into the Arctic and south to the tropics and beyond. Ultimately these voyages led to the opening-up of the Arctic, and in a roundabout, back-to-front way to the discovery of Antarctica.

THE ROUTE TO THE INDIES

In the 14th and 15th centuries Cathay (China), the Indies and the Indian Ocean were well known to European traders. Mentioned by the Egyptian geographer Ptolemy as early as AD 150, they were the source of silks, spices and other goods much in demand in Europe. Following the remarkable journeys of Niccolo, Maffeo and Marco Polo from Venice to Peking in the 13th century, a network of trade routes for Chinese silks and porcelain developed through Palestine, Persia, Turkestan and Central Asia. Spices, fabrics, jewels and perfumes flowed into Europe from Indochina, India and Arabia, along southern routes via the Red Sea and the Middle East. However, the break-up of the Mongol Empire, the rise of the Ottoman Turks and other upheavals along the way made these routes hazardous and expensive, and the need arose for alternative sea routes to the wealth of the Indies.

Under the inspiration of Prince Henry the Navigator, 15th-century Portuguese explorers pressed eastward through the Mediterranean and Red Sea to East Africa and India, and southward along the west coast of Africa. In 1488 Bartholomieu Diaz reached the Cape of Good Hope. In the same year his fellow-countryman Pero de Covilha visited Ethiopia and the east coast of Africa, penetrating south to the Zambesi River. These travels were the prelude to the series of remarkable voyages, mostly Spanish and Portuguese, that within one human lifespan changed the shape of the known world.

Although not everyone at the time believed in a spherical earth, Christopher Columbus was in no doubt that the Indies could be reached by sailing westward from Spain. Having studied the primitive globes of the time, and the works of Ptolemy and Marco Polo, and calculated the angular distance, he estimated that the voyage would take about one month. The four voyages that he made between 1492 and 1504 seemed to bear out his ideas. On the first voyage the first land appeared within a few days of his predicted time, and the country he found bore some relation to Marco Polo's descriptions of Cathay and off-lying Chipangu (Japan). That he had in fact found the Caribbean Sea and the coast of Central America did not matter much in the end; his discovery gave Spain a firm foothold in the New World, to be followed by several centuries of prosperous colonialism.

In 1497–99 the Portuguese navigator Vasco da Gama, pioneering a southerly route across the Atlantic to southern Africa, sailed west almost to Brazil, then followed the trade winds eastward to round the Cape of Good Hope. His voyage opened the seaway to India, and established Portugal as a powerful influence throughout the Indian Ocean. Opero Cabral, following da Gama's route in 1500, sailed a little further west and sighted the coast of Brazil. Within the next two years Amerigo Vespucci, a Florentine navigator in the service of Portugal, had outlined the coast of Brazil as far south as the mouth of the Rio de la Plata.

To map-makers attempting to link these discoveries with those of Christoper Columbus, it was now clear that the Western Atlantic ended in a barrier of continental length, which blocked all further progress toward the west. From 1507 they drew in the barrier firmly, naming the southern portion 'America' in honour of Vespucci.

NORTHERN ROUTES

British and Dutch navigators, inspired by the pioneering voyages of their whaling captains, were among the first to seek trade routes to China via the north. In 1496 John Cabot, a Venetian captain living in Bristol, sailed westward on behalf of King Henry VII to discover land for Britain. He rediscovered and claimed Newfoundland and Labrador, establishing a foothold for Britain's future ownership of Canada and a wide swathe of the Arctic. Cabot failed to return from a second westbound expedition, in which he hoped to find Japan, but his son Sebastian, who had probably sailed with him on his earlier voyage, maintained the family tradition of exploration. After many voyages for both British and Spanish interests, Sebastian settled in Britain and became governor of the Merchant Adventurers, an enterprising British trading company.

In 1555, aged 79, Sebastian joined with London merchants in forming the Muscovy Company to promote trade with Russia. In spring of the following year he was on the quay at Gravesend wishing god-speed to one of his young captains, Stephen Burrough, who was leaving in search of a sea route to Siberia. Burrough reported that the old gentleman 'banketted, and made me and them that were in company great cheere' and that he later 'entered into the dance himself, among the rest of the young and lusty company: which being ended, he and his friends departed most gently, commending us to the governance of Almighty God.'

Burrough sailed his tiny pinnace *Search-thrift* around the northern tip of Norway and the Kola Peninsula and east to the mouth of the Kara Sea, between Novaya Zemlya and the mainland. By early September the pack ice was looming and 'the nights waxed dark', so he turned back and wintered in the primitive Russian village of Arkhangelsk. His was the first attempt by the Muscovy Company to penetrate eastward along the Siberian coast, and one of many to be turned back by impenetrable fields of pack ice.

By 1578 the Dutch too were developing trade with Russia, bringing out furs and timber from Arkhangelsk, and seeking navigable ways further east along the Siberian coast. In 1594 Amsterdam merchants fitted out the small vessel *Mercurius* and instructed Captain Willem Barents, an experienced mariner of Terschelling, to explore for a possible route east in a higher latitude. At the time it was believed that sea ice only formed close to land, so there was sense in heading for open sea in the hope of avoiding it. Barents' first voyage thoroughly investigated the west coast of Novaya Zemlya and the edge of the summer pack ice in the sea that now bears his name, but he found no way through to the hoped-for open water beyond.

A second voyage to the same area failed to make any progress, but in a third, which left Amsterdam in May 1596, Barents discovered Bjørnøya (Bear Island) and Svalbard (Spitsbergen), which he took to be Greenland. He then sailed east and tried to round the northern end of Novaya Zemlya, but in late August his ship was trapped by pack ice and severely damaged. He and 16 Dutch companions were forced to winter ashore. Barents died during the following summer, but most of the others survived to return to the Netherlands.

In May 1607 Henry Hudson, a British captain trained in the service of the Muscovy Company, sailed north in the 80-tonne *Hopewell* on a remarkable voyage that he hoped would take him across the north polar sea to China and Japan. He explored the ice-bound east coast of Greenland as far north as 73°N, then followed the edge of the pack ice eastward to the west coast of Svalbard, which he explored north to a latitude beyond 81°. On his way home he discovered Jan Mayen Island. Around Svalbard, Hudson noted an abundance of whales and 'sea-horses', which he duly reported. Within a few years the area had become a whalers' paradise.

In 1608, again in the tiny *Hopewell*, Hudson tried to sail further north beyond Svalbard, fetching up on the coast of Novaya Zemlya. Like Burrough, he failed to find a way through to open sea. In 1609 he sailed north again, this time in the employ of the Dutch East

A walrus hunt in Arctic seas, from a 1555 edition of Historia de Gentibus Septentrionalibus. *The ivory tusks, which are probably all the artist had actually seen, appear to be growing from the lower jaw.*

India Company. Contrary winds prevented him from exploring further toward the northeast, so he headed westward across the Atlantic Ocean, now seeking a northwest passage. Entering an estuary previously reported by Giovanni da Verazano, he explored the river that now bears his name, establishing a Dutch claim to that area of the New World.

In 1610, once again under British patronage, he made his final voyage to the northwest. He discovered Hudson Strait and explored Hudson Bay, spending the winter of 1610–11 there. But as the *Hopewell* turned for home in June 1611, Hudson's mutinous crew set him adrift in a small boat, together with his son and several others. Neither he nor his companions were ever seen again.

The waters to the north of Hudson Bay were explored initially by John Davis, an Englishman from Devon, who sought the Northwest Passage in three privately funded summer voyages in 1585, 1586 and 1587. With two unbelievably small ships, *Sunshine* and *Moonshine*, of 50 and 35 tonnes, Davis visited southern Greenland (where he charmed the Inuit with fiddle music and dancing) and explored the Davis Strait, Baffin Bay and West Greenland, finding navigable water as far north as 73°. Clearly a man of consequence, in 1588 Davis joined the British fleet that defeated the Spanish Armada. Three years later, off the Strait of Magellan, he discovered and named the Falkland Islands. The northern channel discovered by Davis was explored further in 1616 by

THE FIRST EUROPEANS TO WINTER IN THE HIGH ARCTIC

This distinction fell to Barents and his party in the winter of 1596–7. According to the log of second mate Gerrit de Veer, later published by the Haklyut Society, the time seems to have passed cheerfully enough, despite the latitude, 76°N. Barents and his crew built a substantial house from driftwood and from the timbers of their mortally damaged ship on the shore of a bay they called Icehaven. With a central stove, a Dutch clock, and bedding and stores from the ship, they made themselves as comfortable as possible. On fairly tight rations, they were often cold and hungry, but they were undismayed by their predicament and on the whole healthy, helped by baths in a converted wine cask, prescribed by their surgeon.

The pack ice held them captive until the following May (1597), when they escaped and headed southeast in two improvised boats. Barents died at sea, but the survivors reached Kola, on the Russian mainland, in August, eventually returning safely to the Netherlands.

In 1871 Elling Carlsen, a Norwegian captain, called at Icehaven, where he discovered everything just as the Dutchmen had left it 278 years before. Carlsen catalogued the contents of the hut and took some of them back to Norway, including the clock, salt and pepper pots, books, a flute, and the shoes of the ship's boy, who had died during the winter. From there they found their way to a museum in The Hague, Netherlands.

A polar bear hunt from Gerrit de Veer's 1598 account of the Barents expedition of 1596–97. One oar has been lost in the confusion and two more are about to go the same way. While the bear appears to be climbing over the stern of the boat, those in the bow seem to be debating the way home.

■ ■ ■

Polus arcticus, *a north polar map of 1602, based on Mercator's projection of 1569. Greenland, Iceland, the Davis Strait and northern Scandinavia are recognizable, with fragments representing Svalbard and Novaya Zemlya. However, considerable imagination has been used around the North Pole, which appears to be a continent neatly divided by four rivers.*

Robert Bylot and William Baffin, who reached a remarkable polynya, or pool of open water, in 74°N at the head of Baffin Bay. Curiously, no further exploration followed in this region for 200 years, when whalers rediscovered Baffin's 'North Water' and reaped fortunes from its well-fed whales.

The search for a northeast passage beyond the Kara Sea, seemingly impossible for commercial sailing vessels, was abandoned for at least a century after Barents. Russian traders sailed inshore along the Siberian coast in a narrow channel between land and pack ice, but not until 1725, at the behest of Peter the Great, was a concerted effort made to explore and chart this coast. Vitus Bering, a Dane in the Imperial Russian Navy, was given command of a series of expeditions which, operating from Kamchatka, explored Eastern Siberia and the Bering Sea. In 1728 Bering confirmed the existence of a strait between Asia and America, and in 1741 explored the Aleutian

Islands and the west coast of Alaska. These quickly became important sealing and whaling grounds. Several other voyages by Russian naval officers filled in parts of the northern coast, although the Northeast Passage as a whole remained elusive until it was finally navigated by the Swede Otto Nordenskjöld in 1878–79.

WHALING: THE FIRST ARCTIC INDUSTRY

Stimulated by reports of whales in high latitudes, whalers of several nations redoubled their investment in ships for Arctic waters. The Basques, Dutch, French and British were especially prominent, setting up operations in Labrador, Greenland, Iceland and Svalbard. Most worked from ships, but from the early 17th century onward British, Basque and Dutch whalers established the first Arctic industrial sites, shore whaling stations on Labrador and the Svalbard

■　　■　　■　　**EARLY EUROPEAN EXPLORERS**　　■　　■　　■

1492–1500	Christopher Columbus makes three voyages, discovering the Caribbean Sea and Central America
1497	Vasco da Gama rounds the Cape of Good Hope; John Cabot makes landfall in Newfoundland
1501–02	Amerigo Vespucci navigates the Brazilian coast
1520	Ferdinand Magellan discovers the Strait of Magellan
1577–80	Francis Drake circumnavigates the world
1585–87	John Davis makes three voyages to the Davis Strait and West Greenland
1594–95	Willem Barents rounds the northern tip of Europe to Novaya Zemlya
1607–08	Henry Hudson explores East Greenland and Svalbard
1610	Henry Hudson, seeking a northwest passage, discovers Hudson Strait and Hudson Bay
1616	William Baffin and Robert Bylot discover Baffin Bay and the 'North Water'
1627	Abel Tasman sails to the south of Australia
1634	Thomas Button explores Hudson Bay
1645	Abel Tasman circumnavigates Australia and discovers northern New Zealand
1728	Vitus Bering discovers the Bering Strait
1741	Vitus Bering explores the Aleutian Islands and Alaska
1768–70	James Cook's first voyage: Southern Ocean, New Zealand, Australia
1772–75	James Cook's second voyage: circumnavigation of the Southern Ocean
1776–79	James Cook's third voyage: Cook killed in Hawaii

A native settlement in Russian Lapland, from Jan van Linschoten's Voyagie, 1601. The huts are of turf. Dogs are tethered outside some of them, and almost every dwelling has its rack for drying meat and fish. There are canoes on the shore, and birds and reindeer in the offing. One deer is hauling a boat-like sledge.

This tiny wooden church in Yakutia has the distinction of being the northernmost church in the Soviet Union. It was built by missionaries and pioneer Russian settlers in the late 18th century.

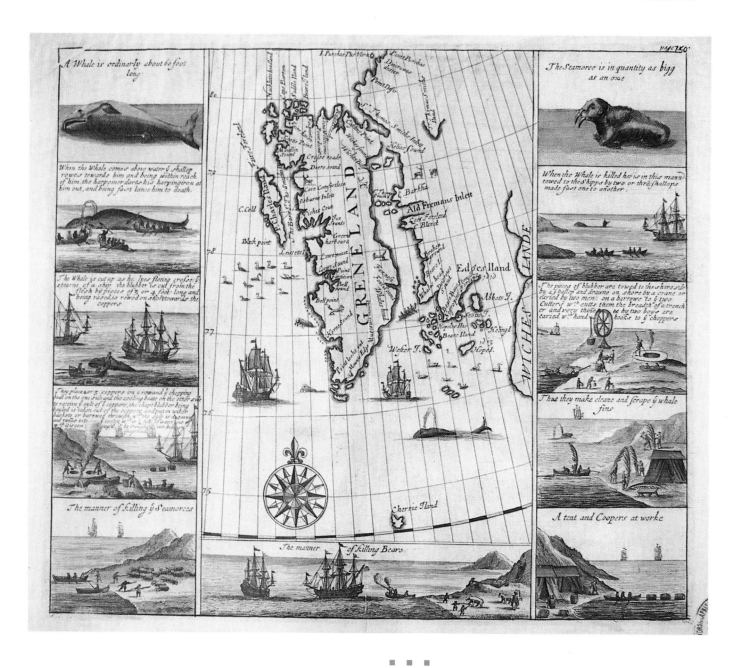

A map of Svalbard (not Greenland, with which it was often confused) dating from 1625, with details of whaling and sealing in the margins. Starting with 'A whale … about 60 foote long' (top left) and 'The seamorce [walrus] … as bigg as an oxe' (top right), the pictures show details of contemporary ships, hunting, tents, try-works for rendering down blubber, whalebone drying, and barrel-making.

archipelago. Initially these were simple tryworks, where blubber could be rendered down for oil, with tents or stone shelters for a few men close by. Later, with the addition of dwelling houses, stores and even churches, some grew to the size of villages, a few even to small towns

Smeerenberg ('Blubber City') on Amsterdam Island, at the northwestern corner of Spitsbergen, was probably the largest. Founded in 1619 by the Dutch soon after their arrival in Svalbard waters, it quickly developed into a town of some size. Recent excavations show that it included rows of trypots, several large living huts (the largest two-storied, and over 25 m/80 ft long and 15 m/50 ft wide), a church, shops, stores and at least one bakehouse, catering for a summer population of over 1,200. In the bay there was anchorage for 100 ships.

At the height of operations, in the early 18th century, over 200 ships were operating off Svalbard, more than half of them Dutch. Whalers were shipped from the Netherlands at the start of each season, as soon as the sea ice moved out, to spend the summer hard at work. At sea and on land there was bitter rivalry between Dutch, Danish, German and British whalers, sometimes developing into open warfare, for each felt justified in destroying each other's property. Overwintering parties remained to guard the factories, and for a time Smeerenberg had a fortress to protect the settlement from Danish and British incursions. Coopers were kept busy through the season, assembling the barrels in which the oil was stored. Now very much in demand for lighting and lubrication, the oil was shipped home at the end of each season and sold throughout Western Europe. Both whales and seals were taken on such a large and intensive scale from the waters around Svalbard that by the middle of the 18th century few were left, and Smeerenberg and other settlements were abandoned.

Then the focus of whaling shifted westward. In 1719 the Dutch began hunting off Davis Strait and the British quickly followed. For over a century the rich waters between Greenland and Canada provided good whaling, receiving a boost when whaling ships began to explore the 'North Water' which Baffin and Bylot had opened up more than a century before. The industry continued spasmodically through the 19th century, declining as whales became scarcer, and finally dying when mineral oils became generally available for heating and lighting.

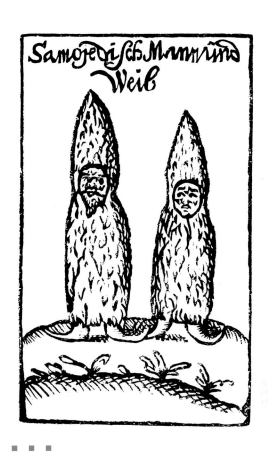

■ ■ ■

A quaint portrayal of fur-clad Samoyeds — natives of northwestern Siberia — from Schleissing's Neu-entdecktes Sieweria, *published in 1693.*

TERRA AUSTRALIS INCOGNITA

The Antarctic continent was discovered by a curious inversion of normal geographical exploration. Africa, the Americas and Australia were stumbled upon by people who had no reason to believe they existed, but were agreeably surprised to find that they did. Antarctica was different. Long before it was discovered, mariners and geographers knew beyond a doubt that a great southern continent filled much of the southern hemisphere. Discovering Antarctica was a process of elimination, of finding out where it was not, lopping huge areas from the maps and finally tracking down the real Antarctica to its fastness among the southern ice.

The Mediterranean geographers who had deduced that the world is round, and postulated hot, temperate and cold zones in both hemispheres, were firm believers in a great southern continent. The most

TYPVS ORBIS TERRARVM.

This is one of many versions of a world map published by the Dutch cartographer Ortelius from 1570 onward. The north polar region contains a large land mass in four parts. Cape Horn has been rounded, and Tierra del Fuego is separate from South America, but still attached to the unknown southern continent; Australia and New Zealand have been discovered but not yet charted.

ancient maps show the Indian and Atlantic oceans bounded by land in the south, and a southern continent in one form or another appeared on most medieval and Renaissance maps. Sometimes labelled 'Terra Australis Incognita' ('unknown southern land'), it usually filled the southern hemisphere from the South Pole almost to the tropics. It had to be large, said the geographers, to keep the world in balance. As late as 1569 Gerardus Mercator, the great Flemish cartographer, wrote of it as 'a continent so great that, with the southern parts of Asia, and the new India or America, it should be a weight equal to the other lands'.

Navigators in search of the Indies were well aware of Terra Australis Incognita; it would have been a splendid bonus to discover a continent in temperate or tropical latitudes, preferably one with gold mines, minerals, good farmland, and plenty of natives to convert to Christianity or trade as slaves.

In rounding the southern tip of Africa, Vasco da Gama effectively cut the first great swathe from the unknown southern land, pushing back its coast to temperate latitudes in the southeastern Atlantic Ocean. The second was cut by Ferdinand Magellan, who in 1520 sailed south in the Western Atlantic to round the southern tip of South America through the winding channel that now bears his name. He correctly described Tierra del Fuego, the land on the southern side of the channel, as one of a group of

islands. But the cartographers would have none of it; Tierra del Fuego was part of the southern continent, and so it was represented on mariners' charts for many years. Sir Francis Drake, who in 1577 was blown backwards round the southern flank of Tierra del Fuego, agreed entirely with Magellan, declaring it to be 'no Continent but broken Islands, but passages among them'. Willem Schouten, a Dutchman from Hoorn, finally rounded Cape Horn in 1616, sailing between the mainland and what he called Staaten Land (now Staten Island). That should have settled the matter, but old legends die hard. He freed Tierra del Fuego from the southern continent, only to make Staaten Land part of it instead.

In the Pacific Ocean, first New Guinea and its offlying islands, then New Holland (northern Australia) and New Zealand were in turn discovered and hailed as the southern continent. With each disappointment the search intensified. Throughout the 17th and 18th centuries several of the competing European nations commissioned their best navigators to comb the southern oceans, gradually moving the search further and further south. All without exception discovered rough seas, lowering skies and treacherous mists. Some made landfalls — tiny islands or green headlands looming out of the fog — that reminded them of cold European shores. The French explorer Yves Kerguelen-Tremarec, who in 1772 discovered the Iles Kerguelen in the southern Indian Ocean, was convinced beyond doubt by their greenness that here at last was the southern continent. Returning a year later with several ships and a party of colonists, he realized that his great discovery was nothing more than a chilly, windy archipelago, and returned to France a disappointed man. His enterprise, however, gave France a lasting stake in the Southern Ocean

CAPTAIN COOK AND THE ELUSIVE SOUTHERN CONTINENT

It fell to Captain James Cook, a Yorkshireman and one of the Royal Navy's most experienced hydrographers, to cut the southern continent down to size. In three outstanding voyages between 1768 and 1779 Cook explored the Southern Ocean thoroughly, keeping mostly south of the 50th parallel. He sailed south of both new Zealand and Australia. Making the first ever crossing of the Antarctic Circle, he then crossed it twice more for good measure, penetrating the Antarctic pack ice several times and reaching the astonishing latitude of 71°10'S. It was his misfortune to bear south each time at points where the continent itself lies far to the south, withholding from him the satisfaction of discovering it.

Cook charted South Georgia and the South Sandwich Islands and visited several areas where land had been reported, only to find open ocean and deep water. During southern winters when conditions at sea were impossible for his small ships, he moved into warmer climates, surveying many Pacific island groups, including the Marquesas, Tahiti and Hawaii.

He also explored the North American coast from Vancouver to Alaska, taking in both sides of the Bering Strait and reaching a furthest-north latitude of 70°44'.

The island of South Georgia interested Cook particularly, for it lay in a latitude equivalent to that of his Yorkshire home. Describing it as a 'savage and horrible' country where 'not a tree was to be seen, nor a shrub even big enough to make a toothpick', he mused on why an island 'situated between the latitude of 54° and 55°, should, in the very height of summer, be in a manner wholly covered many fathoms deep with frozen snow?' He continued: '...a great deal of ice is formed here in the winter, which in the spring is broken off and dispersed over the sea; but this island cannot produce the ten-thousandth part of what we saw; so that either there must be more land, or the ice is formed without it.'

Cook's surveys in the Southern Ocean established that Terra Australis, if it existed at all, could lie only in far southern latitudes. During one of his forays into the southern ice, hemmed in by tabular icebergs that dwarfed his tiny ships, he judged dispassionately that such bergs were being formed on a large land mass far to the south. He further noted that 'the greatest part of this southern continent (supposing there is one) must lie within the polar circle, where the sea is so pestered with ice that the land is thereby inaccessible.' Cook had tracked the southern continent down to its own latitudes, sailed within a few miles of its ice cliffs, and only by sheer ill-fortune failed to discover it. His final conclusion was inevitable in the circumstances: if the continent existed, it would hardly be worth discovering.

7

Later Explorers

The discoveries of the 18th century left geographers with maps of a recognizable world. Climatic zones were known and continents roughed out, with rivers, mountains and pictorial towns for detail. Networks of tracks crossed and re-crossed the oceans. Rashes of dots showed islands discovered — and often re-discovered and named several times, for it was still difficult to determine longitude and fix positions accurately. Even so, there were still great gaps and uncertainties, some to be filled in the 19th century, others even later.

The polar regions were confirmed, but as yet only pencilled in. They were known to be difficult, dangerous and on the whole unrewarding, so special reasons were needed to visit them and explore them further. There were reasons enough to satisfy all tastes.

During the 19th century excitement in simple exploration ran high, for there were clearly new lands to be discovered at both ends of the world. The north polar basin had yet to be penetrated — few explorers had been farther than 80°N, and there was speculation about a still-hidden northern continent. The south polar region was still wholly mysterious. There was also interest in monitoring magnetic variation — the degree to which compass needles are pulled away from true north–south alignment. The subject was a matter of great importance both to deep-sea mariners and to landsmen in high latitudes, for both relied on magnetic compasses to give them direction.

In the north there was also strong motivation to discover northeast and northwest passages from Europe to the Orient, and more immediate economic interest in finding new whaling and sealing grounds, for world markets in oil and pelts continued to grow. In the Southern Ocean there was promise of similar wealth, for Captain Cook and other explorers had reported whales at sea and seals by the thousand on the cold temperate islands they had visited. There were also fortunes to be made in furs from the forests of Siberia and North America.

CONQUEST OF THE NORTHERN FORESTS

The Siberian northlands, loosely held and administered by Muscovite Russia, were acquired for the tsars by the private enterprise of marauding bands. The northern forests and narrow strip of coastal tundra formed a kind of wild back garden to Moscow, costing little to maintain and yielding revenues of furs to the merchant adventurers who exploited them. They had changed little since the time of Ivan IV, who in 1547 became first tsar of Russia, and one the first rulers to realize their potential.

The northern forests were occupied by people of more than a dozen separate nations, living in primitive and widely scattered communities. West of the Urals were the Zyrians, Permians, Cheremis and Votyaks. To the north and east of the mountains were the Samoyeds, Ostyaks and Voguls. On the southern steppes were Tatars, remnants of earlier Muslim invasions. Descendants of all these peoples can be found in the same areas today.

Mainly hunters, fishermen and reindeer herders, these people made their living from forests, rivers and tundra, collecting enough food in summer to last through the long, bitter winters. They were shamanists, believing in spirits both evil and good. Most paid tribute to overlords, who offered protection of a kind, imposed taxes and fought among themselves. Furs were common currency and also much in demand in the world outside.

From time to time their traditional way of life had been disrupted by invaders from the south, for the Tatars valued furs as much as anyone else, and would travel far to acquire them. From the 16th century onward, new invaders came from the west: Tsar Ivan's Russian colonizers and go-getters, motivated by poverty and restlessness, moved east through the Urals along routes that had been known to traders and explorers since the 12th century. There were no roads, only portages through mountain passes, tracks through forests, and long sweeps of river to be navigated in primitive flat-bottomed boats.

The new invasion began in 1581 with a punitive raid by a few hundred Cossacks on a small khanate east of the mountains, which had failed to pay its taxes to Moscow. This set a pattern which continued for well over two centuries. Successive waves of Russian hunters, traders and Cossack adventurers opened up and exploited the treasure-house of furs beyond the Urals, supplying a market that developed and became insatiable both in Europe and in Russia itself. By the mid-17th century the Russians had crossed Siberia to the Pacific coastland and by the late 18th century Kamchatka and the farthest reaches of the Chukot Peninsula had been incorporated into the ramshackle sprawl of the Russian Empire.

THE ANNEXATION OF SIBERIA

Many historians date Russia's invasion of Siberia from the campaign of Yermak, a Cossack leader, against Kuchum, the Tatar overlord of Sibir, in the early 1570s. Sibir was a small vassal khanate on the Irtysh River from which Siberia eventually took its name. In 1571, at which time the Urals marked the eastern frontier of Russia, Kuchum ceased to pay his annual tribute of fine furs to Moscow, and in the following year was responsible for killing emissaries of Tsar Ivan IV. Suspecting rebellion beyond the frontier, Ivan authorized the Stroganovs, a family of merchant adventurers, to establish strongholds east of the Urals on the Tobol, Irtysh and Ob rivers, and restore order. The Stroganovs called in Yermak Timofeyevich, leader of a band of Cossack warriors, to deal with Kuchum.

Yermak began his campaign in September 1581. It appears to have been a desultory fight along rivers — the only practicable routes — between wandering bands of warriors, between Cossacks armed with guns and Tatars armed with swords and bows. Yermak captured Kuchum's stronghold, Isker, late in 1581, then spent a year consolidating his position and awaiting reinforcements. He was killed during further fighting in 1585. Stroganov forces established further Russian strongpoints in the area during the next few years. Kuchum fought on, but was murdered by fellow Tatars after a final campaign in 1598.

The success of such campaigns would have been measured in booty and intelligence brought back to Moscow. The survivors knew that fine furs were there in abundance, and more bands set out to trade or loot. Independent trappers, missionaries and colonial administrators followed. So Muscovite Russia, quietly, with a minimum of organization and little opposition or bloodshed, acquired its sprawling eastern empire.

Similar attention opened the North American forests to trade, missionary zeal and colonial administration. Although Cabot's voyage of 1497 had shown the way, it was Jacques Cartier's discovery of the Gaspé Peninsula and his exploration of the St Lawrence River in 1534–35 that really stimulated the interest of Europeans in North America. The land they coveted was Indian, lived in by several nations who, like their counterparts in the Siberian forests, were hunters, fishermen and shamanists. In rivalry the French and English established the first fur-trading posts, wooed or fought off the Indians, and eventually fought each other, first for trade and ultimately for territorial sovereignty. Under the Treaty of Utrecht in 1713 Britain gained Nova Scotia, Newfoundland and Hudson Bay. Sixty years later James Wolfe's victory at Quebec secured practically all of eastern Canada for Britain.

The Hudson's Bay Company, formed in England under royal charter in 1670, was dedicated to discovering a northwest passage and to occupying and exploiting the land adjacent to Hudson Bay. Eventually, however, it overcame or absorbed both rivals and enemies to become the dominant economic force in Prince Rupert's Land, a huge territory extending from Labrador to the Rocky Mountains, and beyond to British Columbia and Vancouver Island. The company's first factories or trading posts were established in Hudson Bay, but later a chain of posts spread along rivers and lakes far into the interior, gathering furs from local trappers in exchange for trade goods.

Company managers explored and opened up the northern forests, extending their trading influence to the Mackenzie Valley and further. Company prospectors and surveyors looked for minerals and marked their positions on newly prepared maps. Company posts became settlements, acquiring garrisons, mission churches, medical facilities, and eventually police posts and schools. Several ultimately became towns and cities of modern Canada. The Company remained in virtual control until 1867, when many of its powers were surrendered to the newly formed Federation of Canada. It remained an important trading establishment throughout the northlands and is still a significant mercantile firm in Canada today.

THE NORTH POLAR BASIN

While the northlands were being developed, discovery at sea continued. While landsmen pressed eastward through Siberia and westward into Canada in search of furs, their shipborne counterparts continued to seek ways through or past the pack ice. Russian naval explorers inched their way along the ice-bound Siberian coast, linking small settlements on the river deltas, gathering information on ice conditions and navigable channels, and showing the possibility of trade routes that would ultimately carry goods to and from the Siberian heartlands. Further west the search for a northwest passage gathered momentum, aided by the knowledge of whaling captains and stimulated, at least as far as the British were concerned, by cash prizes.

Not surprisingly, the late 18th and early 19th centuries saw many attempts by whalers and others to penetrate northward into the polar basin. Some were lured by glory and cash prizes but hard-headed whalers had stronger motives: their search was always for new whaling grounds — new, rich waters to be exploited for a season or two before anyone else got there — that would make their fortunes.

The problem was always the summer pack ice, an impenetrable barrier to sailing ships in latitudes between 60°N and 80°N. Many headed north each summer along different meridians, hoping to find a way through. The Russians tried east of Novaya Zemlya, and the British and several other nations tried either side of Svalbard, and in all longitudes between Greenland and Novaya Zemlya.

Britain's Royal Navy took the challenge very seriously. In August 1773 Captains Phipps and Lutwidge reached 80°48'N off Svalbard. On board HMS *Carcass*, one of their two vessels, was coxwain Horatio Nelson. The Napoleonic Wars temporarily halted polar exploration, but by 1818 the Navy was ready to sail north again. Encouraged by whalers' reports of unusually ice-free seas in the far north the previous year, two vessels under Commander David Buchan sailed north to Svalbard and two under Commander John Ross sailed northwestward into the Davis Strait, all under orders to penetrate as far as possible into the unknown.

Buchan, accompanied by Lieutenant John Franklin, reached 80°34'N just beyond Svalbard. Here his ships were stopped by ice up to 4 m (13 ft) high

■ ■ ■

Officers of Commander John Ross's naval expedition meeting North Greenland Inuit in the summer of 1818 — the first meeting of this small, isolated community with outsiders. The expedition vessels Adventure *and* Isabella *were the first ships they had ever seen.*

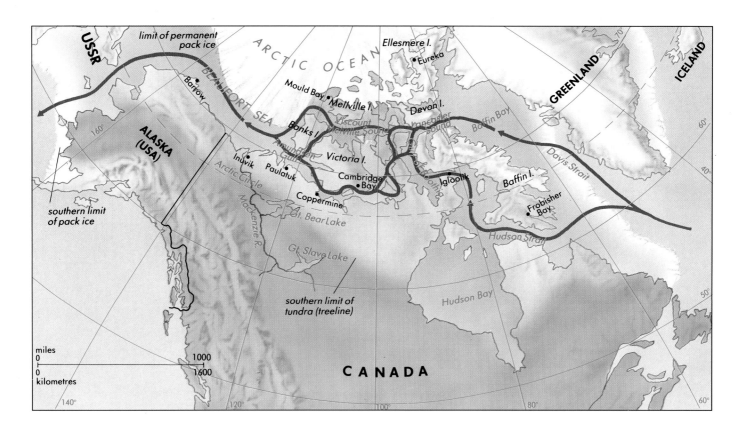

that threatened to bear down on and sink them. Ross, accompanied by Lieutenant William Edward Parry, sailed into Lancaster Sound. It seemed to him enclosed to the west, so he retreated, which was a mistake, for the Sound is now known to be a fairly reliable way through to the Pacific Ocean. Neither expedition was a marked success, but each provided admirable training for its second-in-command. Both Franklin and Parry went on to became famous in polar exploration.

In 1879 a US naval expedition under Commander George Washington De Long tried to penetrate the Arctic Ocean through the Bering Strait, hoping to find new land or reach the North Pole. Caught by the pack ice in 71°N, their ship *Jeanette* was carried westward for almost two years, finally breaking up north of the Novosibirskiye Islands. The crew made their way to the delta of the Lena River, but only 13 of the original company of 33 survived. In small compensation for their pains, they discovered that 'Wrangel Land', supposed to extend from Siberia to Greenland, did not exist, and that Wrangel Island itself was relatively small. Three years later, timbers from the *Jeanette* appeared off southwest Greenland. This supported the idea that the north polar basin was crossed by surface currents and therefore the suspicion that it was empty of land.

■ ■ ■

The North American Arctic and the Northwest Passage. Ships approaching from Europe and seeking a westward passage first tried the St Lawrence estuary and Hudson Bay. The true passages — and there are several alternatives — wind through the ice-choked channels of the archipelago.

THE NORTHWEST PASSAGE

In 1819-20 William Parry, now commanding his own ship HMS *Hecla* and accompanied by the smaller HMS *Griper*, explored Lancaster Sound more carefully. Fully committed to discovering the Northwest Passage, he broke through the ice into Prince Regent Inlet and forced on, managing to reach and cross 110°W, and win £5000 for himself and his crews. The ships wintered in a harbour off Melville Island, but were unable to make progress westward the following year.

Meanwhile John Franklin was leading an expedition overland, by sledge and canoe, from York Factory, Hudson Bay, to link up with the continental

■   ■   ■   MAN-HAULING OVER ICE   ■   ■   ■

In June 1827 Parry anchored HMS *Hecla* in a sheltered cove on north Spitsbergen. Two teams, each consisting of two officers, ten seamen and two Royal Marines, then set out in specially prepared boats 6 m (20 ft) long, equipped with 71 days' provisions. Reaching the ice edge in 81°13'N, they hauled the boats up and began to drag them across the rough pack ice.

It was their misfortune to have started at midsummer — at that time of year temperatures are close to freezing point, the ice is soft, and warm rain gathers in pools underfoot. Hauling loads that averaged more than 112 kg (250 lbs) per man, they made very slow northward progress, constantly wet, alternately rowing and hauling their unwieldy boats over piled-up floes. After several weeks of this, they found that the ice was drifting south faster than they were hauling north. To their eternal credit they reached a point 275 km (172 miles) north of their

ship, in a record latitude of 82°45'N. They returned to *Hecla* after an absence of 61 days.

Although Parry had given his method of travelling much thought, it was in many ways a travesty of native sledging. The Inuit use light sledges, not heavy boats on skids, and dogs take the strain, not men. The loads were excessive, the diet inadequate, the clothing unsuited to wet summer conditions. Not surprisingly, the attempt was a gallant failure.

Sledging marked a distinct advance over surveying from ships. Shipborne survey was adequate for charting ice-free coasts, but sledgers could explore where ships could not, and work unhampered by shipboard routine. Although many profitable hours were spent ashore from ships, in recreation and collecting specimens, sledging journeys could last weeks or months and allow several parties to work simultaneously in different areas.

coast. His companions were a naval surgeon, two midshipmen and an able seaman, and his orders were to investigate the Coppermine River and points eastward from its estuary, using native guides and porters. He achieved a remarkable journey of over 8800 km (5,500 miles), but it tested him to the limit and cost the lives of several of his hired helpers.

In 1821 Parry led a second two-year expedition, this time exploring Fox Channel and the Melville Peninsula. A third expedition in 1824 took him back to Prince Regent Inlet, but after wintering at Port Bowen he lost his companion ship HMS *Fury* in a storm, and had to return home. This was Parry's last attempt to find the Northwest Passage, but not his final expedition. For that he decided to tackle the North Pole, using the sledging techniques that he had seen the Inuit use. Even if his ship were stopped by pack ice, surely a sledging party could continue north over the ice toward the Pole? It was worth a try, but it did not succeed. Parry and his men dragged heavy boats over soft summer ice for a total of almost nine weeks, achieving a northern record in 82°45'N before returning exhausted. From this beginning arose the tradition of man-hauling over ice, a back-breaking technique that for almost a century became insepara-

ble from naval polar exploration.

Although the Act covering the award of prizes was repealed in 1828, successive British governments continued to support Arctic research and to pay honoraria to explorers and their crews. In 1829 Captain John Ross returned to the scene with a private expedition, taking an ice-strengthened paddle steamer, *Victory*, through Lancaster Sound and on to Boothia Peninsula, which he named for the gin manufacturer who had helped to finance his expedition. With his nephew Commander James Clark Ross as second-in-command, he spent four winters in the Arctic, losing his ship to the ice and finally returning to England in a whaling vessel. The expedition achieved little, but gave James Ross an opportunity to visit the North Magnetic Pole, a taste for polar travel, and an apprenticeship in ice-work that would serve him well a few years later in Antarctica.

The mid-19th-century search for the Northwest Passage ended in the disaster of the Franklin expedition of 1845–48. The search parties that combed the north for several years after its disappearance investigated every channel that Franklin might have taken, every coast and island between the mainland and the southern islands of the Canadian archipelago where

THE FRANKLIN EXPEDITION

In 1845 Sir John Franklin, by then a veteran of 59, led a well-equipped British naval expedition that was intended finally to conquer the Northwest Passage. With two equally veteran ice-strengthened vessels, HMSs *Erebus* and *Terror*, ships' companies numbering 139 and three years' supplies, he sailed for Davis Strait. The expedition was sighted in July 1845 by a whaler off Melville Bay, Greenland. After that it was never seen again

In 1848, when still nothing had been heard, two shipborne expeditions and one overland expedition were sent out to search for Franklin. In 1850 five expeditions, three naval and two private, continued the search; one of the private expeditions was funded by Lady Franklin, Sir John's wife, the other by Henry Grinnell, an American newspaper owner. In 1852 four more ships were sent, this time to seek not only Franklin's party but two ships of the 1850 search parties that had failed to return. These widespread searches resulted in the discovery of the graves of three seamen on Beechey Island and evidence that Franklin's ships had wintered there, but very little else.

The Franklin expedition was finally tracked down by Dr John Rae, a medical officer of the Hudson's Bay Company. Between 1851 and 1854 he led independent searches of over 8000 km (5,000 miles), covering the Wollaston Peninsula, Victoria Island, the Coppermine River and the western Boothia Peninsula. Inuit encountered at Pelly Bay told him of white men from broken ships seen off King William Island some years earlier, and of the bodies of over 30 men later found in a starved condition on the mainland. The Inuit had tableware and trinkets from the ships, discovered among the bodies.

A Hudson's Bay Company expedition to the area in 1855 found boat furnishings, tools and tent poles, and a final expedition in 1857–58 under Captain William McClintock found more relics on King William Island and·around the estuary of the Back River. The story pieced together was that *Erebus* and *Terror* had been caught in the ice off the northwest of King William Island in September 1846 and had foundered in April 1848. The men had headed south toward land; some had died crossing the ice, others later while attempting to cross the mainland tundra.

One of the searchers, Commander Robert McClure of HMS *Investigator*, came closest of all to traversing the Northwest Passage. Approaching from the Bering Strait, he sailed eastward close to the mainland shore, then struck across to Banks Island and circled it northward to what is now McClure Strait. Although almost in sight of the westernmost point reached by Parry, with only ice-covered sea between, he was destined never to close the gap. He and his companions spent three years in the area, making excellent sledging journeys. Finally they had to abandon their ship and return on one of the other Franklin rescue vessels.

survivors might have landed. Their efforts added much to geographical knowledge of the area. Although they did not find Franklin or his ships, their searches revealed what had happened and discovered a number of bodies and relics from the expedition. None of the searchers managed to traverse the Northwest Passage, although one of them, Robert McClure, came close enough to be awarded £10,000, half the offered prize. The Passage was finally navigated by the Norwegian explorer Roald Amundsen in 1903–06.

THE SOUTHERN SEALERS

After Cook's voyages in the 1770s little further official interest was taken in the far south. Cook's published accounts made it clear that Antarctica offered virtually nothing to potential colonists — pickings were far richer in Africa, Asia and South America. In any case, expensive wars occupied the European nations and tied up their ships. Not until Napoleon was safely mewed up on St Helena did interest turn again to naval exploration.

By contrast, commercial interest was intense. The Falkland Islands, Patagonia and the tip of South

America were already known for their fur seals, and Cook had reported an abundance of whales and seals throughout the Southern Ocean. The hunters were quick to move in. Commercial sealers were enterprising but secretive folk who explored for profit. With few exceptions their interest in new lands was proportional to the number of seals they found there — good sealing coasts were worth finding, and then worth keeping quiet about. Competent seamen and navigators, the sealing captains kept meticulous logs and made their own charts, but seldom published anything that might help their rivals.

Cook's discoveries came at a time when British and American sealers had almost exhausted the northern stocks of seals. Demand for furs was at a peak, so it made sense for the sealers to head south as fast as possible. Competing ship against ship, company against company, there was no question of conserving stocks. They found their seals and put the gangs ashore, with food and minimal shelter, to kill every animal they could lay hands on. Flensing, drying or salting the skins and packing them into their holds, they sailed off to market (usually in Canton, China), then came back as early as possible in the following season for more.

No accurate records were kept. We do not even know which species of seal — there are several species of southern fur seal — were present on many of the islands. But we do know that South Georgia's fur seals, now estimated conservatively at two to

■ CASH FOR EXPLORATION ■

In 1745 the British parliament passed an Act that granted an award of £20,000 to 'such person or persons, his Majesty's subject or subjects, as shall discover a North-West Passage through Hudson's Straits to the western and southern ocean of America'. This Act was kept in the public eye by amendment in 1753 and again in 1790. Then in 1818 came 'An Act for more effectually discovering longitude at sea, and for encouraging attempts to find a northern passage between the Atlantic and Pacific Oceans, and to approach the Northern Pole'. There were accompanying awards of £5,000 for crossing the 110th meridian north of America, a longitude well into the Passage, and £20,000 for discovering the Passage itself.

Later a graduated scale of awards was introduced for reaching successive northern latitudes: £1,000 for crossing 83°N, £2,000 for 85°, £3,000 for 87°, £4,000 for 88° and £5,000 for 89°N. These were considerable prizes, and they spurred many young British naval officers into polar exploration and research. The Act was repealed in 1828, although prizes continued to be awarded for outstanding exploits.

During the early period of Antarctic whaling only the blubber and baleen (mouth bristles, used for making brushes and stays) were taken from whales. The carcasses were left to rot. Many of the old whaling harbours are littered with whale bones from this period. Here a Weddell seal makes itself comfortable among whale bones, alongside a derelict scow or water-boat.

three million, were cleaned out almost completely within a decade. The sealers then broadened their search, revisiting known islands and discovering new ones within the same latitudinal band. In turn Más Afuera, the South Shetlands, South Orkneys and South Sandwich Islands, Tristan da Cunha, Gough and Nightingale Islands, Marion and Heard Islands, Iles Crozet and Kerguelen, and Macquarie, Campbell, Auckland and Antipodes Islands were stripped of their seal stocks. After fur seals the much larger elephant seals became the quarry. Their hides made good leather, and their blubber yielded a clear oil, as valuable as whale oil for lighting and lubrication.

Toward the end of this grisly slaughter penguins too were rounded up on some of the islands and butchered for their oil. By the late 19th century every island and archipelago in the Southern Ocean had been discovered. Most were irrevocably changed, not only by the loss of seals and penguins, but by fires and the introduction of alien grazing and predatory animals.

A few of the sealing captains were interested in exploration for its own sake. In 1821 Nathaniel Palmer, a young American, was among the first to sight the Antarctic Peninsula. He and William Powell, a Briton, explored the South Orkney Islands. John Davis visited Hughes Bay, further down the Peninsula, and was probably the first man to set foot on Antarctica. In 1823 James Weddell explored the huge embayment in Antarctica that now bears his name, penetrating as far as 74°S in a sea that is usually laden with pack ice. In 1831 John Biscoe discovered Enderby Land, on the continental mainland, naming it after his British employers. In the following year he made discoveries far south along the Peninsula, including Adelaide Island. In 1833 Peter Kemp discovered a stretch of mainland coast close to Biscoe's, now called Kemp Land. These voyages, most of them in ships of 200 tonnes or less, made discoveries no less significant than the more widely publicised voyages of the Arctic naval explorers.

RUSSIA IN ANTARCTICA

The first expedition to follow Cook into Antarctic waters was a Russian naval operation. In the tradition of many Russian Arctic expeditions, its officers were experienced ice navigators, and it brought into the field a well-equipped, experienced group of scien-

tists, draftsmen and cartographers. Its commanding officer, Captain Thaddeus von Bellingshausen, was a thoughtful German with long service in the Imperial Navy, and a great admirer of Cook, whose charts and publications he had studied.

In the southern summers of 1819 and 1821 *Vostok*, a 600-tonne corvette, and *Mirny*, a slightly smaller transport, made voyages that between them circumnavigated Antarctica. One of Bellingshausen's main objectives was to complement Cook's voyages, sailing south where he had been forced north, and to get as close as possible to the polar continent, or indeed to the Pole. Bellingshausen's skill and leadership realized these objectives in full measure. Reading his published accounts of the voyages, it is sometimes difficult to remember that he and his second-in-command, Mikhail Lazarev, were in none-too-manoeuverable sailing ships, negotiating contrary winds and currents, trying to reach their objectives through icy seas, often among flotillas of icebergs that dwarfed their ships and could easily have broken them to matchwood.

Vostok and *Mirny* added substantially to Cook's incomplete surveys of South Georgia and the South Sandwich Islands, visited several other Southern Ocean islands, and forced their way south into the ice. They crossed the Antarctic Circle no fewer than six times and came within sight of the Antarctic mainland on several occasions.

During his first voyage, at a point slightly west of the Greenwich meridian, Bellingshausen sailed among towering tabular icebergs within 30 km (20 miles) of an ice-bound coast; the mainland ice cliffs may well have been in sight, although unrecognized for what they were among the jumble of icebergs. Toward the end of his second voyage Bellingshausen discovered remote Peter I Island (now Norway's Peter I Øy) and charted and named the mountains of Alexander Land, clearly seen but unapproachable because of heavy pack ice, near the base of the Antarctic Peninsula. Bellingshausen Sea in this region was named for him, and other Russian names commemorating his officers and crew are liberally sprinkled around Antarctica.

This was Russia's first foray into Antarctic waters, and highly successful. Although probably realizing that he was close to a continent, Bellingshausen made no claims to have seen land. His chartwork, compared with modern maps, makes it clear that he

was several times within a few kilometres of the ice-cliff coast. His modestly stated narrative and observations, and those of his scientists and cartographers, have stood every test of time. On the strength of his voyages the Soviet Union today claims a historic interest in Antarctica and the Southern Ocean, but makes no claims to ownership of Antarctic territory.

Between 1837 and 1843 three major national expeditions, French, American and British, added detail to the map of Antarctica. Each carried scientists as well as expert navigators, spending two or three summers in the ice. They described many new geographical features, rock formations, plants and animals, adding substantially to knowledge of the southern hemisphere. No less important was their chartwork: the coastlines they plotted in their maps and charts made clear, for the first time, the true size and continental proportions of Antarctica.

TERRE ADÉLIE

The French were first in the field. In 1837 Captain Jules Dumont d'Urville of the French Navy, carrying personal orders from King Louis-Philippe, sailed south with two well-founded ships, *Astrolabe* and *Zélée*. A man of culture and science, Dumont

■ ■ ■

Dumont d'Urville's Astrolabe *and* Zélée *in the ice off Adélie Land. Ships under sail were always at a disadvantage in approaching Antarctica. Offshore winds cleared the sea of ice but made the approach difficult. Onshore winds took ships close-in but brought the ice in with them, leaving little sea room. Here the crew take to the floes to haul the ship's head round and steer away from the ice cliffs.*

d'Urville had already won fame by bringing the Venus de Milo to Paris. Concerned mostly with surveying and collecting among the islands of the Pacific Ocean, his expedition made two strikes toward Antarctica.

During the first, in February 1838, he was caught and held in the ice off the Antarctic Peninsula, but managed to escape without serious damage. He surveyed parts of the peninsula coast and named several of the offlying islands. His second voyage, after a year spent in the Pacific Ocean, was more productive. *Astrolabe* and *Zélée* sailed south from Tasmania, entering the pack ice and forcing their way south until halted by an ice cliff. In January 1840, skirting the ice of what seemed to be a mainland coast, they discovered and landed on a group of small islands. Their point of landing, named Pointe Géologie, was heavily occupied by small black and white penguins, which vigorously contested the intrusion. Dumont d'Urville served wine to his jubilant officers and crew, claiming the coast for France and naming it Terre Adélie after his wife. The penguins, which his naturalists recognized as a new species, acquired the same name. Adélie penguins are the archetypal, entertaining species found all around the Antarctic continent, much loved by explorers and all who see them.

The French government upheld Dumont d'Urville's claim. Terre Adélie — a narrow slice of the Antarctic cake, about 270 km (170 miles) wide at the coast and tapering all the way to the South Pole — remains a French possession. Jules and Adélie Dumont d'Urville earned one other small, unwelcome claim to fame. In 1841, shortly after his return to France, they took an excursion by train and died together in one of the world's earliest railway accidents.

CHARLES WILKES AND THE US EXPLORING EXPEDITION

Almost simultaneously with Dumont d'Urville, an expedition of six US naval ships left port to spend nearly four years exploring the southern oceans. Largest of the fleet, *Vincennes*, was a 780-tonne sloop. The smallest, *Flying Fish*, was a schooner and former New York pilot boat that should never have gone anywhere near the ice. Commanding the expedition was Lieutenant Charles Wilkes, whose brief included hydrographic work all over the southern hemisphere and voyages of exploration in Antarctic waters.

There has seldom been a less happy polar expedition. From its grudging acceptance by Congress to its ignominious return, followed by courts-martial for several of its officers and ungrateful repudiation for its commander, the United States Exploring Expedition seems to have borne a curse. First excur-

■ ■ ■

Adélie penguins nest in a packing case left by Shackleton's 1907–09 polar expedition, Cape Royds, Antarctica. The case, zinc-lined, once contained a reel of steel sounding wire. With others it was hastily thrown ashore on the headland close to Shackleton's hut when bad weather forced his ship to leave in a hurry.

■   ■   ■   POLAR EXPLORATION 1801 – 1900   ■   ■   ■

1801	Edmund Fanning and others take a record catch of over 120,000 fur seal skins from South Georgia
1806	Auckland Islands, south of New Zealand, discovered and cleared of fur seals
1810	Macquarie Island, south of Tasmania, discovered and a large catch of fur seal skins taken
1819	Edward Parry penetrates west of 110°W in the Northwest Passage
1819	British merchant William Smith discovers the South Shetland Islands; sealers move in
1819–20	John Franklin leads an overland expedition to the Coppermine River, Arctic Canada
1819–21	Bellingshausen in *Vostok* and *Mirny* circumnavigates Antarctica — first sighting of continental Antarctica
1821	American John Davis in *Huron* makes first landing on the Antarctic Peninsula in Hughes Bay
1821	Nathaniel Palmer in *James Monroe* and John Powell in *Dove* discover the South Orkney Islands
1821–25	Edward Parry leads a second and third attempt on the Northwest Passage
1823	James Weddell in *Jane* and Matthew Brisbane in *Beaufoy* reach 74°15'S in the Weddell Sea
1827	Edward Parry attempts to sledge from Svalbard to the North Pole
1829–32	John and James Ross explore the Boothia Peninsula and discover the North Magnetic Pole
1831–32	John Biscoe in *Tula* discovers Enderby Land and Adelaide Island
1833	Peter Kemp in *Magnet* sights Kemp Land, continental Antarctica
1837–1840	Jules Dumont d'Urville circumnavigates Antarctica, discovering Terre Adélie and islands off the Antarctic Peninsula
1838–40	Charles Wilkes leads the US Exploring Expedition in two Antarctic voyages
1839–43	James Clark Ross leads a scientific expedition to Antarctica, discovering the Ross Sea, Ross Ice Shelf and Victoria Land
1845–48	Sir John Franklin's expedition to the Northwest Passage ends in disaster
1848–54	Franklin search expeditions to the Northwest Passage region — Franklin relics discovered
1872–76	HMS *Challenger* explores oceanography of the Southern Ocean
1873	Eduard Dallmann in *Grönland* explores Antarctic Peninsula waters for right whales
1879–81	De Long makes a bid for the North Pole in USS *Jeanette* — ship and many of the crew perish off the Siberian coast.
1878–80	Adolf Nordenskjöld in *Vega* navigates the Northeast Passage
1888–89	Nansen makes first crossing of the Greenland ice cap
1892–93	Dundee whaling expedition explores the northern Weddell Sea for right whales
1892–94	Norwegian whaling ships under C. A. Larsen visit Antarctic Peninsula waters in search of right whales
1894–5	Bull and Kristensen search for right whales in Ross Sea, Antarctica; first landing on continental Antarctica at Cape Adare
1897–99	*Belgica* Antarctic expedition under Adrien de Gerlache winters in pack ice of Bellingshausen Sea
1898–1900	Borchgrevink leads British Antarctic Expedition to winter at Cape Adare

❄

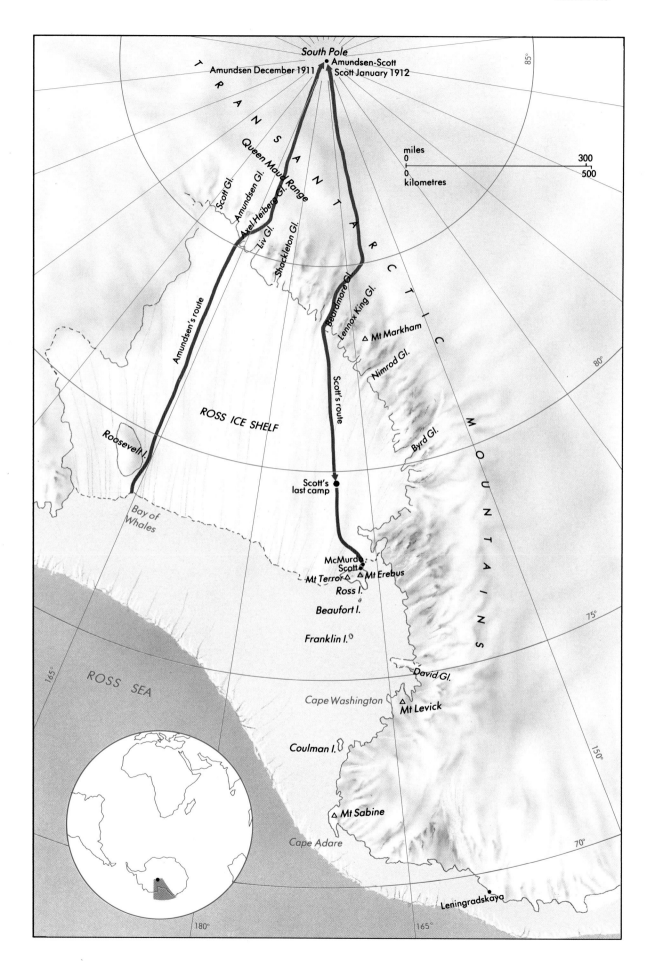

South Pole

Amundsen December 1911
Amundsen-Scott
Scott January 1912

TRANSANTARCTIC

Queen Maud Range

Scott Gl.

Amundsen Gl.

Axel Heiberg Gl.

Liv Gl.

Shackleton Gl.

Beardmore Gl.

Lennox King Gl.

△ Mt Markham

Nimrod Gl.

miles
0   300
0   500
kilometres

Amundsen's route

Scott's route

Byrd Gl.

M
O
U
N
T
A
I
N
S

ROSS ICE SHELF

Roosevelt I.

Scott's
last camp

Bay of
Whales

McMurdo
Scott
Mt Terror △   △ Mt Erebus
Ross I.

Beaufort I.

Franklin I.

David Gl.

ROSS   SEA

Cape Washington
△ Mt Levick

Coulman I.

△ Mt Sabine

Cape Adare

Leningradskaya

85°

80°

75°

150°

70°

165°

180°

165°

sions into the ice off the Antarctic Peninsula in February 1839 confirmed what Wilkes had suspected all along: his men were ill-equipped and his motley collection of ships were ill-founded for work in any ocean, least of all in the ice-bound Southern Ocean. His men were cold, damp and dispirited, and he soon found reason to doubt the loyalty and dedication of several of his officers. One of his smaller ships, the schooner *Sea Gull*, survived the ice off Cape Horn only to be lost with all hands off Chile.

The expedition wintered in warmer seas. The store ship *Relief* returned home, and the remaining four refitted as best they could in Australia. For his second Antarctic voyage Wilkes left Sydney in late December 1839 and headed south again toward the pack ice. *Vincennes*, and *Porpoise*, a 230-tonne brig, entered the ice and reached 64°S, at which point they found themselves halted by bergs and an ice cliff and turned westward, hoping to find a way south. Joined by *Peacock*, a sloop slightly smaller than *Vincennes* although far less manageable in the ice, they then continued westward, keeping as far south as the ice would allow.

It was an unrewarding trek, for this is an all-ice coast with no rock outcrops to show convincingly where the land starts. Constantly dodging bergs and brash ice, Wilkes sketched and logged a succession of ice-covered mounds far inland, naming a number of icy features which he was sure represented land underneath. That his ships were close to land became apparent from soundings — they were sailing over a deep but certain continental shelf. An emperor penguin taken as a scientific specimen obliged with additional evidence: its crop contained basaltic pebbles from a sea floor, a fair indication of land close by.

■ ■ ■

The Ross Ice Shelf and routes to the South Pole. James Clark Ross's expedition of 1839–43 was the last great shipborne exploratory expedition to either pole. Scott's route to the pole in January 1911 followed that pioneered by Shackleton in 1907, starting from McMurdo Sound and ascending the Beardmore Glacier to reach the polar plateau. Amundsen started from the Bay of Whales, an indentation in the ice front, and ascended the steeper but shorter Axel Heiberg Glacier.

In late January 1840 *Peacock* suffered damage by running stern-first into an iceberg and had to return to Sydney. The two remaining ships stayed on station until mid-February, when *Porpoise* broke off and headed north. Wilkes in *Vincennes* headed westward for a further week before shaping course for Sydney.

During their six weeks in the ice the US ships in effect outlined about one seventh of the coast of Antarctica. Wilkes completed his maps and reports and sent them back to the United States. After spending a further year in the Pacific Ocean he returned home himself, to be given a hostile reception. Officers who had returned earlier had complained publicly of his leadership. Some of the charts and logs sent on ahead were already suspect, if not completely discredited. The navy set up a board of enquiry and Wilkes was court-martialled on several charges, most of which were withdrawn during the hearings. The final reports of his voyages, meticulously compiled by himself and a few loyal staff, were ungraciously curtailed by the navy and printed only in limited edition, making them virtually inaccessible to the scientific world.

Although Wilkes's chartwork contained errors and not all of his conclusions have been substantiated, his achievements against heavy odds are now recognized. His expedition results, controversial when first reported, are now regarded with greater favour — it was not half so bad an expedition as his countrymen in office at the time wanted to make out. Wilkes, a flawed personality, made the best of a bad situation. Whatever its shortcomings, the expedition returned with the first real evidence that the Southern Ocean contained a land mass of continental size.

Strongly anti-colonial, the United States had no wish to claim any of the territory that Wilkes had discovered. However, the name Wilkes Land on a substantial sector of Antarctica, and the application of his names to many features along that sector of coast, are generally regarded as a well-deserved tribute to a dedicated explorer.

JAMES CLARK ROSS IN ANTARCTICA

Within a few years of returning from his uncle's expedition to the Arctic, James Clark Ross found himself leading a major Royal Naval expedition to Antarctica. The year was 1841, and the occasion marked a brief revival of British interest in Antarctica,

◾ ◾ ◾

Erebus *and* Terror *dwarfed by pack ice. Most celebrated of polar sailing ships, these were strongly-built naval monitors, reinforced to carry large guns and therefore strong enough to enter and negotiate open pack ice. They sailed to Antarctica with James Clark Ross in 1839–43 and to the Arctic with Sir John Franklin in 1846, foundering two years later in the ice of the Northwest Passage. This striking painting is by Beechey.*

■ ■ ■ THREE SCANDINAVIAN EXPLORERS ■ ■ ■

Fridtjof Nansen (1861–1930) a zoologist and a scientist on the staff of Bergen Museum, established his reputation by a first crossing of the Greenland ice cap and subsequent studies of the Inuit, with whom he wintered in 1888–89. Between 1893 and 1895, inspired by the drift of relics of USS *Jeanette* from Siberia to Greenland, he attempted to reach the North Pole by drifting across the Arctic basin in *Fram*, a ship specially designed to be frozen into pack ice

Fridtjof Nansen,
aged about 35.

without sustaining damage. The drift started in the Laptev Sea, not far from where *Jeanette* had foundered. After 18 months, realizing that *Fram*, although safe, would miss the Pole, Nansen left with a companion, F. H. Johansen, and sledged with dog teams toward the Pole, turning back in 86°14'N to head for Franz Josef Land. After overwintering in a stone and sealskin hut, he and Johansen made their way toward Svalbard, eventually meeting a British expedition which helped them back to Norway. Nansen helped to found the study of oceanography, making many deep-sea cruises. In 1906 he was appointed Norwegian Minister to London, led the Norwegian delegation to the League of Nations in 1920, and worked for the League in repatriating prisoners of war and in famine relief, for which he was awarded the Nobel Peace Prize.

Roald Amundsen (1872–1928) read medicine for a time, then went to sea, qualifying eventually as a mate. In this capacity he joined Adrien de Gerlache's *Belgica* expedition, so becoming one of the first to overwinter in Antarctica (1897–98). In 1903–06 he took *Gjoa*, a 21-m (70-ft) yacht, through the Northwest Passage. In 1910 he planned to take Nansen's *Fram* to the North Pole, but hearing that Peary had got there, changed his plans and went instead to the South Pole. In a well-planned, fully professional operation he drove dog teams across the Ross Ice Shelf and up the Axel Heiberg Glacier to reach the Pole on 14 December 1911. During the 1920s he completed a Northeast Passage voyage, then flew with American Lincoln Ellsworth in an airship across the Arctic basin from Svalbard to Alaska. Amundsen was lost when an aircraft, seeking survivors from another flight, disappeared.

Knud Johan Victor Rasmussen (1879–1933), born in Jakobshavn, southwest Greenland, became the most accomplished Greenland explorer and Arctic anthropologist of his time. One-quarter Inuit, brought up in Greenland with native companions, he absorbed the Inuit languages and their skills of living off the land and dealing with cold. After formal education in Denmark (which included training as an opera singer), he returned to spend much of his life on expeditions to different parts of Greenland. As a young man in 1902–04 and again in 1906 he wintered in northwest Greenland among the polar Inuit, and in 1905 considered how to introduce reindeer to the West Greenland economy.

In 1910 he and a companion set up a trading station at Thule, northwest Greenland, using the profits to finance more expeditions. In 1912 he made a far-northern crossing of the Greenland ice cap, and in 1916 began a two-year survey of the North Greenland coast; 1919 found him in Angmagssalik, studying the East Greenland Inuit; and between 1921 and 1924 he sledged from Greenland to Canada and across North America to Barrow, Alaska, making studies of all the Inuit communities he met on the way. Later he returned for further field-work in southeastern Greenland. Although Arctic travel and the company of Inuit were his main enjoyment, Rasmussen took trouble to write reports both for fellow scientists and for the public, and to publicise Inuit culture in its many forms, from sculpture to songs.

■ ■ ■ THE CANADIAN ARCTIC EXPEDITION ■ ■ ■

Funded by the Canadian Government, the Canadian Arctic Expedition was an attempt to explore the Arctic Ocean between the Canadian archipelago and Alaska, where Stefansson thought there was further land to be discovered. A southern party would work in Coronation Gulf and a northern party would explore westward from Prince Patrick Island. Stefansson's scientific staff included oceanographer James Murray and surgeon Alistair Mackay, who had served with Shackleton in Antarctica. His photographer was George Hubert Wilkins.

Stefansson's qualities of leadership and organizing ability became apparent from the start of the expedition in Wrangell, Alaska — a scene of utter confusion over stores, loading, destinations and expedition plans. Three ships left in June 1913, intending to rendezvous at Herschel Island on the north coast. They reached the coast but in early August *Karluk*, the main expedition ship, became caught in the inshore ice. On 20 September Stefansson and four companions, with two dog teams, left the ship to hunt caribou on the mainland, expecting to be away ten days. In their absence the ship became separated from the shore by a wide lead, and began to drift westward with the ice. Carried for five months toward Siberia, it was finally crushed some 300 km (190 miles) north of Wrangel Island.

Under the stolid, reliable leadership of the ship's captain, Robert Bartlett, the complement of 25 scientists, crew and Inuit, plus the ship's cat, struggled for two months over the ice toward the relative safety of Wrangel Island. They travelled in small parties. Eight, including the two Antarctic veterans, may have decided to go directly for the mainland, but disappeared and were never seen again. With the rest of his party on dry land, Bartlett and an Inuit crossed with dog teams to the Siberian coast in a desperate bid for help. By the time a rescue ship reached Wrangel Island, in September 1914, two of the remaining castaways had died from hardship and a third had shot himself. The cat, thoroughly bewildered by events, was one of the survivors.

Having left his expedition to the mercies of the friendly Arctic, Stefansson spent five years exploring with a small group in the western islands of the Canadian archipelago, discovering Brock, Borden, Meighen, Lougheed and other new islands. His expedition reports ensured that this, rather than *Karluk*, was the exploit for which the Canadian Arctic Expedition is particularly remembered. The southern party under Dr Rudolph Anderson, which had the good fortune to travel in other ships and operate independently, undertook three years' arduous but successful scientific work on the Canadian coast between Alaska and Coronation Gulf. Captain 'Bob' Bartlett died in 1946, honoured by all explorers. Stefansson died in 1962, controversial to the end.

---

stimulated by the French and American expeditions that had already entered the field.

A veteran of five Arctic expeditions, in one of which he had reached the North Magnetic Pole, and now of appropriate naval seniority, Ross was undoubtedly the right man to lead a south polar naval expedition in which magnetometry was a main objective. For what it is worth, he was also said to be the handsomest officer in the Royal Navy. His ships, *Erebus* and *Terror*, were heavily-built monitors stressed to carry large guns. They carried Ross safely through the Antarctic ice, but were later lost with Sir John Franklin in the heavier ice of the Northwest Passage. Rawdon Crozier, Ross's second-in-command in Antarctica, was one of the 139 who lost their lives with Franklin.

Ross sailed in October 1839 for Hobart, Tasmania, with a small group of scientists and elaborate instructions concerning his itinerary and the scientific studies expected from his staff. En route he set up magnetic observatories at St Helena and Cape Town, and in Christmas Harbour, Iles Kerguelen, where he spent five months. In Tasmania Ross met Sir John Franklin, then Lieutenant Governor of Van Diemen's Land, who arranged for a cheerful gang of convicts to build him an observatory close to town.

Sailing in November 1840, he called at the Auckland Islands and Campbell Island for further magnetometric observations, and in mid-December headed south for Antarctica. Knowing where Wilkes

■ ■ ■

Base G, Admiralty Bay, a
British scientific station of
the late 1940s on the South
Shetland Islands. For several
years the hut housed a small
team of scientists who
recorded the weather and
studied the geology of the
area. Now no longer in use,
it is maintained as a refuge
for emergencies.

had sailed (Wilkes had left copies of his charts for him in Hobart), Ross determined to work further east. As he must quickly have realized, it was a fortunate decision. Barging into the expected field of pack ice, he found himself unexpectedly sailing straight through it into open water beyond. Then for days he headed serenely southward through thin pack ice, insignificant in comparison with the Arctic ice he was used to, with a splendid panorama of Antarctic mountains and glaciers opening off his port bow. He reached and passed the southern record (74°15'S) established by Weddell on the opposite side of the continent in 1823. He had but one complaint: the ships' compasses told him that the magnetic pole lay to the west among the mountains, but a band of heavy coastal pack ice prevented him from sledging over to it.

Ross had discovered the sea that now bears his name, and the long stretch of mountainous coast now

called Victoria Land, forming part of New Zealand's Ross Dependency. He sailed on south to discover Possession, Beaufort and Franklin Islands, and an ice-girt island dominated by twin peaks, one of them an active volcano. The island is now Ross Island, and the peaks bear the names he gave them, Erebus and Terror. The deep bay close by, which he saw but could not penetrate, he named McMurdo Sound after his first officer. Turning eastward, Ross found himself sailing along a high, impenetrable ice cliff, an ice barrier now known to be the edge of the Ross Ice Shelf. Short of time and unable to move further south, he returned to Hobart for the winter.

In the following summer he returned to explore the barrier further, then skirted the pack ice eastward, making for Cape Horn and the Falkland Islands. After wintering in the Falklands he spent his third Antarctic summer trying to enter the Weddell Sea. *Erebus* and *Terror* rounded the tip of the Antarctic Peninsula and tried to head south, but were turned back by heavy ice — it was not the right season for exploring in that sector. James Ross Island and Erebus and Terror Gulf, east of the Peninsula, mark the passage of his expedition. Ross returned home to an enthusiastic public, a gratified Board of Admiralty, and scientists who acclaimed his work unstintingly.

POLAR PRIVATEERS

Ross's was the last of the great seaborne exploratory expeditions to either polar region. For the rest of the century small expeditions became the rule. Usually land-based, privately financed, and operating mainly ashore, they filled in the details left out by those who had gone before. A wide range of motives prompted those who led and those who took part. For leaders, polar regions made reputations and sometimes (though rarely) fortunes. Followers gained experience, developed their sciences or professional skills, and learnt a great deal about themselves.

Even when geographers called for international research in polar regions (for example in the International Polar Year of 1880), and again when there was a call for cooperative Antarctic research in 1895 (to which Britain, Scotland, Sweden and Germany responded), it was usually left to private societies or individuals to organize expeditions, seeking whatever funds they could wring from their governments. The tradition of private enterprise continued well into the 20th century, when polar exploration again became a national concern and large, government-sponsored expeditions were required.

Almost every Arctic country has generated its quota of explorers, both professional and amateur. Not surprisingly Scandinavians took the lead. Fridtjof Nansen and Roald Amundsen are perhaps the best-known of all polar explorers. Nansen, primarily a zoologist and oceanographer, worked entirely in the north; Amundsen, a professional seaman and adventurer, was equally successful at both ends of the world. Denmark and Greenland produced Knud Rasmussen and a number of other devoted Greenland explorers.

Sweden's main contributions were the Nordenskjölds. Adolf Erik Nordenskjöld, a geologist and geographer at the Swedish State Museum, led scientific expeditions to Svalbard, Greenland and Siberia from 1858. In July 1878 he began a one-year journey in Vega, a tiny steam-driven sealer, that achieved the first-ever transit of the Northeast Passage. Adolf's nephew, geologist Otto Nordenskjöld, took part in several Arctic expeditions, and in 1901 led a Swedish expedition to the Antarctic Peninsula and Weddell Sea. In 1911 Otto joined with British scientists to develop a combined Swedish/British expedition to Antarctica, but World War I put a stop to their plans.

Imperial Russia produced a succession of navigators and scientists of many disciplines who investigated the Siberian northlands. Prominent among the later ones were Eduard Vasilyevich von Toll, a geologist who worked extensively on the islands north of Siberia at the end of the 19th century, and Aleksandr Vasilyevich Kolchak, naval officer, oceanographer and general scientist who spent many years on northern expeditions around the turn of the century. Toll

was lost on an expedition to the Novosibirskiye Islands. Kolchak found himself commanding White Russian forces in Siberia after the Bolshevik revolution, and was shot by firing squad in 1920 Many did brave and distinguished work, but surprisingly little is known of their explorations outside their own country. The Soviet Union has maintained the tradition, encouraging Arctic and, in recent years, Antarctic, research through its many polar-oriented expeditions and institutes.

In both Russia and North America, where a polar regions sits firmly in the back yard, the product tends to be polar citizens rather than polar explorers. Pioneer inhabitants of the prairie towns, and the unnamed thousands who opened up backwoods Alaska and Siberia, often did their day's work in conditions no less arduous than those faced by polar explorers, although they made less fuss about it and attracted far less attention. They seldom became prominent, or even involved, in the more spectacular forms of polar exploration.

Canada's notable exception was Vilhjalmur Stefansson, born in Manitoba to immigrant Icelandic parents in 1879. Stefansson spent much of his working life among Eskimos in the Canadian north. An anthropologist by training, from 1906 to 1912 he worked especially among the Mackenzie and Copper Inuit to familiarize himself with their ways. Then, as leader of the Canadian Arctic Expedition, he spent five years (1913–18) in the far north. This expedition was not an unqualified success, for its ship Karluk was wrecked and eleven of its crew were subsequently lost. Stefansson, who thrived on controversy, was among the first to consider the possibility of using aircraft and submarines in expeditions, and the first to appreciate the future importance of the Arctic in long-distance flights. His attempt in 1920 to claim Wrangel Island for Canada failed with the death from starvation of four of the five Inuit colonists he installed there. The basis of Stefansson's reputation was his enthusiasm for 'the friendly Arctic', a concept that other Arctic explorers judged dangerous in the extreme, and one that from time to time must have puzzled those who survived his expeditions.

Curiously few of the Americans who distinguished themselves in 19th- and 20th-century polar exploration were of northern origins. De Long was a New Yorker. Neither Frederick Cook nor Robert Peary, both professional explorers who claimed to have

■ ■ ■ SCOTT, SHACKLETON AND THE SOUTH POLE ■ ■ ■

Commander Robert Scott, a career officer in the Royal Navy, was selected in 1901 to lead the first and only British naval expedition to explore Antarctica. He followed James Clark Ross's route to McMurdo Sound, penetrating the Sound to winter his ship *Discovery* as far south as possible on Ross Island. From there he and his colleagues man-hauled sledges to the high polar plateau, which was clearly a possible route to the South Pole. Ernest Shackleton, a young merchant service officer on the expedition, sledged with Scott and physician Edward Wilson, reaching a record 82°S.

In 1907 Shackleton returned to McMurdo Sound with a privately funded expedition. With three companions he made a bid for the South Pole, over 1300 km (800 miles) from his base at Cape Royds, but had to turn back when only 180 km (112 miles) from it. Scott returned, also with a private expedition, in 1911, and with four companions reached the South Pole on 17 January 1912, only to find that Amundsen had arrived there 34 days earlier. Scott and his party died on their way back from the Pole.

In 1914 Shackleton planned an expedition that would cross Antarctica via the South Pole, but lost his ship *Endurance* in the pack ice of the Weddell Sea. After drifting for several months he got his men ashore on Elephant Island, in the South Orkneys, then sailed in a lifeboat to South Georgia to seek assistance for them. All were eventually rescued.

Sir Ernest Shackleton, British Antarctic explorer, known affectionately as 'The Boss'. He sledged to within 145 km (90 miles) of the South Pole. Here, accompanied by Frank Hurley (photographer, left), he warms himself by a blubber stove at Patience Camp, on the pack ice.

❉

exploration were northerners, although many had learnt how to cope with extreme cold during a Midwestern childhood. Byrd followed the professional approach of Amundsen rather than the inspired amateurism of Scott in his dealings with Antarctica, leading three successful expeditions which made full use of aircraft for the first time.

The non-polar countries were no less productive of polar explorers. Germany's first contribution was Eduard Dallman, a sealing and whaling captain who in 1873 led the first whaling expedition to Antarctic waters. His ship, the sealer *Grönland*, was the first steamship to work the Antarctic Peninsula region.

They caught no whales, but surveyed and added a number of German names to the charts. Wilhelm Filchner, an army officer and explorer with experience in the Pamirs and Himalayas, headed a German expedition in 1910, funded by public subscription and lottery. He planned to cross Antarctica from the Weddell Sea to the Ross Sea. His ship *Deutschland* penetrated the ice of the Ross Sea and a hut was built on the Antarctic shelf ice, but the ice broke away and the expedition had to retreat. *Deutschland* became trapped in the pack and drifted for nine months before being released unscathed. Germany's third explorer, Erich von Drygalski, a practically-minded

■ ■ ■

*Scott's first Antarctic hut,
used by his 1901–03
expedition in McMurdo
Sound, is now ringed by a
chain fence for protection.
In the background are the
modern buildings of US
scientific station McMurdo,
and the volcanic ridges of
Ross Island.*

trapped in the pack and drifted for nine months before being released unscathed. Germany's third explorer, Erich von Drygalski, a practically-minded professor of geography at Berlin University, led expeditions to Greenland in 1891–95 and to Antarctica in 1901–04. A much later fourth was Captain Alfred Ritscher, who in 1938–39 led a seaplane survey expedition to Dronning Maud Land, Antarctica. The seaplanes, catapulted from a mother ship, *Schwabenland*, took many hundreds of aerial photographs and dropped darts to stake Germany's claims to this corner of the continent.

Japan produced a curious and unexpected scientific expedition to Antarctica in 1910–12, under naval Lieutenant Nobu Shirase, but did not follow it up until after World War II. Italy's General Umberto Nobile, an aviator and engineer with interests in dirigibles, made a pioneering flight across the Arctic basin by airship in 1926, accompanied by Roald Amundsen and Lincoln Ellsworth. France's most attractive contribution to the list of explorers was Jean-Baptiste Charcot, whose two expeditions to the Antarctic Peninsula in the early years of this century were followed by many to Greenland and other Arctic locations. A physician of independent means, his hobby was sailing his small but well-equipped

expedition ship *Pourquoi-pas?* on scientific cruises, taking like-minded scientists to wherever they needed to work. This facility enabled many French scientists, from anthropologists to zoologists, to develop Arctic interests.

From Belgium came Baron Adrien de Gerlache de Goméry, a naval lieutenant who in 1897–99 commanded *Belgica*, the first expedition ship to winter in Antarctic waters. Among his crew were mate Roald Amundsen, and Frederick Cook, a popular and effective American medical officer who later made a bid for the North Pole. Adrien de Gerlache later worked in Greenland and in the Kara and Barents Seas.

Britain continued to produce polar explorers throughout this period. They ranged from wealthy yachtsmen who chose to sail every summer to the Arctic ice, to such dedicated semi-professionals as Robert Falcon Scott, whose naval career was enhanced by Antarctic exploration, and Ernest Shackleton, an adventurer whose qualities of leadership and courage flourished best in a polar environment.

From Britain and the Empire came many polar scientists, including geologists Douglas Mawson, Raymond Priestley and William Edgeworth David, who served with the Antarctic expeditions of Scott or Shackleton. Polar adventurers abounded. One such was George Hubert Wilkins, an Australian, who worked for four years as a photographer with Stefansson in Arctic Canada, flew with the Australian Flying Corps, joined Shackleton's last expedition as an ornithologist, became a pioneer bush pilot in Alaska, made some of the first flights from Antarctica during the 1920s and again in the 1930s, and between-whiles became involved in an unsuccessful bid to reach the North Pole by submarine.

Through the 1920s and '30s the Arctic was a proving ground for dozens of young British university men. In their long vacations, on shoestring expeditions, they sledged across Greenland, explored corners of Svalbard, studied waders on Jan Mayen or surveyed glaciers on Ellesmere Island. Some scraped funds together for serious over-wintering parties, for example the British Arctic Air Route Expedition of 1930–32, led by Gino Watkins, which investigated year-round flying conditions across southern Greenland. This involved over a dozen members, surveys by aircraft, sledges and boats, shore bases, and an ice-cap weather station.

■ ■ ■

Captain Robert Scott and his British party, photographed at the South Pole in January 1912, having lost the race for it. Ill-equipped, and man-hauling to the point of exhaustion, all died on the way back to McMurdo Sound. Sitting left to right are Bowers and Wilson; standing left to right are Oates, Scott and Evans. Bowers took the photograph with a cord attached to the camera.

■ ■ ■

Roald Amundsen and his Norwegian polar party aboard Fram *in Hobart, Tasmania, on their return from the South Pole. They reached the Pole in December 1911. Their success was based on the use of skis and dog sledges, and meticulous planning. Left to right are Hansen, Bjaaland, Amundsen, Wisting and Hassel.*

8

Polar Politics

Politics is the practice of government, and polar politics is the government of lands and oceans remote from centres of power and sparsely populated. For hundreds of years political issues beyond the polar circles have been ignored or neglected, and mishandled when they could no longer be swept under the carpet. Polar politics today focus on two key problems: Who owns the polar lands and oceans and what are their responsibilities? And what are the rights of the people who live there?

Empty of voters, with fewer than five people per square kilometre (fewer than 13 people per square mile), polar lands have generated little political heat, either nationally or internationally, in the past. Few feathers have been ruffled over polar issues, few battles fought, few elections lost or won. Until recently polar disputes caused only the smallest wars. Problems at local, national and international level, from hunting rights to questions of sovereignty, have usually been settled amicably in warm government offices, far from snowdrifts and pack ice. But as the world has shrunk, polar issues have quite suddenly grown in importance. The polar regions have, begun to warm up, politically speaking.

At the start of this century the Arctic was little-known. Much of its land was virtually unclaimed — outsiders did not want it, and the indigenous inhabitants saw no point in claiming what so patently belonged to everybody. But by the 1950s half a dozen nations had explored it and taken possession of every square metre. The major powers seemed poised to make it the most likely place for the start of World War III. NATO and Soviet hawks glared at each other across the Arctic basin, submarines played war games in and under the pack ice, surveillance aircraft buzzed overhead, and boffins plotted missile trajectories high in the upper atmosphere.

At the start of the century the south polar region had hardly entered human consciousness either. But by the 1950s it was claimed, at least half-mapped, and the subject of intense scrutiny by scientists of a dozen nations. It had even developed a promising crop of its own political problems. The cold war brushed Antarctica too — in the 1950's Soviet and American task forces, ostensibly supporting scientific expeditions, jockeyed for strategic positions on the continental rim. The Antarctic Peninsula, claimed by three nations at least, and the Falkland Islands,

claimed by two, were rapidly developing trouble spots. In 1957 Argentine troops fired angry shots at Britons in Antarctica, but fortunately missed. In 1982 there was earnest open warfare between Britain and Argentina over the Falkland Islands, South Georgia and southern sovereignty.

What brought the two polar regions so precipitately onto the world stage? More was involved than mere pride of ownership. In the Arctic, long-distance air transport was a key factor. Arctic lands remained unclaimed until the 1920s, when far-sighted explorers pressed for airfields that would open up the north and provide staging posts for intercontinental passenger flight. In the Antarctic, the initial spur was whaling. Although several nations reserved rights to claim sovereignty, none bothered to do so until the start of Southern Ocean whaling, when land-based facilities were needed. Once one country had claimed Antarctic territory for this unappealing purpose, others dusted off their own claims, and Antarctic politics was born.

At the moment both polar regions are in a peaceful mode. For the first time in many years the Arctic nations have ceased to posture, and finding ways of cooperating in the name of science and conservation. In this respect Antarctica is well ahead of the Arctic. For over 30 years the Antarctic Treaty System has provided a political framework for international cooperation among scientists and administrators, extending over the whole of the continent and, in some issues at least, into the Southern Ocean as well. There are still political problems at both ends of the world, but just now, in the last decade of the 20th century, solutions seem possible and even likely.

THE ARCTIC 'MEDITERRANEAN'

The Arctic nations are, by definition, those whose shores lie within the Arctic Ocean or the Greenland Sea, or whose territory lies within the Arctic Circle. They include the four Scandinavian countries (Norway, Sweden, Denmark, Finland), the Soviet Union, the United States, and Canada. These lands form an almost continuous ring around the Arctic Ocean, comparable with the ring which Southern Europe, the Middle East and Africa form around the Mediterranean. The northern shores of Greenland, Canada and Alaska together form a coastline roughly as long as the Mediterranean coastline from Morocco to Israel. Greenland is about as far from Alaska or the Siberian shelf islands as Spain is from Turkey. From Iceland to Norway is as far as from Italy to Egypt.

In the Arctic the United States and Soviet Union rub elbows — at its narrowest point the Bering Strait is only 85 km (53 miles) across, the distance of Sicily from Tunisia. North Greenland and Canada face each other across Baffin Bay.

Throughout history humanity has ebbed and flowed around the Arctic basin, with all but the Inuit, the Sami and the sub-polar Indians and Siberians held at bay by the cold, unwelcoming environment. But within the last century the tide has turned. Humanity is now converging on the Arctic from all sides. The immediate consequence we have already seen. Northern lands and oceans were quickly claimed and assimilated, and any international problems that arose were just as quickly settled — nobody wanted the bother of war or prolonged international law-mongering.

More lasting and less tractable problems have been the fate of indigenous northern folk all around the Arctic. Theirs has been a sad history. Life before the arrival of Europeans was never easy. High infant mortality and periodic starvation were the usual lot of nomadic populations, and even at its best the Arctic is an unforgiving environment. Early contacts with seamen, traders and missionaries introduced them to European wants, religious preoccupations, social systems, diseases, justice and injustice, and penalties well outside their previous experience. They took willingly to knives, guns and other artefacts that eased their hard lives, but they paid for them in furs, walrus ivory and other natural products which were never abundant and quickly became scarce.

Those who survived the epidemics of influenza and measles, tuberculosis and alcoholism, lived to see their beliefs and values scorned, their communities wrecked, their traditional ways of life irrevocably altered. Later generations have found themselves the 'ethnic minorities' of large, foreign-tongued nations, plunged into a puzzling world of census forms, schools, institutional goodwill, finance, unemployment, and arbitrary decisions by distant authorities. Therein lie the major challenges in Arctic politics today.

SCANDINAVIA

Norway, Sweden and Finland are true Arctic countries with territories north of the polar circle. Denmark stops well short of the Arctic Circle, but includes within its sovereignty the distant, indisputably Arctic province of Greenland. While each of the Scandinavian countries has its own character and attitudes to the Arctic, the northlands of Norway, Sweden and Finland have much in common. Geographers refer to them as the Nordkalotte or 'northern cap' of Scandinavia and treat them as a geographical, social and economic entity

THE NORDKALOTTE

The northern provinces of Norway (Nordland, Troms and Finnmark), Sweden (Norbotten) and Finland (Lappi), lying on or above the Arctic Circle, together form Scandinavia's 'northern cap'. This is wild, spectacular country, thinly populated. The west is mountainous and rugged, with deep coastal fjords, high tablelands and fast-flowing rivers. The valleys are forested, the uplands grass-covered, with a narrow strip of tundra along the northern coast.

Warmed by the North Atlantic Drift or Gulf Stream, the western flank remains almost completely ice-free through the year, although the mountains attract heavy snowfall in late autumn and winter. The east is a gentler, rolling plateau strewn with lakes, slower-flowing rivers and bogs, and covered with forest and sparse grasslands. All but the northernmost rivers flow toward the Gulf of Bothnia. The eastern upland comes under strong continental influences: it is warm and dry in summer, but very much colder than the western mountains in winter. The Gulf of Bothnia is frozen over for four or five months each winter, and the surrounding land is heavily snow-covered.

This is 'Lapland', the homeland of some 30,000 Sami or Lapps. Traditionally it extends eastward across the Soviet border into the Kola Peninsula as well, and in former times the Sami were free to wander where they pleased. Now national boundaries cut Lapland into provinces of four sovereign states. Sami continue to move freely across Scandinavia with little regard for frontiers, but they are separated from their few remaining kinsfolk in the Soviet Union.

Northern Norway and Sweden especially are well endowed with minerals. Kiruna, Gällivare, Malmberget and Svappavaara, in Swedish Norbotten, export high-grade iron ores by rail to Narvik on the Norwegian Sea and Lulea on the Gulf of Bothnia. Lower-grade ores are mined at Norway's Kirkenes, near the Barents Sea, and Finland's Kolari, on the Torne River which forms part of the border with Sweden. Lead is mined at Bleikvassli in Norway and Laisvall in Sweden. Other centres produce copper, zinc and chrome. Mining, refining and transportation are facilitated by abundant hydroelectric power. Generated from the rivers of all three countries, some of it in international schemes, it compensates for lack of coal or oil in the region, and the surplus is exported to the south.

Although one of the wealthiest and most progressive regions of the Arctic, the Nordkalotte has generated a range of economic and social problems, many of them common to all three countries and indeed to Arctic development as a whole. Highly technological industries employ outsiders rather than locals, who lack the necessary skills and training. Low-tech employment pays poorly, causing local dissatisfaction and a haemorrhage of manpower. Many hands disappear to the south, but there are also migrations from poorer to wealthier countries, e.g. from Finland to Sweden.

Industrialization has brought inevitable environmental problems to the north. Hydroelectric schemes conflict with reindeer herding and ruin traditional fishing waters. Mining and smelting destroy large areas of native countryside, pollute the clear Arctic atmosphere, and poison forests and rivers. Timber-milling, paper-making and other forest industries feed hungrily on trees, in areas where forests are slow to regenerate. Local people are demanding more say in decisions that affect them. These problems are to some degree being addressed jointly. The Nordic Council, which represents the Norwegian, Swedish and Finnish governments, has given rise to a Nordic Lapp Council, where problems common to all the northern areas can be resolved.

■ ■ ■

An oil installation on Endicott Island, Prudhoe Bay, on the Arctic Ocean shore of Alaska, one of the starting points of the Alaska pipeline. Oil is a political issue. In Alaska, and in Canada, it has brought the question of native rights to the fore.

NORWAY AND SVALBARD

Norway is in every way the most polar of all European countries, not only in geography but in history, economy and general orientation. Its concerns extend to the Antarctic as well as the Arctic. Historically a loose-knit confederation of coastal settlements extending far into the Arctic, Norway has always lacked the resources to keep its young men at home. From the earliest days it has produced Arctic explorers. Norsemen from southern Norway established the first Arctic empire, ruling their Icelandic, Faroese and South Greenland settlements like any

latter-day colonial power. From its ports fishermen, sealers and whalers sailed north every year into the pack ice, to Jan Mayen Island, Bjørnøya and distant Svalbard, always searching for new seas and new shores to hunt.

Norwegians kept their identity through the period of the Kalmar Union in the 14th century and through their later attachment to Sweden. After years of disaffection and subordination, they finally regained their independence in 1905, continuing to develop an economy based on what they knew best — fishing, sealing and whaling in local Arctic and sub-Arctic

THE SCANDINAVIAN COUNTRIES

Norway, a kingdom on the western and northern flanks of the Scandinavian peninsula, has an area of 324,219 km² (125,182 sq miles), and a population of 4.2 million. About one-third of the country lies north of the Arctic Circle, but its climate is considerably warmed by the North Atlantic Drift. In the central and northern mountains there is extensive tundra and forest.

Svalbard, north of Norway on the 80th parallel, is an ice-capped archipelago of five large and many smaller islands. Older maps call it Spitsbergen, the name of the main island. The total land area is 62,422 km² (24,101 sq miles), and about 60 per cent of this is ice-covered. Svalbard (meaning 'cold coast') is under Norwegian sovereignty, but is demilitarized and subject to an international treaty which gives other countries mining rights. It has a population of about 3,500, mostly Norwegian and Soviet miners.

Sweden, occupying the Baltic flank of the Scandinavian peninsula, is a kingdom of 449,964 km² (173,731 sq miles), with a population of 8.3 million. Its mountains and uplands are ice-covered all the year round. Among the world's wealthiest and most socially advanced countries, its main sources of mineral wealth lie north of the Arctic Circle.

Finland, Europe's northernmost state, is a republic of 337,032 km² (130,128 sq miles), with a population of 5 million. It is peneplaned by ice-

sheets, heavily forested, and liberally sprinkled with lakes which freeze over in winter. About one-third of the country lies north of the Arctic Circle and is inhabited mainly by Sami (Lapps).

Denmark, occupying the peninsula of Jutland and neighbouring islands, has an area of 43,069 km² (16,629 sq miles) and a population of just over over 5 million. A kingdom, and far from polar, it includes the polar province of Greenland and the sub-polar province of the Faroe Islands, both self-governing but economically linked to Denmark.

Greenland has an area of 2.176 million km² (840,000 sq miles), four times the size of France, and a population 55,000. When Greenland left the EEC in 1985, the population of the Community was barely affected but its area was cut by half. Ice covers 84 per cent of the land to a mean depth of 1500 m (4,900 ft), which means that Greenland contains about 8 per cent of all the world's ice. Politically, Greenland is a self-governing province of the Kingdom of Denmark.

Iceland, a large island south of Greenland, has a total area of 103,000 km² (39,768 sq miles) and a population approaching 250,000. Lying athwart the Mid-Atlantic Ridge, it is volcanically active, with volcanoes and hot springs, and made up mainly of recent lava fields. Mixed with the volcanoes are small remnants of glaciers and ice fields. The highest point, Öraefajökull, rises to 2119 m (6,954 ft). Formerly a dependency of Denmark, Iceland became a sovereign state and republic in 1944.

❄

waters, and shipping. At the same time they diversified into shipbuilding, maritime trading, mining, smelting, engineering, timber products and hydrocarbons, which are the basis of the country's prosperity today.

Farming is locally important, encouraged along the western seaboard by the warmth of the North Atlantic Drift (Gulf Stream). For centuries reindeer herding has been the economic mainstay of the inland Sami of the Nordkalotte. Links with the Arctic were strengthened in 1920 when the Spitsbergen Treaty gave formal custody of Svalbard to Norway. In 1927 Norway also acquired Jan Mayen Island, between the mainland and Svalbard, after years of maintaining a meteorological station there. Legislation to control hunting on Svalbard and Jan Mayen quickly followed, in particular to protect fur-bearing species of land mammals such as foxes, polar bears and reindeer, which by then were severely threatened. Norwegian geologists and prospectors played their part in exploring both Svalbard and Jan Mayen for minerals, and Norwegians were among the first to mine coal on Svalbard, using it to solve a growing fuel problem at home.

Norway's many polar personalities include the two most celebrated of all polar explorers, Fridtjof Nansen and Roald Amundsen, and Harald Sverdrup, doyen of oceanography, who worked especially in the Arctic Ocean. Whaling has always held a special significance for Norwegians, for social and ethnological reasons as well as economic. In its time a skilled and honoured profession, whaling was especially important to a country with few natural

■ ■ ■

A late 19th-century steam whale catcher operating in Siberian waters. The gunner standing on the bow has fired the harpoon, which is embedded in the whale. After its death, the whale will be towed to a nearby factory for flensing. Steam catchers and harpoons with explosive heads allowed whalers to hunt fast-moving rorquals, or baleen whales.

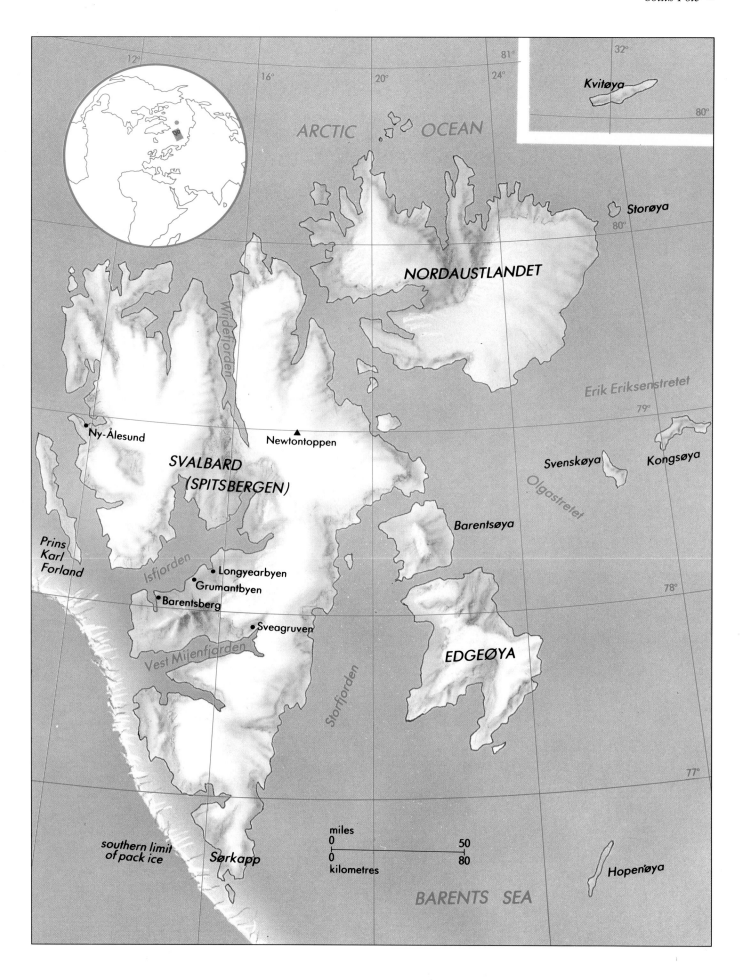

12°

16°

20°

24°

81°

32°

Kvitøya

80°

ARCTIC   OCEAN

Storøya

80°

NORDAUSTLANDET

Erik Eriksenstretet

79°

Ny-Ålesund

Newtontoppen

Svenskøya

Kongsøya

SVALBARD
(SPITSBERGEN)

Olgastretet

Barentsøya

Wijdefjorden

Prins
Karl
Forland

Isfjorden

Longyearbyen

Grumantbyen

Barentsberg

78°

Sveagruven

EDGEØYA

Vest Mijenfjorden

Storfjorden

77°

miles

0

50

southern limit
of pack ice

Sørkapp

0

80

Hopen'øya

kilometres

BARENTS   SEA

SVALBARD

Lying north of central Norway, in the latitude of northern Greenland, Svalbard is an extensive archipelago of five large and several smaller island. Some of the islands are mountainous, with high tablelands capped by ice and carved by glaciers; Newtontoppen on eastern Spitsbergen is the highest point, rising to 1717 m (5,633 ft). Fjords cut deeply into Spitsbergen and Nordaustlandet, providing fine harbours. For most of the year Svalbard lies within the pack ice. Warmed by the tail-end of the North Atlantic Drift it has relatively mild summers, and successive explorers from Viking times onward have discovered and re-discovered it by following the ice edge north. Barents and Van Heemskerck reported it in 1596, and Hudson in 1607 charted some of its coasts, mentioning that there were abundant whales in its inshore waters. Dutch and English whalers hunted there from 1611, followed by French, Germans and Scandinavians. Small factories, usually little more than one or two iron trypots on brick foundations near the shore, with primitive living huts nearby, were set up in many harbours. A few, like Smeerenberg, became large-scale industrial settlements.

Svalbard has never had a native population. After whaling and sealing declined in the late 18th century, syndicates of Russian hunters set up camps along the coasts, first on Edgeøya and later on the larger islands, taking seals and walruses in summer and trapping for furs in winter. Some became permanent residents. From the early 19th century onward, Norwegian trappers based in Tromsø and Hammerfest established regular summer camps for sealing and whaling. Later, prospectors of many different nationalities discovered coal, iron ore and other minerals, and claimed rights of exploitation. Coal was first mined by a British company at Adventdalen in 1904, and later by an American company at Longyearbyen, which eventually became the administrative centre.

Mining raised the question of who actually owned Svalbard, and in 1912 the islands were agreed to be *terra nullius* by Norway, Sweden and Russia, the three countries most concerned. The issue was resolved in 1920, when an international treaty made Svalbard part of the Kingdom of Norway.

The islands were at the same time demilitarized, and rights to exploit minerals were granted to all signatories — Britain, Denmark, France, Italy, Japan, Netherlands, Sweden and the United States; the Soviet Union signed the treaty later. After the treaty, both Norway and the Soviet Union developed coal mines at several sites on the eastern side of Spitsbergen, the Norwegians at Longyearbyen, Sveagruva and Ny-Ålesund, and the Russians at Barentsberg, Grøndal and Pyramiden. Both continue to export coal to their home countries, mainly during summer when unprotected cargo ships can use the harbours.

Svalbard acquired strategic importance in World War II when it became necessary for the Allies to maintain shipping lanes to northern Russia. The mines were evacuated and destroyed, and British forces from time to time prevented Germans from using the islands. However, hidden German meteorological stations provided radio reports of great value to German operations in Northern Europe. An airstrip at Ny-Ålesund now maintains regular services with Tromsø. Relatively easy of access, the islands are well studied by glaciologists, ecologists and other scientists, and are a popular tourist venue in summer.

A Soviet mining settlement on Spitsbergen, Svalbard. Good-quality coal has been mined in this high-Arctic setting by Norwegian and Soviet companies since the early years of this century.

resources of its own to exploit. The skills and mysteries of the industry, centered on the northern settlements of Sandefjord and Tønsberg, were a source of pride to all Norwegians, particularly after the late 19th-century revival when steam replaced sail.

Norwegian inventiveness produced the bow-mounted explosive harpoon, the specially equipped high-speed catcher ship and the stern-slipway factory ship that made pelagic (open-sea) whaling possible. The skill and industry of the whalers themselves changed and developed with each generation. In 1904, after centuries of Arctic whaling, Norwegians followed whaling captain C. A. Larsen to Antarctic waters, where they dominated the immensely successful Southern Ocean whaling industry until the 1960s. In the 1920s and '30s Norway provided highly skilled gunners, icemasters and flensers for almost every other whaling fleet in the world, and also took responsibility for international record-keeping. Details of every whale taken in the Southern Ocean were logged and are on record in a remarkable scientific archive at the Norwegian Bureau of International Whaling Statistics.

During the same period Norwegian whalers explored many miles of ice-bound Antarctic coast, substantiating Norway's later claims to Dronning Maud Land, a large sector of the Antarctic continent, and to Bouvetøya and Peter I Øy in the Southern Ocean. In 1960 Norway was among the first half dozen nations to sign the Antarctic Treaty.

SWEDEN

Unlike Norway, Sweden has no coast facing the Arctic Ocean, and unlike Norwegians, Swedes have no special interests in the Arctic beyond the borders of their own country. The Swedes' gateway to the world outside has always been their long coastline on the Baltic Sea. While pre-mediaeval Norwegians explored the Arctic, Swedish Varangians created an empire across the Baltic in northwestern Europe and Russia, trading as far afield as Greece and Asia Minor, and founding the first Russian state around Novgorod.

Breaking free of the Kalmar Union in 1523, and already in control of Finland, the Swedes fought practically all of their Baltic neighbours, including Denmark and Norway, to gain control of the Gulfs of Bothnia and Finland, the Baltic Sea, and outlets to the North Sea. The Swedish Empire reached its widest bounds in 1660, then declined in a succession of disastrous wars. In 1721 the East Baltic provinces, Karelia and part of Finland, were lost to Russia and Poland, and West Pomerania was restored to Prussia. The rest of Finland became a Russian Grand Duchy in 1809.

Southern Sweden, like Norway, is warmed by the North Atlantic Drift. About three-quarters of the country is forested. Throughout the imperial period and for long after, Sweden subsisted on agriculture, forestry and fishing. Acute rural poverty during the 19th and early 20th centuries forced many Swedes overseas in search of a better life, notably to the North American

■ ■ ■

Kiruna, a modern mining
town north of the Arctic
Circle in Swedish Lapland.
Founded in 1899, the city
stands at a railhead
among iron-rich
mountains. Most of the ore
is sent by rail to Narvik, on
the Norwegian coast.

Midwest. Sweden's current prosperity is based largely on 20th-century industrial and mining developments, many of them located in the Nordkalotte. Arctic-based industries include lead and iron mining on a vast scale, ore treatment, and hydroelectric power generation. In the same area, reindeer husbandry remains an important source of food and local wealth.

Although Sweden as a nation has shown little political ambition in polar regions, Swedish scientists have taken a lively interest in polar research since the mid-19th century. Otto Torrell's pioneering expeditions to Svalbard from 1858 were the first systematic attempt by scientists to study a polar area. The reports of his teams on the geology, glaciology, botany, zoology and geophysics of the more accessible islands were models that other expeditions have since followed. New maps were produced, and

■ ■ ■

A Northern Sami family,
photographed toward the
end of the last century.
The turf hut uses a building
material that is plentiful
on the tundra, with good
insulating qualities.

Torrell found strong evidence for his own theory that an ice cap had once covered much of Scandinavia. Funded mainly by private subscription, these expeditions started several young Swedish scientists on polar careers, among them Adolf Erik Nordenskjöld and his nephew Otto.

Swedish geologists were active in prospecting Svalbard, and in 1911 a Swedish company opened a coal-mine, Sveagruven, which operated for several years. Swedish scientists worked intermittently in Svalbard, Greenland and Iceland throughout the 1920s and '30s. In 1949–52 Sweden joined Norway and Britain in an expedition to Dronning Maud Land, Antarctica. In 1978, celebrating the centenary of the first Northeast Passage transit, the Swedish government lent strong support (including its icebreaker *Ymer*) to a major international oceanographic expedition, Ymer-80, in which scientists of nine nations explored the far-northern oceans between Greenland and Franz Josef Land.

In 1984 Sweden set up a Polar Research Secretariat to supervise Swedish research in both polar regions, and in 1988–89 fielded SWEDARP, a major expedition to the interior mountains of Dronning Maud Land, Antarctica. Since 1984 it has been a full consultative member of the Antarctic Treaty.

FINLAND

A country of rolling, ice-scoured plains, Finland is heavily forested, rising to moorlands in the northwest. Over 50,000 lakes dot the plains, laced together by rivers and marshlands, and all are ice-covered in winter. About one-third of the country lies north of the Arctic Circle. The Finns are of diverse origins. Some came from Sweden, some from Estonia and points south, and some from Karelia and the southeast. About 90 per cent speak Finnish, a language completely different from Swedish or Norwegian (which are very similar), akin to Hungarian and shared only by Estonians. Some 7–10 per cent speak Swedish, especially in the west. Many speak both languages, and both are used officially. In the far north of the country are the Finnish Sami or Lapps, probably representing the original inhabitants of Finland, who speak two or more varieties of Lappish. Most educated Finns speak English, Russian, or both.

The Finnish language has helped the Finns to maintain their identity in adversity down the ages. During the 16th and 17th centuries they were vassals first of Sweden and then of Russia, achieving independence only in 1917, from a Russia weakened by revolution. Shortly afterwards Finland gained a narrow corridor to the Barents Sea at Petsamo (now Pechenga), between Norway and the Soviet Union. This was lost, together with southeastern Karelia and other border territories, in the peace treaty following war with Russia in 1944.

Enmity with Russia caused Finland to ally itself with Germany in World War II, a decision that cost

THE SAMI

The origins and history of the Sami are obscure. They have lived in Lapland for at least 2,000 years, maintaining their ways of life against waves of incomers from the south. About 40,000 Sami are still identifiable, although there are many more in the northlands with Sami blood. They fall into three cultural groups, with considerable overlap. Coastal Sami were semi-nomadic hunters and fishermen of the western and northern seashores, and some of them were also reindeer herders; they maintained a circuit of long-stay camps, moving between them at the turn of the seasons. Forest Sami, also semi-nomadic, lived inland, hunting forest reindeer and fishing the freshwater lakes and rivers. Mountain Sami, the smallest group, were true nomads, living and travelling in full symbiotic association with their reindeer herds. All three kinds of Sami have to some degree altered their way of life to meet present-day needs. Many intermarry with incomers, who now outnumber them heavily; those who do so tend to lose their Sami identity or retain it only on special occasions. Many have joined modern life, moving to the towns and cities, taking up professions, entering the mines, working in the heavy industries of the north, or serving the tourist industry. Those who still identify with the Sami lifestyle have settled to crofting, commercial fishing or reindeer herding on industrial lines, supplying ready markets for venison in southern Scandinavia and Germany. The southern Sami herds were hard hit by the Chernobyl nuclear reactor disaster of 26 April 1986. Heavily irradiated carcasses unfit for human consumption were destroyed or fed to mink, and for a while reindeer meat was virtually unsaleable throughout Scandinavia.

Sami reindeer herders of northern Norway at a slaughterhouse during the first winter after the Chernobyl incident. Reindeer feed on lichens which tend to absorb radioactivity; as a result, many carcasses were unfit for human consumption.

the country dear in war damage. During the Lapland War of 1944–45, German, Finnish and Soviet forces devastated northern forests and settlements, destroying half the buildings and 90 per cent of the bridges, slaughtering reindeer, cattle and horses and scattering the population. Even more of the Finnish forest was subsequently cut to pay reparations to those who won the war.

Finland takes its own Arctic sector seriously, but has few other polar interests. Most of its prosperity comes from forest products. Birch, pine and spruce forests grow further north in Finnish Lapland than anywhere else in the world, and even the slow-growing northern forests, properly managed, are made to yield profit. Mixed farming and fishing in the Baltic are also important, and iron, copper, gold and other metal ores are mined and processed. Hydroelectricity is the main source of power, some of it produced jointly with neighbouring countries and exported for profit. Heavy industries include steel production and shipbuilding — Finnish shipyards have a well-earned reputation for designing and building a wide range of icebreakers, for use in Baltic and oceanic waters. Reindeer herding is important in Lappi, Finland's northern province above the Arctic Circle.

DENMARK AND GREENLAND

Denmark has a long tradition of working the maritime Arctic. A nation of fishermen and sea hunters, from early mediaeval times onward Danes sailed north each summer, seeking new fishing grounds and exploitable stocks of whales and seals. Often they competed fiercely with Norwegian, Dutch and British entrepreneurs. Many became mercenaries in the service of other countries; Vitus Bering, for example, who explored the Bering Strait, the Bering Sea and Alaska, served in the Imperial Russian Navy.

Danes and Norwegians, united under one crown, maintained strong colonial links with settlements in southern Greenland, Iceland and the Faroe Islands. In 1814, when the Treaty of Kiel gave Norwegian sovereignty to Sweden, Denmark retained interests in all three communities. Iceland broke away in 1944 to become a sovereign nation but Greenland and the Faroes remain Danish possessions. Greenland's early Norse colonies flourished for several centuries, then disappeared. Adverse climatic changes,

chronic sickness, neglect by communities at home, and Inuit hostility have all been blamed. The date of their disappearance is not known, but Martin Frobisher was unable to find them on his visit of 1578.

In 1721 a Norwegian Lutheran missionary, Hans Egede, resettled the site of Godthaab, hoping to discover the lost Norsemen and bring them the benefits of Christianity. Backed by Danish capital, he founded a religious colony and trading community among the Inuit, authoritarian and in many ways destructive to native interests. Missions of other denominations followed, equally despotic and insensitive to the real needs of the native communities.

In 1774 the Kongelige Grønlandske Handel (KGH) or Royal Greenland Trading Company was founded. In 1782 it gained monopoly rights and effectively closed Greenland to other nations, and from that date Denmark controlled Greenland in a fiercely protective colonialism, a curious mother-child relationship that lasted for almost 170 years. It guarded the Inuit from some of the worst outside influences that were then pressing hard on native communities elsewhere, but tended to concentrate them in small areas and overexploit the natural resources on which they depended. Ultimately Danish rule insulated them from progress and the realities of a changing world. The benevolence originally intended took long to achieve. Economically the colony was never self-sufficient — subsidies were inadequate — and by the mid-19th century standards of health and welfare in the native settlements were scandalously low. Later in the century the Danish government introduced much-needed reforms. Boards of guardians were created, including elected native representatives, and efforts were made to encourage the Inuit to resume their traditional ways of life.

Danish explorers and scientists took full advantage of Greenland, mostly in small private expeditions. Over the years archaeologists, biologists, geologists and surveyors built up a substantial body of knowledge, to which British, French, German and other nationalities contributed. Prominent among the Danes was Knud Rasmussen, Greenland-born and part Inuit, who was unusual in living with the native peoples, speaking their language fluently and absorbing their culture. G. C. Amdrup, Mylius Ericksen and Einar Mikkelsen explored the east coast, Lauger Koch

■ ■ ■

*Jakobshavn, north of the
Arctic Circle in Disko Bay,
West Greenland, is now a
busy fishing port. The large
buildings by the shore are
fish-processing factories.*

crossed the ice cap, and many other Danes made major contributions to discovery in Greenland.

Although Denmark reserved claims to the whole of Greenland, its control was initially limited to the west coast between Cape Farewell (the southern tip) and 74°30'N. In 1894 it extended jurisdiction to Angmagssalik, a new mission and trading station on the ice-bound east coast; ten years earlier, the Danish explorer Gustv Holm had discovered a hitherto-unknown people, the East Greenland Inuit, on the site of Angmagssalik. In 1917 Denmark traded its West Indian Virgin Islands to the United States, which needed them to protect the approaches to the newly-opened Panama Canal. Buying the islands for cash, the United States renounced any possible future claims to parts of northwestern Greenland. This left Denmark free, in 1921, to extend its jurisdiction over the whole island.

When the Danish administration closed Greenland's settlements to all foreign ships, Norway protested strongly, recording a counter-claim to part of the northeast coast and setting up a small token colony there. The resulting dispute, taken to the International Court of Justice in 1933, was settled in Denmark's favour, and the Norwegians withdrew.

During World War II, with Denmark under German occupation, the government in Greenland turned to the United States, making land available for airfields and military bases that helped the Allied war effort. German commando units established clandes-tine meteorological stations at remote sites along the east coast. During the war years, Greenland prospered, gaining a sense of independence. When the war ended and Danish control was restored, local people, who more and more identified themselves as 'Greenlanders', made it clear that they would not welcome a return to colonial status. Since then the country has evolved toward independence and self-government

Greenland still has far to go before it achieves economic independence. Its problem is to provide, from very meagre natural resources, an acceptable standard of living for its widely scattered people — a population currently numbered at 55,000 and growing rapidly. 'Acceptable' means 'high' by world

■ ■ ■

*Pack ice invests much of
Greenland's east coast
throughout the year. The
southwest coast, where most
of the population lives, is
relaticely ice-free even in
winter. When Greenland left
the EEC in 1985, the land
area of the Community was
reduced by half. The ice cap
contains 8 per cent of all
the world's ice.*

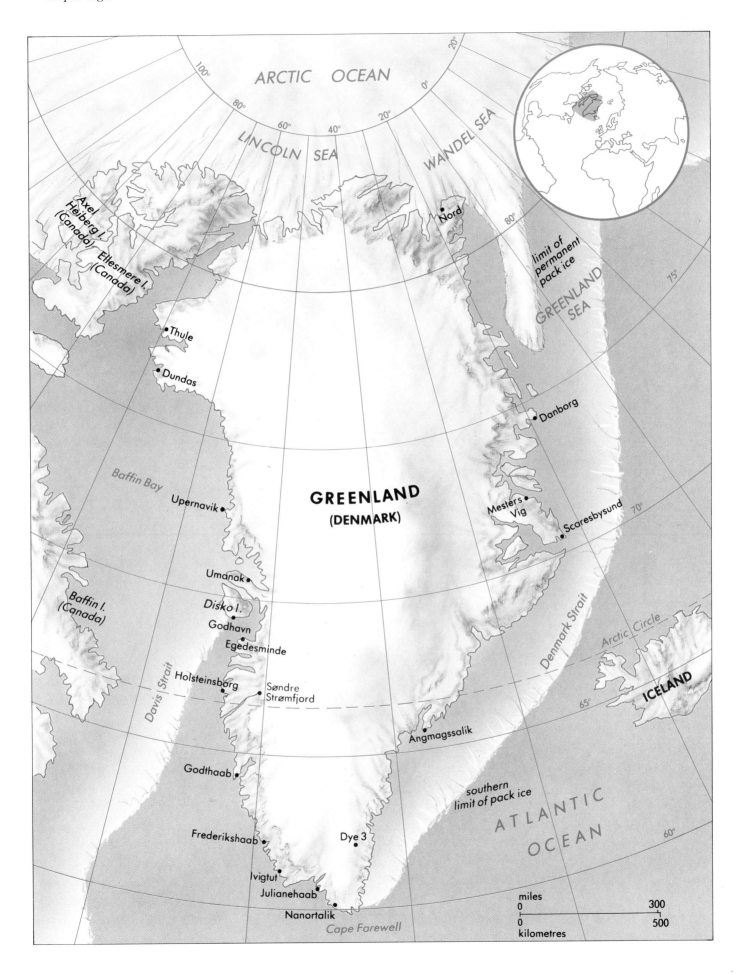

ARCTIC OCEAN

100°

80°

60°

0°

40°

20°

LINCOLN SEA

WANDEL SEA

20°

80°

Nord

limit of permanent pack ice

GREENLAND SEA

75°

Axel Heiberg I. (Canada)

Ellesmere I. (Canada)

Thule

Dundas

Danborg

Baffin Bay

GREENLAND
(DENMARK)

Upernavik

Mesters Vig

Scoresbysund

70°

Umanak

Baffin I. (Canada)

Disko I.

Godhavn

Egedesminde

Davis Strait

Holsteinsborg

Søndre Strømfjord

Denmark Strait

Arctic Circle

ICELAND

65°

Angmagssalik

Godthaab

southern limit of pack ice

ATLANTIC

OCEAN

Frederikshaab

Dye 3

Ivigtut

Julianehaab

Nanortalik

Cape Farewell

60°

miles
0   300
0   500
kilometres

HOME RULE FOR GREENLAND

When Greenland sought independence in 1945, Denmark was unwilling to relinquish its protectorate immediately, but in 1948 a combined Greenlandic/Danish commission explored the problems, preparing the way for the development of a completely new relationship. In 1953 Greenland became a province of the Kingdom of Denmark, and Greenlanders received full Danish citizenship. In 1955 a Ministry for Greenland was established and, at great cost to the Danish taxpayer and with the full consent of Greenland's two National Councils, Denmark developed an Arctic policy aimed at modernizing Greenlandic society and the economy on which it was based. Modern deep-sea fishing became the mainstay of the economy, replacing subsistence sealing and trapping. New townships replaced scattered settlements. Hospitals, schools, fish-processing factories, communications, transport and other centralized facilities were improved and extended, and capital was invested in mining.

This fast-moving policy gave rise to many problems. Immediate improvements in living standards were balanced by social disruption and rootlessness. Much of the new work, from building construction to schoolteaching, had to be done by an imported Danish workforce, as Greenlanders lacked the necessary skills. Pay differentials left Greenlanders impoverished in their own society, and the growing influence of Danes in every sphere of life became intolerable. Greenlanders were increasing rapidly in population, but not so fast as the Danes. In the colonial days of 1945 it took 340 Danes to run Greenland. By 1979 there were over 7,000 administrators, almost one-fifth of the island's total population, their numbers increasing daily as the complexity of life increased.

In 1975 Denmark set up a further commission, and in 1979 instituted Home Rule, involving a further level of independence for Greenlanders. In a phased programme of delegation, churches, schools, social services, production and transport were the first operations to come under Greenlandic control, followed by housing, power and telecommunications, health, fishing and environmental responsibilities. Defence policies remain Danish, while mining and hydrocarbon development are joint responsibilities.

One of Greenland's first acts on achieving Home Rule was to leave the European Economic Community. Continued membership, it considered, would seriously prejudice its control over the deep-water fish stocks that would now provide its chief source of income.

standards, for Greenland's role model is Denmark, which has some of Europe's highest standards of education, social services and social responsibility. To reach these goals, the Greenlanders have little more than the fish and shrimps of northern waters.

There are minerals, for example cryolite at Ivigtut, lead and zinc ores at Mesters Vig, and low-quality coal at Disko, but demand is currently low and the capital costs necessary to exploit them are high. The few remaining outlying communities continue to hunt for meat and furs for their own use, and at one time many produced surplus pelts for export. However, conservationist lobbying, typified by a recent EEC ban on seal products, has destroyed the once valuable export market and deprived northern hunters of a much needed source of income. Sheep farming in the warm southwest provides meat and fleeces, and tourism is a growing source of foreign exchange, although still on a small scale and dominated by Danish entrepreneurs.

There are few current industries other than those connected with fishing and fish-processing, and few others that are feasible without large-scale capital investment. Unemployment is high. Instead of leading self-sufficient lives in their own small communities, many Greenlanders now find themselves technically unskilled or semi-skilled, and very much at a disadvantage in town. Since there are no roads and railways, all goods travel by ship or by plane, which adds substantially to the cost of living, especially for communities in the far north. The fish stocks on which almost everything else depends are subject to fluctuations, and may already be overtaxed. Denmark continues to support Greenland's economy, but the burden is great and will one day be laid down.

Greenland has become a unique experiment in Arctic administration, one that is being watched closely in other Arctic countries with similar populations. Should its economic and social problems prove insoluble and standards of living decline, depopulation seems the most likely consequence. Young Greenlanders will have the choice of remaining within their Arctic heritage or leaving for a new life in Denmark and the world outside.

ICELAND

Today Iceland lies just south of the Arctic Circle, but in early mediaeval times the Circle was drawn further south and Iceland lay within it. Seven or eight centuries ago, it was a much colder country, closely matching its name. Iceland lies on the Mid-Atlantic Ridge, a northeast-southwest rift in the ocean floor, marked by earthquakes, volcanic upheavals and outpourings of basaltic lava. Most of the ridge lies in deep water, but between Greenland and Scandinavia the lava has piled up into a submarine platform. On this platform, some 20 million years ago, grew the island we now call Iceland. The rift continues to open around the island at a rate of 2–3 cm (about 1 inch) per year.

Living on the edge of the Arctic poses fewer problems than living alongside a submarine ridge. Icelanders long ago came to terms with both. Washed by the North Atlantic Drift, ice-free except for inland glaciers, Iceland is a sub-Arctic island, warmer throughout the year than southern Greenland. Winters are mild and summers cool, with plenty of rain and snow. The island's permanent glaciers, small by Greenland standards, nevertheless cover a greater area than all the glaciers of Europe combined. They produce vigorous streams of cloudy water, with occasional surges when they meet underground volcanic activity. The characteristic vegetation is moorland, with stunted forests and groves of trees in sheltered valleys.

Iceland's 200-odd volcanoes add excitement to daily life. The countryside is dotted with fissures and fumaroles, which from time to time grumble and belch like angry walruses. Icelanders accept philosophically the appearance of new offshore islands, such as Surtsey, which arose with a roar off the south coast in 1963. They recalculate their country's total area, declare the new islands protected, and send ecologists out to study the flora and fauna that move in to colonize them.

Icelanders are used to lava and ash spilling over summer pastures, diverting rivers and creating interesting new situations — used too to finding their cattle and sheep dying from poisonous volcanic fumes. When in 1973 the prosperous little township of Vestmannaeyjar, on the Heimaey archipelago, began to disappear under ash from a neighbouring volcano, they were not at a loss. They evacuated the 5,200 inhabitants, pumped seawater ashore to divert the lava flows, dodged hot ash and lava bombs to shift furniture, livestock, cars and valuables to safety, and re-sited the town's all-important fish-processing factories. A year later Vestmannaeyjar was back in business just a few hundred metres from the old site. Its restored population enjoys the benefits of a new harbour provided by the lava flows, and free central heating from the hot ashpile covering the old town.

Whereas Greenland's early Norse colonies declined and disappeared, Iceland's managed to survive. Politically independent for its first three centuries, Iceland developed an orderly society of widely scattered communities of mixed Nordic and Celtic origin governed by a parliament of local chiefs. In the 13th and 14th centuries, when it became a colony first of Norway, then of Denmark, its population seems to have numbered about 50,000. They lived by subsistence farming and fishing, and already had an enviable reputation for music, poetry and sagas. Prosperity and numbers rose and fell with fluctuations in the climate, and also at the whims of the volcanoes. The Industrial Revolution and social reforms of the 18th and 19th centuries bypassed the island completely, with the result that Iceland entered the 20th century a poor, neglected and rapidly depopulating community.

Restored to parliamentary self-government (although still a Danish colony) during the early years of this century, Iceland embarked on a programme of development which cleared many of the outlying crofts, brought new towns and villages into being, and gradually modernized the economy. In 1944, while Germany occupied Denmark and Iceland was occupied and governed by Allied forces, it took the opportunity to declare its independence from colonial rule and form a republic.

Iceland has no forests or minerals of economic

value, but fast-flowing rivers yield cheap and plentiful hydroelectricity, and so the country has been able to modernize. When more energy is needed, Icelanders have only to harness the power of their fumaroles, which already provide cheap domestic heating in many towns and settlements. Enthusiastic geothermal energy is never far below the surface in a country that straddles the Mid-Atlantic Ridge.

Fishing and fish-processing currently provide much of Iceland's prosperity, which is only slightly less than that of Denmark and other Scandinavian countries. Protecting and controlling its all-important fish stocks during the 1970s involved the country in 'cod wars' with other Western European states, notably Britain, whose own deep-sea fishing fleets had worked the Iceland banks for many years. Sheep and cattle farming, field and greenhouse crops, and fishing continue to provide most of Iceland's food, although cereals are imported. Aluminium smelting, light engineering and other energy-intensive industries mark the way ahead for this Arctic-fringe society, so precariously poised on the edge of the abyss.

THE SOVIET ARCTIC

The Soviet Union extends 8000 km (5,000 miles) from east to west and 3000 km (1,800 miles) from north to south, and has a total area of 22.4 million km² (8.75 million sq miles). State planners define roughly half of this huge area as 'the Soviet north' — the area so designated extends south to 60°N in European Russia and to 50°N in Eastern Siberia. In these northlands, which are both polar and sub-polar, human populations are thin, averaging five people per square kilometre (13 people per square mile). In summer it is cold in the far north but warm in the south. In winter the Arctic cold spreads south and is ubiquitous.

The Trans-Siberian Railway, completed in 1905, opened up Siberia to immigration and made modern development possible. Little was done in the final years of tsarist rule, but the Bolshevik revolution brought the northlands into the 20th century. Soviet planners, needing to marshal all their country's resources, examined and assessed the potential of Siberia for the first time.

■ ■ ■

Nadym, near the Arctic Circle, is one of the main centres of the Yamal-Nenets gas-extracting industry. It was built as a model Siberian town in the late 1970s.

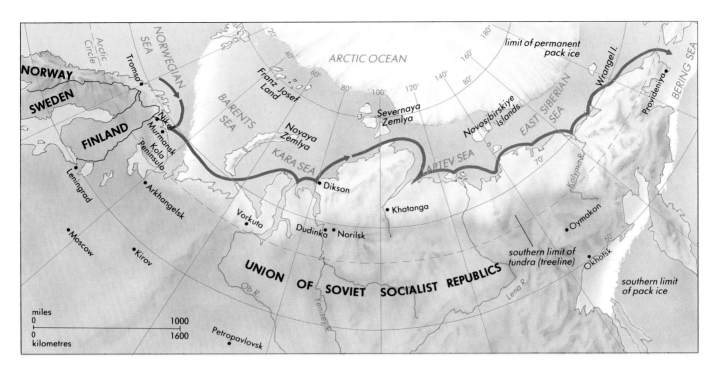

■ ■ ■

The Northern Sea Route,
formerly sought by explorers
as the Northeast Passage,
or northeastern sea route to
China, is now a busy trade
thoroughfare. It is kept open
by icebreakers in all but the
coldest months, and links
all the northern ports of
the USSR.

The northlands, especially the Arctic, were found to be rich in a variety of metal ores and coal. Development costs were high and a transportation network and infrastructure of settlements had first to be established. Throughout the 1920s and '30s and again after World War II, in successive five-year plans, the Soviets developed huge industrial centres for mining and smelting throughout the north, concentrating mainly on high-value minerals. Nowhere else has the Arctic been challenged on such a scale, or manipulated so successfully for economic development.

Products range from alluvial gold, dredged from many of the northern rivers, to coal and heavy metals. Nickel is worked at Pechenga (formerly Finnish Petsamo), at Nikel on the Kola Peninsula and at Norilsk, a new city (now of 200,000 inhabitants) close to the Yenisey delta. Copper, selenium, platinum and other minerals are also smelted. Kola has important

iron mining and smelting centres, and is a major source of apatite, the raw material for superphosphate fertilizer. Arctic tin and tungsten ores occur mainly in the central and far eastern regions. Coal is mined close to the Arctic Circle at Vorkuta for use locally and throughout the northwest.

Enormous underground fields of oil and gas have been developed since the 1960s, in Tyumen Oblast between the Urals and the Yenisey, and in the Timan-Pechora basin. There are further fields near Yakutsk and in the far east around Anadyr and on Sakhalin Island, and exploration now extends to the inshore waters of the Barents Sea. Fields now in production provide over 60 per cent of the Soviet Union's annual consumption. The gas fields, generally lying north of the oilfields, stand on the world's largest known reserves. Daily production of oil and gas in the Soviet north is currently five to six times that of Canada, and approaches the overall daily production of the United States. A network of pipelines links wellheads and refineries with consumers in the northern industrial areas and in the south. Hydroelectric and tidal power have been developed at several northern centres, mainly for local smelters and industrial settlements.

Industrial development so rapid, and on so vast a scale, necessitated the construction of new towns and villages, roads, railways, powerlines and infrastructure, all carved in haste from virgin tundra and forest. Countless engineering problems special to the Arctic — how to build on permafrost, for example, and

Mikhail Gorbachov, visiting the nuclear-powered icebreaker Rossiya *in Murmansk, October 1987. This was the occasion of his historic policy statement inviting worldwide cooperation to make the Arctic a zone of peace.*

how to use materials and operate equipment at low temperatures — were met and dealt with in pioneering spirit. Not surprisingly, improvisation, faulty planning and cost-cutting became apparent in many operations.

Most of the development involved skilled work by incomers from the south. Indigenous people did the unskilled jobs and were generally encouraged to maintain their pastoral roles. Some of the development was carried out by slave labour, for the Soviet authorities maintained and developed the tsarist tradition of Siberian penal camps, occupied by criminals and political prisoners who worked for their keep. No less ugly under socialism than they were under capitalism, the camps are a lasting blot on Russia's reputation, detracting from the country's fine achievements in the Arctic.

To human brutality must be added the charge of environmental insensitivity. Extensive environmental destruction in the Arctic, previously ignored or brushed aside, is now freely admitted by Soviet engineers. Industrial pollution is widespread. Thousands of hectares of forest on the Kola Peninsula have been destroyed and tundra pastures contaminated by spoil tips and noxious gases. Across the Arctic basin in Alaska, atmospheric scientists regularly monitor industrial haze from the Nikel and Norilsk smelters, recognizable by their metallic signatures. Observers have criticized the quality of life in many of the industrial settlements — Arctic workers receive special bonuses, but standards of housing are low. Town planning has been unimaginative, with few

concessions to winter storms and snow management.

However, the magnitude of Soviet achievement in Arctic development is unmatched. Northern industrialization kept the Soviet Union going in World War II, when its western industrial centres were overrun by invading Germans, and has since provided work and a measure of prosperity for millions of Soviet citizens. *Perestroika* may bring about some of the improvements in quality that are so badly needed and so richly deserved by a hard-living community.

Arctic and sub-Arctic reindeer herding, forestry, hunting, fishing and farming have had mixed success under collectivization. Furs retain their economic importance — fur farms and hunting collectives have been established and markets organized to produce high-quality sable, mink, beaver, ermine and squirrel pelts, selecting the best for export. Timber is exported during the ice-free months from northern river ports. Reindeer, cattle, horses and river fish provide food for the north, with a little over for export. The efforts of Soviet agronomists to extend cereal growing and market gardening to the northlands seem to have failed. Hay is the main crop, with only a few collective farms producing significant quantities of potatoes or green vegetables.

Huge maritime fishing fleets operate from Murmansk and Arkhangelsk in the west and from Petropavlovsk, Kamchatka, in the far east. Arctic cargo fleets operate the Northern Sea Route between Murmansk and Bering Strait, a route well over 5000 km (3,100 miles) long, linking a dozen important Arctic ports. The fleets, which include many large ice-strengthened cargo ships, are aided by some 75 ice-breakers. Sixteen of these are among the world's largest and four are nuclear-powered. Polar icebreakers of this size can cut steadily at walking pace through ice up to 2 m (6 ft) thick. The United States has two icebreakers of similar capability, and Canada one.

In August 1977 *Arktika*, pride of the Soviet fleet and the world's most powerful icebreaker, took time out from mundane duties to visit the North Pole. To get there she broke through over 2000 km (1,250 miles) of heavy multi-year ice, achieving the first-ever visit of a surface ship to the Pole. In 1987 *Sibir*, another Soviet giant, made a similar journey. Four further nuclear icebreakers will join the fleet during the 1990s.

The Soviet Union's northernmost island territories, Novaya Zemlya, Franz Josef Land, Severnaya Zemlya and the Novosibirskiye Islands, did not formally become Soviet territory until the 1920s. In the late 19th century Wrangel Island, easternmost of the Siberian islands, seemed as likely to become American or Canadian as Russian, for a US naval captain made the first recorded landing in 1881, and the Canadian explorer Stefansson later made a bid for Canadian ownership. The Soviet Union claimed it formally in 1924, and two years later landed a small group of Chukchi reindeer herders to colonize it.

These northern islands are of no current commercial interest, although they do give the Soviet Union some political justification for declaring the Northern Sea Route 'internal waters' and therefore subject to Soviet control. Two-hundred-mile-wide Exclusive Economic Zones drawn from baselines joining the islands give the Soviet Union rights over very wide swathes of the Arctic Ocean and its shallow continental shelf. Only one area is currently in dispute: Norway and USSR disagree over the precise boundary for fishing rights in the waters between Svalbard and the Norwegian coast.

ALASKA AND THE CANADIAN ARCTIC

The Canadian northlands occupy some 7 million km² (2.73 million sq miles), about 70 per cent of the country as a whole. Low-lying and gently undulating, except for a mountainous eastern fringe, the area has only recently emerged from beneath an ice cap that, in its time, was broader and wider than the present Antarctic cap, although never so thick. The bedrocks, geologically known as the Canadian Shield, are hard, honed-down granites and gneisses, covered in places by folded sedimentary and metamorphic rocks, with a threadbare covering of soils. The northern third is tundra-covered, grading away to polar desert on the dry archipelago. The southern two-thirds lie under conifer and birch forest, liberally laced with rivers and lakes.

Alaska, a western extension separated only by a political boundary, has an area of 1.52 million km² (586,400 sq miles). Practically all of it is northland.

■ ■ ■

The township of Frobisher Bay (Iqaluit), Baffin Island, Canada. Little more than a trading post in 1920, it was the site of an important World War II airfield and later an operations centre for stations of the DEW (Distant Early Warning) line.

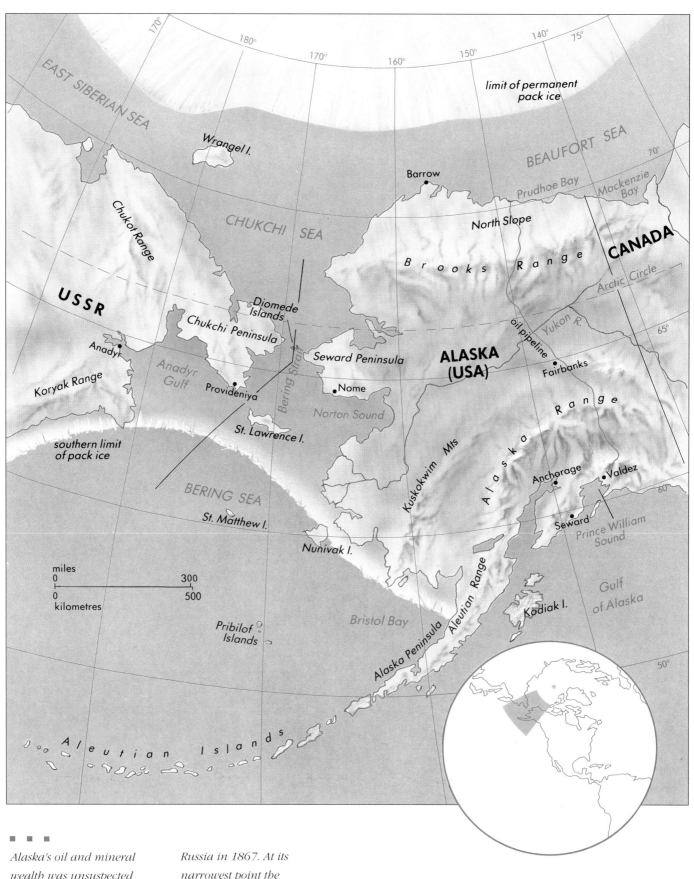

■ ■ ■

Alaska's oil and mineral
wealth was unsuspected
when the United States
purchased the colony from

Russia in 1867. At its
narrowest point the
Bering Strait is a mere
85 km (53 miles) wide.

Geologically complicated by the alpine chain of the great western American cordillera, it has tundra-covered northern coastal slopes and mountains, and southern valleys filled with tundra, forest and grassland. To the west its mountains extend into the sub-Arctic chain of the Aleutian Islands. In the Bering Sea, the Pribilof Islands, Nunivak, Hall, St Matthew and St Lawrence Islands are part of Alaska. So is Little Diomede, in the Bering Strait, but Great Diomede, only 4 km (2.5 miles) away to the east, is Soviet territory, for the international boundary lies between them.

In both Canada and Alaska, tundra coasts and northern rivers belong to the Inuit, while forests and southern waters are mainly Indian country. Of different stocks, ethnic backgrounds and cultures, Inuit and Indians have less in common than Europeans were originally inclined to believe. Alaskan and Canadian Inuit, by contrast, like Alaskan and Canadian Indians, have a great deal in common. The political boundary along 141°W is a southerners' artefact, of no special significance to either people.

Canada's northlands were colonized by Europeans arriving mainly from the east and south, spreading along its rivers and lakes in search of furs, and exploring its northern waters in the hope of finding the Northwest Passage to China. Alaska, by contrast, was occupied from the west. Siberian natives had been aware of it for millennia. Vitus Bering in 1741 was the first European to note officially its wealth of furs, a view echoed by James Cook during his visit of 1778. Russian trappers and fur traders quickly spread along the mainland coast and onto the islands, under the nominal control of the Russian–American Company. Founded by Tsar Paul I and granted exclusive rights to the colony in 1799, the Company developed Sitka as its capital and administrative centre, organizing the native Aleuts and Indians to collect furs for export. Under Russian benevolence the native population of the Aleutian Islands dropped from an estimated 20,000 in the late 18th century to fewer than 2,000 in the 1860s.

By the mid-19th century Russian fur-trading settlements extended down the Pacific coast to central California, but stocks of fur-bearing animals, pirated by American, British and Japanese sealers, were becoming seriously depleted. With no other resources to develop, the colony became unprofitable, and in 1867 Russia was glad to sell Alaska to the United States for $7.2 million. The border with

Canada was finally determined in 1903, along 141°W and the watershed of the southern Coastal Mountains, giving Alaska a narrow 'panhandle' alongside British Columbia.

Neither Alaskan nor Canadian colonists found much use for the tundra. Although whalers visited Inuit coastal settlements, devastating several of them with introduced diseases, the tundra and many of the remote communities that lived there remained relatively untouched until the early 20th century. Forests, on the other hand, were heavily exploited from the outset, and the Indians within them organized for gathering furs, which was the prime motive for colonization. Trading posts set up by companies such as the Hudson's Bay Company became villages where nomadic natives were encouraged to settle, initially to encourage trading, later for ease and economy of administration. North American methods, although perhaps less harsh than Russian, were not wholly beneficial: diseases unfamiliar to the natives decimated some communities and destroyed others, and alcoholism became widespread.

Alaska became part of the United States at a time of rapid expansion. With the West almost won, there were plenty of restless immigrants eager for the opportunities that the new possession offered. A salmon fishing industry began in the 1870s, with canneries along the west and south coasts. Goldfields discovered in and behind the panhandle, and later at Nome and in the Tanana valley, brought growth to local settlements and prosperity to the community as a whole. Territorial status was granted in 1912. Forests provided local timber and a surplus for export. Copper was mined at Kennecott, and coal, silver and other readily exploitable minerals at several localities. Huge reserves of copper, coal, iron and more valuable minerals were identified elsewhere in the territory. Railways threaded inland linking Skagway to Whitehorse, Seward to Fairbanks, and mining centres along the Copper River. In the absence of roads, Alaska's major rivers were used for transportation, determining the sites of some of the larger inland settlements. Farming developed in a few favoured areas, helped by government subsidies.

World War II saw Alaska in the firing line. Some of its outer islands were occupied by Japanese forces, and others were fought over or bombed. Thousands of American service men and women gained first-hand experience of their northernmost territory, and

THE ALASKA PIPELINE

lthough by no means the first pipeline to be laid in the Arctic, the trans-Alaska pipeline was by far the longest and widest, and the operation to install it was arguably the world's largest-ever engineering project. The pipeline solved the problem of how to get oil from the wellhead at Prudhoe Bay, on the North Slope of Alaska, to markets in the United States. Anywhere else in the world large oil-tankers would have provided the answer, but Prudhoe Bay is frozen for more than half the year. Neither the seasonal use of icebreakers, nor the suspension of production in winter, nor attempts to store the oil would have made economic sense.

Almost 1300 km (800 miles) long and 122 cm (48 inches) in diameter, the pipeline crosses tundra, mountains and forest to reach Valdez, in southern Alaska. Much of the ground it crosses is permafrost, frozen solid in winter but thawing to shallow depths in summer. The oil emerging from the ground is warm, about 80°C (176°F), and flows best if it can be kept warm. The pipe, made of lengths of welded steel 1.3 cm (1/2 in) thick, is therefore heavily lagged. The original plan was to bury the pipe, but delays caused by public enquiries and objections from environmental groups gave the planners time to think further. Laying a warm pipeline, even an insulated one, directly on or in permafrost would invite trouble, for the ground would thaw in summer and the pipe would sag and break. Northern Alaska is also an earthquake zone; a pipeline enclosed in ground that is liable to crack would be very much at risk, and difficult to repair if it broke.

The Alyeska Pipeline Service Company, which designed and laid the pipe, had to determine an optimal route and thoroughly investigate the soils along the way. After building various experimental lengths of line to test various ways of supporting it, they eventually decided to keep only about half the pipe above ground, resting on H-shaped steel supports. The posts of the supports are hollow, topped with cooling fins and containing refrigerant; their function is to conduct winter cold 8 m (26 ft) or deeper into the ground and so reduce summer thawing. The pipeline, resting on the crossbar of the support, is free to move 3–4 m (9–13 ft) laterally, allowing for expansion under the summer sun and also for earthquake movements. Rivers presented

particular problems, for they are mostly wide, with shifting beds. Special places were left for caribou to cross the pipeline, and many other concessions were made to conservation groups concerned with the effects of the pipeline on the local environment.

Considerable thought was also given to the siting of pumping stations (needed at intervals along the line to keep the oil moving), and to the gravel beneath the line and the accompanying service road. Despite its many novelties, the design seems to have been entirely successful. The pipeline currently carries up to 200 million litres (53 million gallons) of oil per day, and could double its throughput if necessary.

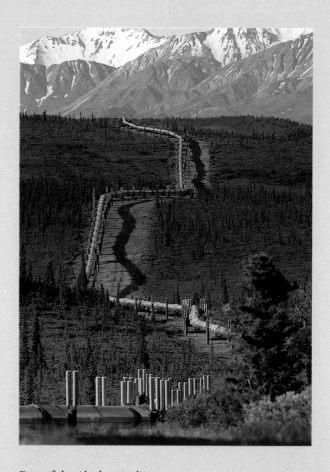

Part of the Alaska pipeline, carrying oil from North Slope oilfields to the southern port of Valdez. The bends allow for expansion and contraction.

Alaska gained a valuable international all-weather highway linking it, through Canada, with the rest of the United States. In 1946 it became the largest state of America, with an area more than double that of Texas.

After the war Alaska became an important base for Cold War operations. Its continuing growth and prosperity were based largely on defence spending, the cash flow helping to develop small industries and enterprises throughout the state. Fisheries, fur trapping and forestry continued to employ most native Alaskans, although many also took unskilled employment related to defence contracts. Oil production, a small but significant part of the economy since the 1920s, developed remarkably in the late 1960s with the production of petroleum and natural gas from wells on the barren North Slope. Petroleum now dominates the Alaskan economy. In the 1960s petroleum revenues amounted to less than 10 per cent of state revenues, but by the 1980s they had risen to 50 per cent and more, and the prosperity of the state now depends heavily on world market prices for oil. The pipeline linking production areas on the North Slope with the southern port of Valdez ensures a reliable, continuous flow of oil from the wells to consumers in the southern states of America.

THE CREATION OF CANADA'S NORTHERN TERRITORIES

The war of 1812 determined the international boundary along the 49th parallel, separating the loyal British colonies of the north from an independent United States. The northern forests and plains, rich in furs, were originally divided between the Hudson's Bay Company, which controlled Prince Rupert's Land (within the catchment area of Hudson Bay), and the Northwest Territory, controlled by the North-West Company. Following open warfare, the two companies were amalgamated in 1821, and the reconstituted Hudson's Bay Company held sway over practically all of the northern territories.

In 1867, when the four colonies of Nova Scotia, New Brunswick and Upper and Lower Canada (now Ontario and Quebec) amalgamated to form the Dominion of Canada, the new federal government bought out most of the Hudson's Bay Company's lands and rights. Manitoba (formerly the Red River Colony) became a province in 1870; Vancouver Island and British Columbia (separate colonies since 1849 and 1858) united in 1866 and joined the federation in 1871; and in 1880 Britain incorporated the islands of the Canadian archipelago into the northern territory.

The Gold Rush of 1896 resulted in a massive influx of population to the area, and in the formation of a separate Yukon Territory administered from Whitehorse. A further influx into the Canadian Midwest during the early 20th century resulted in the development of two new provinces, Saskatchewan and Alberta, finally restricting the Northwest Territories and Yukon Territory to the area north of the 60th parallel. Until the 1920s both territories were controlled largely by the Royal Canadian Mounted Police. Territorial administration commenced with the start of large-scale mining.

Canada's Yukon and Northwest Territories (NWT) grew more slowly. Whaling and fur trading were the first two industries. Explorers and prospectors, fur traders, missionaries and teachers made contact with native communities and established settlements, with the Royal Canadian Mounted Police patrolling and keeping order. Title to the Arctic islands was strengthened from 1922 onward, when police posts and post offices were established on Ellesmere Island and neighbouring islands, and an RCMP patrol vessel made regular summer visits. Only when gold was discovered in the Yukon River basin in 1896 was a formal administration set up in what is now Yukon Territory. Discovery of oil near Fort Norman on the Mackenzie River led to the establishment of a Northwest Territories administration.

Gold, copper, silver and lead were mined in the Yukon during the 1920s and '30s, but by the late '30s, the territory was in severe economic depression. In the rest of the Canadian north only the Mackenzie Valley fared as well. Prosperity built up slowly from the development of oil at Norman Wells in the 1920s and of gold, silver and pitchblende mining near the Great Bear and Great Slave Lakes in the '30s. These demanded the extension of river, rail and road transport systems and the provision of minimal social infrastructure, and brought some paid employment to native peoples.

World War II and its aftermath accelerated development in several areas, notably along the southern border of the northlands. The first long-distance pipelines were built to carry oil from Norman Wells to Whitehorse and other centres in Alaska. New roads and airfields appeared, and mining and hydroelectric power schemes proliferated. Lead, zinc, tungsten, iron, asbestos, gold, silver, copper, bismuth and other ores were mined, providing steadily increasing revenues. However, with the return of peace, demand for ores fell and the less economical mines closed. Huge reserves of minerals still lie untapped, awaiting some future time when their development will again be worthwhile.

Post-war oil and natural gas discoveries spread from the mainland to the northern islands, and offshore into the Sverdrup Basin of the Arctic Ocean. With government support, wells have been drilled and huge reserves proved in several areas of the northlands, and both oil and gas are now exported continuously to the south. Although the boom fuelled by the Cold War is now over, and many of the mines are worked out or temporarily closed, the Canadian northlands have been left with a social infrastructure, good rail, road and air links, and a sharp appreciation of their economic potential.

In both Alaska and Canada economic development has moved fast, faster on the whole than the development of educational and training facilities for native peoples. As in other northern areas, the natives tended to be left on the fringes of development, with no voice in decision-making and unable to participate in economic life except as unskilled or semi-skilled labourers. Even tourism, which is developing fast across the northlands, tends to be controlled by entrepreneurs from the south, who employ other southerners as managers and natives only as guides. Although the native inhabitants benefit from the better schools, hospitals and other welfare services allowed by higher revenues to local administration, many have felt left behind in the race to develop their lands and natural resources. The last two or three generations, facing the greatest changes of all, have found adjustment to white ways particularly hard, with resulting health and social problems.

Native pressure groups and political organizations, first encouraged in Alaska, spread quickly to Canada and developed along separate lines. In recent years they have done much to establish native rights to land, to bring natives effectively into decision-making, and to ensure adequate compensation for lost or alienated rights and resources. In Canada a turning point was marked by the Mackenzie Valley Pipeline Enquiry, a two-year investigation into the impact of a proposed pipeline to transport gas south along the Mackenzie Valley. Mr Justice R. T. Berger, leading the commission of enquiry, took pains to discover native views on the matter. His report of 1977 recommended that construction be delayed for ten years to allow full consideration of native rights — a matter that would hardly have been considered for discussion a generation earlier.

Native participation, now encouraged at all levels of decision-making and government, has slowed down rates of change and to some degree hindered progress, but happier and more democratic communities are the result. Some legislators are discovering that Inuit and Indian attitudes to the Arctic environment may in fact be ecologically sounder and more practical than southern attitudes — what once seemed obstructionism makes good sense in a northern context. If the objectives of development leave room for wisdom, there is wisdom in plenty among those who know the Arctic best.

THE POLITICS OF ANTARCTICA

Compared with the north, the politics of the Antarctic are simple and straightforward. There is no permanent human population within the polar circle or the 10°C (50°F) isotherm. For the present, questions of continental ownership have been shelved under the Antarctic Treaty, and development of any kind is limited, if not made impossible, by climate, remoteness and cost. Because nobody belongs to Antarctica, nobody cherishes it as their own country. There is nobody to fight, as Inuit and Indian have fought, the quiet, constant battle to keep scientists and planners in order.

Ownership of most of the temperate or sub-polar southern islands is not in dispute. By right of discovery and present or recent occupation, France claims Iles Kerguelen, Crozet, Amsterdam and St Paul. On similar grounds, including inheritance from the British Empire, the Republic of South Africa claims Marion and the Prince Edward Islands, Australia

claims Heard, Macdonald and Macquarie Islands, and New Zealand claims Campbell Island and the Auckland, Bounty and Antipodes Islands. On similar grounds Britain lays claims to Tristan da Cunha, Gough and Nightingale Islands, of which ownership is not disputed, and to the Falkland Islands, South Georgia and the South Sandwich Islands, which Argentina has disputed to the point of invasion and open warfare.

On continental Antarctica Britain claims a pie-shaped sector called British Antarctic Territory, extending from 20°W to 80°W. This overlaps with similar claims by Chile to Territorio Chileno Antártico (90°W to 53°W) and of Argentina to Antártida Argentina (74°W to 25°W), which also overlap each other. Norway claims the adjacent sector, called Dronning Maud Land, from 20°W to 45°E. Norway's claim does not extend to the South Pole, but throws in Peter I Øy and tiny Bouvetøya for good measure.

Australia claims two pie-shaped sectors, called Australian Antarctic Territory, inherited from Britain and extending between 45°W and 160°E. These are separated by a narrow French sector, Terre Adélie, between 136°E and 142°E. Finally, New Zealand claims the Ross Dependency, from 160°E to 150°W, and extending to the Pole.

The bases of all these claims go back to individual voyages of discovery and announcements of possession, but the claims themselves tend to be more mod-

ern. Exceptionally, Britain's first claim to the 'Falkland Islands Dependencies' was lodged in Letters Patent of June 1843, shortly after the visit by James Clark Ross. Most other claims date from the 20th century, starting at the onset of the whaling era. Thus Britain restated its claim to the Antarctic Peninsula and adjacent islands in 1908, at a time when the Norwegians were seeking whaling stations in the area. New Zealand's control of the Ross Dependency began in 1923 when Britain, responding to the presence of whaling ships in the Ross Sea, claimed the area in an Order-in-Council and placed it under the control of the Governor-General of New Zealand. In the following year, and no doubt as a direct response, France staked her claims to Adélie Land and the southern islands, placing them under the sleepy control of her colony Madagascar.

Australia's claims date from a British Order-in-Council of 1933, following a combined British, Australian and New Zealand shipborne expedition that explored the coastline of this long sector. Norway's claim, dated 1939, followed two decades of exploration by whaling ships in that sector, but was also a direct response to the presence of a German survey expedition in the area. Chile followed Norway's example in 1942, and Argentina followed Chile shortly afterwards.

These claims left open a substantial sector of West Antarctica between 150°W and 90°W, which nobody

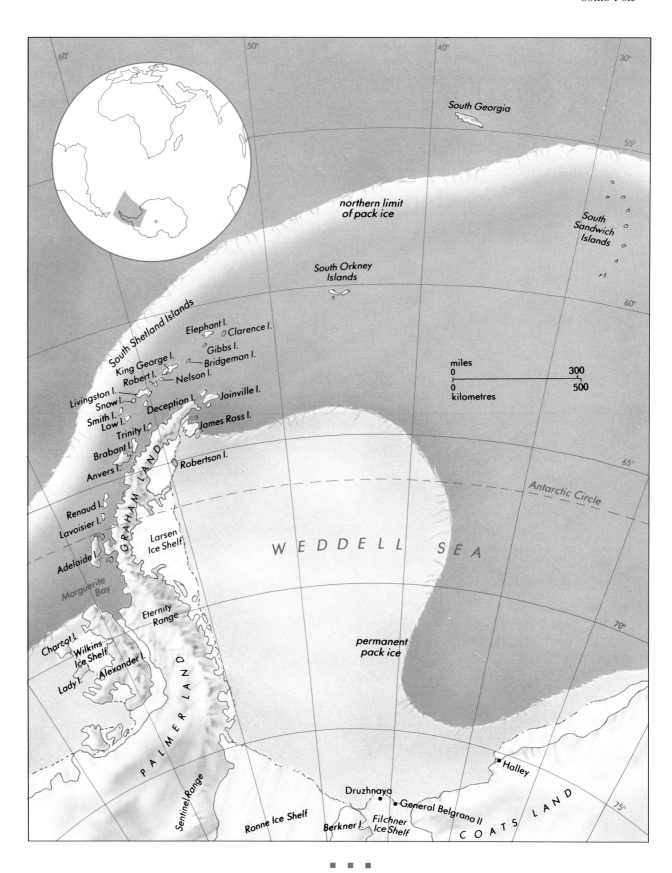

The Antarctic Peninsula
and the islands of the Scotia
Arc are claimed by Britain
and Argentina; Chile's
claim is to the Peninsula
and part of the
Bellingshausen Sea.

appeared to want. It is no coincidence that, because of heavy pack ice offshore, this has always been the most difficult sector to reach by sea. The claims gave satisfaction to those that made them and were to some degree recognized by other claimant nations, but they were by no means universally respected. At a time when they agreed on little else, for example, the United States and the Soviet Union made no territorial claims in Antarctica and made it clear that they had little time for anyone else's claims.

The claims were indeed questionable or even invalid under international law. At the times they were made, they were not followed up by occupation and effective administration, a requirement that is generally agreed upon even for polar lands. Britain took whaling responsibilities seriously, perhaps because they were a source of revenue. From the arrival of the first whaling stations on South Georgia and the South Shetland Islands magistrates were appointed to keep records and sell postage stamps, and from 1924 onward operated the Falkland Islands Dependencies Research and Development Fund.

In 1943, although heavily engaged in World War II, Britain further substantiated claims to the Falkland Islands Dependency sector (for which Argentina and Chile were by then active rivals) by establishing permanent survey bases in the area — the first-ever long-term habitations in Antarctica. In response, both Chile and Argentina increased their own presence in the area, sending naval ships south and setting up bases of their own. Although a few of these stations are still occupied, today the Antarctic Peninsula and nearby islands are littered with semi-derelict huts, non-functional navigation beacons and piles of rubbish from this period, to the despair of those who knew them in better times and to the disgust of visitors.

In 1946–47 the United States put the first of a series of large exploratory expeditions into the field, involving icebreakers, aircraft and thousands of men, that between them surveyed most of Antarctic. By doing so the United States established a convincing

right to claim a substantial interest in the future of the continent. The French opened stations in Terre Adélie and on some of their southern islands, and the Australians and New Zealanders established annual expeditions to some of their southern possessions. In 1949–52 came a combined Norwegian, British and Swedish scientific expedition to Dronning Maud Land, and in 1955–57 a British aerial survey of parts of the Antarctic Peninsula area. Cold War strategists began to consider Antarctica's possible role in modern warfare. Airline planners dusted off schemes, dating from the 1920s and '30s, for establishing international airports on some of the southern islands — even on Terre Adélie — for intercontinental flights. Late but unmistakably, Antarctica was joining the 20th century.

THE IGY AND THE ANTARCTIC TREATY

The years 1957–59, designated International Geophysical Year and International Geophysical Cooperation Year, brought new influences to bear on Antarctica. Scientific expeditions of a dozen nations began working on the continent in a concerted effort of scientific and geographical exploration. Although the Cold War raged elsewhere, in Antarctica American and Soviet explorers met and cooperated as civilized folk should. Chilean, Argentine and British scientists took tea together and traded ideas. The French and the South Africans, Australians and New Zealanders cooperated in international programmes. Above all, claimant nations made a point of inviting everyone else to use 'their' territories.

So eminently sensible was this arrangement that everyone concerned agreed that it should continue. From it arose two separate but linked developments, the Antarctic Treaty and the Scientific Committee on Antarctic Research, which between them have ensured several decades of political and scientific cooperation in Antarctica and the surrounding oceans. These, and their possible implications for Arctic cooperation and research, are discussed more fully in Chapters 9 and 10.

9

Science in a Cold Climate

Science is a confusing word and, as such, thoroughly unscientific. It is the name we give firstly to a method of approaching and tackling questions, and secondly to the masses of facts and information that have been assembled under the headings of the different scientific disciplines. As a method of investigating the world, science is practical but limited — in some fields an immensely powerful tool, in others worse than useless.

It helps us discover, mainly through setting up and testing 'models' or 'hypotheses', how things work, how to manipulate processes or events in our favour, and how to store information in forms that we can recover, use, and add to later. Models and hypotheses are developments of what non-scientists call hunches. Testing them is often a matter of experimenting, or predicting possible consequences and matching models with reality.

Scientific method is excellent for answering some kinds of questions but hopeless for others. Ask scientists what Antarctica is made of, and the earth scientists will step forward and tell you in as much detail as you want to know, possibly more. Ask scientists who Antarctica belongs to, and the political scientists will have a sound view, although not necessarily one that everyone will accept. Ask scientists 'Who made Antarctica?', and they can give you no satisfactory account based on science. They may give you an answer, for that is what they like to do, but in this case an honest answer will be based on faith, hope or guesswork rather than science.

The earth scientists would base their views on a huge, generally agreed body of knowledge extending from seismology to mineralogy, knowledge that further research is likely to add to and refine, rather than upset. The political scientists would give their answer in the light of current conceptions of how ownership is established and maintained. Their methods, they tell us, are no less rigorous than those of other scientists, but the rules they apply are man-made, open to several interpretations, and so less definitive or certain. Hence the possibility of fundamental disagreement on what may seem to be a simple issue.

The question of who made Antarctica is impossible to tackle scientifically, for the word 'who' carries a loading — it assumes one kind of answer that scientific method cannot investigate. The question is not meaningless, but for science it needs to be re-shaped.

The best scientists in any discipline are those who have learnt the trick of posing questions in ways that make them soluble by scientific enquiry. That keeps them busy enough, and free to dodge (well, postpone thinking about) the questions that they cannot reshape satisfactorily.

The methods of polar science are not basically different from those of other kinds of science. Scientists who work in polar regions sometimes feel restricted if they are called polar scientists — they can practice their crafts just as readily elsewhere, and indeed may have to when their current research grants run out — but some scientific enquiries *must* be pursued in polar contexts and others are *best* pursued there, and these are the true substance of polar science.

COSTS AND BENEFITS

One major problem limiting polar science is its cost. Not all polar enquiries have to take place beyond the polar circles, but most problems in polar science require field work, and the costs of field work are high. During the 1930s, when undergraduates from Oxford and Cambridge spent summer vacations on scientific research and survey in the Arctic, they could rent fishing boats cheaply, live on next to nothing in tents, beg or borrow equipment, make simple, basic observations of value, and come home vastly enriched in experience and knowledge. Those days, sadly, are past.

There are still a few small private expeditions to polar regions, run on shoestrings by young people for fun and adventure. There are a few more on a larger scale, that rely on the charisma of their leaders or on the public's memory of 'heroic' expeditions to raise funds for their support. Depending as they do on media attention, they often need to give an attention-catching performance, and sometimes behave outlandishly. No expeditions have yet set out to walk backward or push perambulators to either pole, but there is every chance that one will before long. Some of these expeditions try to to include scientific enquiry in their programmes, test new methods, or push the human body to the limits of endurance. A very few return with credible results.

In a different category are private expeditions undertaking logistic research, investigating, for example, the feasibility of using ice runways to land wheeled aircraft in the Antarctic interior. These may be paid for in part by tourists, who welcome the adventure and can afford to pay for it. Then there are true tourist expeditions, composed of hardy folk who make well-organized, air-supported ski marches to one or other of the poles, perhaps taking a few scientific observations on the way, and pay handsomely for the vacation of a lifetime. But most modern polar research is institutionalized: both the research and the institution are usually financed by governments or their agencies. As in the days of the old naval expeditions, polar science has again become a direct expense on taxpayers.

In terms of costs, polar science has gone very up-market. Scientific stations are no longer the cosy, lamp-lit huts that they were in the time of Amundsen, Scott and Shackleton. Today they are permanent installations, for year-round or recurring summer expeditions. Built and equipped to the highest specifications, they cost far more to install and maintain than would their equivalent at home. Expeditions also tend to be bigger than before, and far more costly. Standards of living and in-hut entertainment are higher, to offset boredom and maintain morale — needs that seem to have crept into expedition life while no one was looking.

The cost of transporting people and loads of equipment to the ends of the earth is very high. Scientific equipment seldom comes cheap, especially with the packaging and stocks of spare parts that expedition conditions demand. Icebreakers, transport ships, survey aircraft, helicopters, snowmobiles and skidoos all escalate costs, and all require trained operators and expensive maintenance crews. Safety measures — good radios, back-up transport, medical facilities, rescue teams on stand-by — always cost money and are now considered essential and no longer luxuries.

Field scientists and support personnel form the front line. In the rear are the bureaucracies, managing, ordering and shipping tonnes of stores, organizing salaries, insurance premiums and pensions — all in the cause of polar scientific research. Almost inevitably, within a few years of any national expedition starting up, administration absorbs far more of the available money than science. Ultimately, expeditions cease to employ scientists, relying instead on those supported by universities, institutions or other grant-giving bodies.

Government support and larger cash flows have made everyone more ambitious. Since World War II a succession of government-funded expeditions — notably Australian, British, French, New Zealand, Soviet and American — has poured money and effort into exploring Antarctica. Without these expeditions, Antarctica would still be a relatively unknown continent, for there is little chance of financial return from exploring it, and private enterprise could not possibly have operated on so huge and continuous a scale. Extensive flying programmes to map the ice cap and underlying rocks would never have happened. Continuous records from long-term stations would not have been gathered. Polar plateau stations, how-

■ ■ ■

Dye 3, a radar station on the South Greenland ice cap, a far cry from the wooden huts used by early polar scientists. Several kinds of glaciological research are done here. Periodically the station has to be jacked up to keep it above the rising level of the snow.

ever desirable, would have been out of the question — installing and maintaining them would have proved completely prohibitive.

Even small, relatively local polar expeditions are costly. Each year Norway, the United States, Canada and other northern countries set aside substantial budgets to maintain relatively small programmes of scientific work in the north. For northern-hemisphere countries to run substantial programmes in the south — for Poland to maintain a station on the South Shetland Islands, for Germany to run a research icebreaker and an ice-shelf station, for France to maintain stations on Iles Kerguelen, Crozet and Amsterdam as well as Antarctica, for Britain, Japan, the United States and the Soviet Union to keep ships, stations and aircraft in the southern ice — is costlier by many orders of magnitude.

Ask spokesmen of any of these countries why they are going to all this trouble and expense, and they will probably speak first of contributions to international polar science. There must be something very special about polar science to justify such huge expenditure — or is there more to it than that? Keep asking and listening, and an honest spokesman will sooner or later admit what is abundantly clear to everyone: national prestige is also involved, with the possibility — the faint, remote possibility — of some useful return for the money and effort expended.

Ultimately the taxpayer is entitled to ask why. Who are these polar scientists, with their insatiable demands for public money? What is the value of their science, that is so much more expensive than closer-to-home kinds of science? What is this prestige that is so alluring? Would significant prestige be lost if the money were spent instead on housing, aid for the Third World, famine relief, or even armaments? What is the case for polar science or polar prestige, and why are they linked?

CUMULATIVE KNOWLEDGE

Polar science began in the early days of exploration, with individuals who were inquisitive in approach and systematic in recording their observations. Some were trained scientists retained especially for the purpose, but many of the best were observant ships' officers, whaling captains, surgeons and passengers. Their records of what they experienced — climate, cloud formations, pack ice, icebergs, natives, natural

history, rocks and a host of other phenomena — are still of value. The scientific success of a cruise in the early days was judged immediately by the bulk of specimens brought back for museums, and later by the bulk of reports written and published in bound volumes. Of no less lasting value are the private logs, letters and papers of those who travelled and recorded what they saw, for often they saw with fresh, unprejudiced eyes.

Early published works tend to be descriptive rather than deductive, although a few true scientists — not always those with first-hand experience — generalized about polar regions from the loose ends collected. As in practically all other science then and now, the information gained and the ideas it engendered were freely interchanged between nations. Von Bellingshausen knew of Cook's observations and those of his naturalists, and built substantially on them. Wilkes passed his navigational results to Ross. Various scientists wrote copious letters to each other — often agreeable, leisurely exchanges of views of a kind few scientists have time for today. The libraries that accompanied later scientific voyages were well stocked with the published results of earlier expeditions, publications still valued, although they are now rare documents.

So the knowledge slowly built up, and the polar regions gradually became part of the world of science. Everything we have learnt from polar regions has its own intrinsic value, but in a few particular fields of enquiry polar information has been essential to our understanding of how the world works, and the expense and effort of securing it has been fully justified.

TERRESTRIAL MAGNETISM AND AURORAS

Captain James Ross's enthusiasm for locating the magnetic poles was part of a general interest in terrestrial magnetism, of great practical value to 19th-century mariners. As magnetic compasses improved and standards of navigation rose, it became necessary to understand the patterns of variation in Earth's magnetic field. Magnetic declination, the angle between true north and magnetic north, was one of the first variables measured over Earth's surface. The first map of declination was published by Edmund Halley in the early 18th century. Ships' officers made measurements whenever they could, and magnetometry became an essential feature of polar expeditions.

THE DRIFTING MAGNETIC POLES

Earth's magnetism is based on electric currents set up by movements of the planet's molten core, and its magnetic field of force is similar to that which would appear if the earth contained a bar magnet, flexible and slightly mobile, aligned about 15° from the axis of rotation. The geomagnetic poles, representing the ends of the magnet, lie some 1600 km (1,000 miles) from the geographic poles, not quite antipodally to each other, as though the magnet were slightly bent. Each pole drifts continuously, pirouetting from hour to hour and travelling long distances over the years. Observers know they have reached one or other pole when a dip-needle (a bar magnet on horizontal bearings) points vertically into the ground.

The North Geomagnetic Pole, which Ross first visited in 1831, dodges between northern Greenland and the islands of the Canadian archipelago.The South Geomagnetic Pole has wandered in historic times from behind the Ross Sea coast to the northern coast of Antarctica close to Terre Adélie. Ross failed to reach it, for in the 1840s it lay several miles inland, beyond a belt of pack ice that his ships could not penetrate. Not until January 1909 was it finally visited and flagged, by a sledging party under the Australian explorer Douglas Mawson. They found it highly mobile. Approaching to within a few kilometres and calculating its speed of movement, they seriously considered waiting for the geomagnetic pole to come to them.

Long-term shifts occur slowly and are to some degree predictable. The lines of force between the two magnetic poles, revealed by compass needles, can be mapped accurately and their rates of change calculated. To navigate effectively with magnetic compasses, we need to keep abreast of these changes. Close to the magnetic poles, where the lines of force converge, magnetic needles become sluggish and useless for direction-finding, especially if there are magnetic rocks close by. Navigators in high latitudes close to the magnetic poles prefer to use gyroscopic compasses or navigate by the sun.

Local, unexpected variations were found and traced to bodies of magnetic rock. Then repeated observations over long periods revealed secular variations: the strength and direction of the field slowly changed over time, as though a magnet inside the earth were moving. To study this, long-term monitoring was required, close to the magnetic poles, where variations and secular changes are most marked. Magnetometry was one of the sciences studied at Arctic stations during the first Polar Year (1882–83), and in the early years of the 20th century the US government supported a special survey vessel, *Carnegie*, made of non-magnetic materials, that voyaged all over the world recording terrestrial magnetism. Magnetometer records are still maintained at some modern polar stations.

Auroras, the northern and southern lights, are related to Earth's magnetic fields. Aurora means dawn — occasionally both the northern Aurora Borealis and the southern Aurora Australis look like a false dawn, especially when seen low in the sky from sub-polar latitudes. A weak aurora is a greenish, reddish or white glow that suddenly spreads across the sky — a loom of light over a city that isn't there. A full display throngs the sky with curtains and shafts of light, with greens and reds predominating, radiant, unearthly, and brighter than the fullest full moon.

Auroras can be seen almost anywhere north of 45°N and south of 45°S. The best and brightest tend to appear in fairly narrow bands, or auroral zones, up to 400 km (250 miles) wide and ringing the North and South Geomagnetic Poles at a distance of up to 2500 km (1,000 miles), like geomagnetic polar circles. In the northern auroral zone, for example in southern Greenland, Iceland, northern Norway or northern Alaska, auroras occur as often as 240 nights per year — a show almost every winter night — although many are obscured by heavy cloud. Away from the zones, auroras are much less frequent. In the north polar basin, which lies north of the zone, and in northern Siberia and central Canada to the south of it, the lights can appear 100 nights a year. In Vancouver or Edinburgh they can appear 25 nights a year and in southern Alaska, London or New York no more than five nights a year. The further one goes from the zones, the less spectacular the aurora. Northern Alaskans often get the full treatment; southern Alaskans, like Londoners, seldom see more than a glow.

NORTHERN AND SOUTHERN LIGHTS

■ ■ ■   ■ ■ ■

Although auroral curtains sometimes seem to hang low, almost touching the ground, they actually occur in the upper atmosphere between 80 and 320 km (50 and 200 miles) above Earth's surface. Their light is due to collisions between electrons from the sun and widely scattered atoms and molecules of the thin rarefied atmospheric gases, especially oxygen and nitrogen.

Electrons escape from the sun all the time, impinging on the earth in a 'solar wind' of varying strength, and light is generated wherever they collide with high atmospheric gases. All over the top of the atmosphere a faint 'sky glow', often confused with starlight, brightens the night sky. However, over the magnetic poles Earth's magnetic field concentrates and channels the electrons, creating the patterns of light associated with the northern and southern auroras.

The colours emitted are mostly reds and greens, in a range of wavelengths and intensities. The *International Auroral Atlas* distinguishes six colour types of aurora. The highest, occurring over 200 km (120 miles) above the earth and extending upward to many hundreds of kilometres, are blood-red and very constant. Below them form the green arcs, rays and curtains so characteristic of the Aurora Borealis, often with a red lower border only 80 km (50 miles) above the ground. However, auroral displays are infinitely varied, shifting in the course of an evening, often with a second, quite different show after midnight. 'Sun spots' mark surges of energy from the sun when the flow of electrons increases. Not surprisingly, auroras tend to be most spectacular when sun spots are active, usually starting 18–36 hours after a flare. One memorable sun spot episode in February 1986 gave spectacular night-long performances over Svalbard, and glorious demonstrations all over Western Europe from the Arctic coast to the Bay of Biscay.

❄

The southern hemisphere auroral zone passes south of the Weddell Sea across Dronning Maud Land and Byrd Land, and cuts a swathe over the cloudy Southern Ocean. Nobody lives in most of this vast region, so the lights of the Aurora Australis play nightly to whales, seals and penguins. Although they can be as brilliant as those of Aurora Borealis, observers who have seen both tend to find the southern lights disappointing.

Auroras have been studied simultaneously at both ends of the earth, for example from two aircraft, equipped with all-sky cameras, flying over Alaska and over the 'conjugate point' (the equivalent geomagnetic latitude and longitude) above the Southern Ocean. These studies, which can be made only in March and September, when it is equally dark in both hemispheres, show that northern and southern auroras tend to be similar, synchronous, but slightly displaced from exact geomagnetic symmetry. Auroras play far above the weather and have no direct influence on climate. Scientists study them for their own sake, for the information they provide about the earth's magnetic field, and because of their links with sunspot activity and terrestrial magnetism. One prac-

tical link involves radio communications; solar storms that intensify auroras are likely to interfere with radio signals in polar areas.

STUDYING WEATHER AND CLIMATE

Weather phenomena occur in the lower atmosphere, mostly within 15 km (9 miles) of the ground. Quite different phenomena occur in the upper atmosphere, between 15 and 50 km (9 and 30 miles) up. Both kinds of phenomena are being studied in polar regions.

There is a long-standing tradition that mariners record the weather — they are always alert to it, and usually take the trouble to report it accurately in the ship's log. Virtually every ship and land expedition to polar regions has taken barometers and thermometers, and kept accurate records of weather phenomena. Some of these early records have now become extremely valuable. Although incomplete and not always taken as meticulously as they would be today, they provide excellent material for comparison with modern data. They are important baseline studies, from which we can see how climate has changed over the last two or three centuries.

∎ ∎ ∎

The red phase of an auroral display above a harbour in southern Greenland. In the auroral zones auroras are the rule rather than the exception on winter nights, although cloud cover often obscures them. Light emissions at the red end of the spectrum are associated with collisions between high-energy electrons and high-atmosphere gas atoms at altitudes 200 km (120 miles) or more above Earth's surface.

Only in the last 100 years have meteorological stations been established in polar regions and taken standard observations in ways that make their data fully comparable with records from temperate and tropical regions. In the early years of this century, when Scandinavian meteorologists began to study the upper atmosphere and discover how weather is generated, it became apparent that movements of polar air masses play a key role in determining temperate and even tropical climates. Their work was helped by a sudden increase in the number of Arctic weather stations during the 1930s, mainly providing information for the growing needs of polar aviation.

With the advent of Arctic flying it suddenly became important to understand surface, atmospheric and upper-atmospheric conditions and their seasonal variations. Canadian bush pilots and Alaskan airline pilots flew more safely with a network of weather information, and many North American meteorological stations date from this period. World War II brought more airfields and weather stations to the

Arctic fringe. The Alaska Highway, built in 1942, was originally a supply route to Ladd Field, Fairbanks, an important staging post for aircraft flying to Russia across the Bering Strait. At about the same time the Soviet Union completed its third five-year plan to develop the Northern Sea Route, involving new ports and new airfields. In the 1950s and '60s these became part of an Arctic War scenario. In 1917 there were fewer than 20 scientific stations in the Russian Arctic; by the end of 1945 there were 77, many of them providing regular schedules of weather data.

In the Cold War period weather stations were established on North Greenland, the Canadian archipelago and the most northerly Soviet islands. Starting in 1947, the US Air Force flew daily weather reconnaissance flights from Fairbanks, Alaska, across the Arctic basin to 85°N. The Russians, Americans and Canadians also established floating scientific stations that drifted about the Arctic basin with the pack ice and automatic weather stations (first used in wartime) that could be dropped in inaccessible

■ ■ ■

Here the northern lights are in a green phase. Great curtains and draperies of light move rapidly across the sky, turning and folding, intensifying and fading, in a constantly changing display. The brightest auroras are associated with complex, large-scale instabilities within the Earth's magnetosphere triggered by fluctuations in the 'solar wind'.

places. These transmitted weather data at scheduled intervals.

Antarctic meteorology was slower to take off. All the major expeditions took pains to record the weather, and ships in the Southern Ocean, including whaling fleets, made observations from which both forecasts and useful climatological studies were derived. However, up until World War II there were only two long-term stations in the whole Antarctic region. One was on Laurie Island, in the South Orkneys, set up by the Scottish explorer William Bruce during the *Scotia* expedition in 1903 and taken over by the Argentine government in 1904 when the expedition ended. The other was at Grytviken, a major whaling station north of the pack ice zone on South Georgia, where observations began in 1905.

In 1944 a British naval expedition, Operation Tabarin, established stations at Deception Island on the South Shetlands and at Port Lockroy on the western flank of the Antarctic Peninsula. From these small beginnings arose the post-war Falkland Islands Dependencies Survey, which then became the British Antarctic Survey, operating both bases and sledging parties to provide more continuous climatic records. New Zealand ran wartime stations on the Auckland Islands and Campbell, maintaining the latter after the war.

During the late 1940s and '50s Antarctica and the Southern Ocean islands received permanent French and Australian stations, and the International Geophysical Year 1957–59 saw the start of many more permanent stations dotted about the continent, including Amundsen-Scott at the South Pole itself. Since then there have usually been about a dozen stations on the Antarctic Peninsula, 20 or more on mainland Antarctica, and a scattering on the Southern Ocean islands (see frontispiece map). This is meagre coverage for so large an area, but enough to allow fairly reliable forecasting for field operations and provide material for long-term climatological studies.

Polar climatic research is currently of great value in establishing the norms and limits of world climate. We know that climate varies, that many human populations depend on climatic cycles for their livelihood, and that some live in regions where small, lasting changes of climate would destroy their way of life. We need to know how the worldwide climate machine works, to be alert to its changes, to understand what causes them, and to detect when changes

■ ■ ■

A polar meteorologist taking weather observations. Standard screens of this kind are used all over the world to ensure comparability of data. They are a standard height above the ground and almost identically instrumented.

shift from minor to major. Polar climates, we suspect, may be useful indicators of change: if the earth is warming or cooling, the changes may be detectable in polar regions before they appear elsewhere.

ATMOSPHERIC AND OZONE STUDIES

The polar regions are popularly thought to be pristine and pure, untouched by human hand. Polar air should be clean, shouldn't it? There's nothing going on in polar regions to make it dirty, is there? This was certainly true for both polar regions until the early part of this century, and since then the Antarctic has fared better than the Arctic. Regrettably, Arctic air is now unclean — nowhere as filthy as temperate air, but still polluted, at times and in patches, with industrial gases.

The first to notice this were Canadian and Alaskan bush pilots, who wondered about the layers of haze that sometimes hung about for days. Greenland hunters saw the sky taking on an ominous bronze tinge. Canadian Indians smelt smoke that was not from their familiar wood fires. Aircraft fitted with sampling devices flew through the haze, and atmospheric chemists studied the samples. It became clear that all these phenomena were linked: the Arctic atmosphere is invaded from time to time by smoke from industrial areas on the Arctic fringe or beyond.

It became clear too that the Arctic atmosphere is peculiarly disposed to receive and hold pollution. In winter especially the atmosphere is made up of stable layers. The pollution, a mixture of industrial gases and fine particles, invades the layers, finding its own level and spreading like very thin filling in a sandwich. No turbulence disperses it and no rain washes it out, so it persists and spreads. Eventually it has to fall somewhere, probably onto Arctic lands and into the rivers and ocean. It is unlikely to improve the Arctic. Whether or not it does measurable harm remains to be seen.

Chemical analysis has shown that some of the pollution appearing over Alaska has distinctive signatures of heavy metals, pointing to North Siberian refineries as the source. Continuing studies of upper wind patterns and monitoring of the pollution itself have made it possible to pinpoint the source of almost every haze 'event'. Blame can be apportioned and offenders could be urged to clean up their emissions, an expensive but by no means impossible task.

Does it matter if haze sometimes veils the Arctic sun? The Inuit think it does, and it is their atmosphere that is being polluted. International cooperation is needed to see that it stops.

There is nothing especially polar about upper-atmosphere studies, but it so happens that a phenomenon of great general interest has been highlighted in a polar region: the ozone hole over Antarctica. Polar scientists were the first to spot the phenomenon and draw attention to its possible implications. All scientists now use it as an example of the value of routine observations.

In the high reaches of the upper atmosphere, far above the weather, the several gases that make up the atmosphere are present in minute amounts. Thin though they are, and completely invisible, they form a veil which has useful properties. The veil filters the incoming sunlight, absorbing some of its energy, especially energy at the ultraviolet (UV) end of the spectrum. It also retains some of the heat energy (at the infrared or IR end of the spectrum) reflected from Earth's surface. In this respect it acts rather like a blanket, keeping the heat in. Different gases are responsible for these two functions. Ozone (a special form of oxygen) is the filter, while carbon dioxide, methane and several other gases contribute to the blanket effect.

During the early 1980's routine observations of incoming radiation at Halley station disclosed a sudden loss of ozone above Antarctica every spring. Scientists felt it wise to explore further. The loss, monitored eventually through international cooperation involving satellites and high-flying aircraft, was found to be matched by a high incidence of an alien gas, chlorine monoxide, which should not have been there at all.

The presence of so much chlorine at the top of the atmosphere was ascribed to chlorofluorocarbons (CFCs), man-made industrial gases used in refrigeration, aerosols and plastic foams. These rise into the upper atmosphere and react with the ozone to form chlorine monoxide. Their damaging effect over Antarctica during early spring is due to a build-up during the sunless months and a sudden depletion of ozone when the sun returns.

An ozone hole over Antarctica each spring is not in itself a serious matter — it is not a first indication that the sky is falling in. But it is a warning that CFCs are eating into the ozone layer all around the world. If ozone continues to disappear faster than it is formed, the protective veil will thin and we shall all experience higher levels of UV.

Ultraviolet radiation in low doses gives us a healthy tan and helps us to maintain vitamin D balance. In higher doses it can be damaging, leading to sunburn and more serious skin conditions. Other animals, plants and bacteria are also sensitive to UV, although it is readily absorbed by thick cloud or a thin layer of water. We experience stronger-than-usual UV when we live under constantly clear skies, especially in mountains or on high plateaus where the atmosphere above us is thinner. People who live in such places tend to have a higher-than-usual incidence of skin cancer and cataract (opacity of the lens of the eye). If the ozone layer thinned, these conditions might become more general, or need to be guarded against more carefully.

■ OZONE OVER ANTARCTICA ■

Ozone, made up of three linked atoms of oxygen, is generated constantly from gaseous oxygen (made up of two linked atoms) wherever high-energy sources are close at hand. For example, it occurs around electrical equipment, where sparks provide the energy input, and during rainstorms, when lightning penetrates the lower atmosphere. It also forms in the uppermost layers of the atmosphere, when strong ultraviolet light from the sun impinges on it. In the upper atmosphere conditions are right for ozone to form and also for it to be broken down. So the ozone layer constantly forms and re-forms.

Over the polar regions a high-level belt of circular winds (the polar vortex) tends to concentrate the ozone into cap-like layers. This effect is especially marked over Antarctica because the vortex effect there is stronger. The ozone layer can be detected by spectrophotometry, which is done routinely at stations all over the world, including those in the polar regions. When plenty of ozone is present in the upper atmosphere, much of the expected UV radiation in sunlight is absorbed by it and is therefore missing from the spectrum. A sudden increase in incoming UV means that the veil has become ineffective — the ozone has disappeared and more of the UV is pouring through.

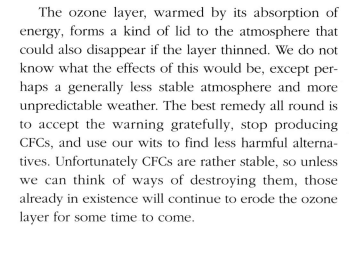

The ozone layer, warmed by its absorption of energy, forms a kind of lid to the atmosphere that could also disappear if the layer thinned. We do not know what the effects of this would be, except perhaps a generally less stable atmosphere and more unpredictable weather. The best remedy all round is to accept the warning gratefully, stop producing CFCs, and use our wits to find less harmful alternatives. Unfortunately CFCs are rather stable, so unless we can think of ways of destroying them, those already in existence will continue to erode the ozone layer for some time to come.

EARTH SCIENCES

Naturalists on early polar expeditions, who often included geology in their background, brought back mineral samples and rock specimens. A few provided excellent field notes, including sketches of rock formations, on which later scientists were able to build. There was practical interest in discovering precious metals, ores and coal. But there was also real interest in fossils, and in sedimentary deposits and other evidence of past ages, for geologists of the 18th and 19th centuries were foremost in propounding theories of evolution and world history, and sought evidence wherever they could find it.

Almost every modern polar scientific expedition has included geologists; indeed many have been geological expeditions. Even scientists in other disciplines accept that knowledge of earth structure is fundamental to an understanding of the polar regions, and geologists were among the first to pro-

■ ■ ■

The Clean Air Building at Amundsen-Scott station, South Pole. Set up some distance from the main station to avoid contamination, the building contains instruments which analyse the composition of South Polar air. Cumulative records indicate rising levels of pollution.

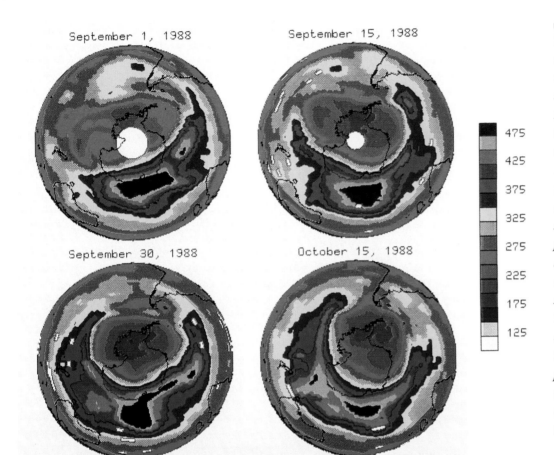

September 1, 1988   September 15, 1988

September 30, 1988   October 15, 1988

475
425
375
325
275
225
175
125

■ ■ ■

These four images, recorded by the Total Ozone Mapping Spectrometer on US Nimbus-7 statellite, show the development of an ozone hole between 1 September and 15 October 1988, at the onset of the Antarctic spring. The hole appears purple in the central blue areas. The white areas are not significant — they simply indicate 'no data'. The ozone layer is constantly formed and broken down by natural processes, but the presence in the upper atmosphere of CFCs currently favours breakdown.

vide time scales against which biological and glaciological events could be measured. Geological studies in polar regions have paid off handsomely, although not always in the most obvious ways.

Returns from minerals have been mixed. Siberia, which has been most thoroughly and systematically explored, has yielded rich deposits of gold, silver, tin, copper, nickel and many other precious or valuable metals, together with the fuels needed for smelting and energy production. Norwegians and Russians continue to mine coal on Svalbard. Canadians, Alaskans and Greenlanders, having explored their northlands well although perhaps less exhaustively, have felt less obliged to exploit what they have found. They have invested in and drawn on sources of oil and natural gas but on little else. Other minerals have been mined, but only briefly, and only when they were cheaply available. Currently there is little mining in the North American Arctic. At the moment, ores can be obtained more cheaply elsewhere.

Antarctic minerals are something of an enigma and likely to remain so. The Antarctic Peninsula, geologically a continuation of the Andes, might be expected to contain the mineral wealth of the Andes. However, fairly intensive surveys over several decades have failed to reveal even a fraction of that wealth in the ice-free areas exposed to geologists' hammers. Continental Antarctica has huge stocks of coal, of varying ages and qualities, exposed in the mountains of southern Victoria Land. Shackleton's polar party discovered coal alongside the Beardmore Glacier in 1908, and there was fossil-bearing coal in the geological samples carried by Scott's party on their ill-fated return from the Pole in 1911. However, Antarctic coal lies far from any practical means of transport and even further from any market. The world will need to be very short of coal before anyone mines it.

There are other mineral deposits in Antarctica, at least in the 2 per cent of it which is not covered in ice. In the Australian sector, for example, there are precious metal ores that, were they elsewhere, might just be regarded as exploitable. In the sea bed offshore there is evidence of hydrocarbons. Common sense dictates that so vast a continent is likely to have all kinds of mineral wealth, but distance and climate make it extremely improbable that anyone will exploit it in the foreseeable future.

Yet earth scientists have not wasted their time in polar regions. Using dozens of different techniques, from seismology to sea bed drilling, they have worked out the structure and history of Earth. Antarctica was one of the keys to understanding continental drift. We now know that the mainland occupied a central position in Gondwana, the southern half of the original land mass from which all the southern continents derive; that the sea bed all around Antarctica is expanding; and that available rocks on the mainland match those of Australia, Africa and southern India, even down to containing similar fossils. All this evidence was needed to convince the world that Wegener's concept of continental drift was basically right. As Darwin freed us from the concept of fixed, immutable species, so Wegener freed us to model a world in which even the continents are on the move.

UNDERSTANDING ICE AND SNOW

The term 'glaciology' was first used in the mid-19th century to describe the study of glaciers, but the extensive discipline we know today, covering all manifestations of snow and ice, barely existed before World War II. The earliest glaciologists worked in temperate regions, on transient snow fields and Alpine glaciers. Only a few enterprising or wealthy ones managed to spend time in the Arctic, and even fewer reached the Antarctic. Physicist Charles Wright and geologist Raymond Priestley, who served with Scott's South Polar expedition, were well ahead of their time in publishing a 'glaciology' expedition report in 1922.

Compared with other disciplines, glaciology may seem dispensable. Who really needs to know about ice and snow? Yet glaciologists are curiously practical people who do far more than watch snowflakes falling. Access to polar regions gave them welcome new perspectives on their subject. From studying the properties of ice and snow, and the mechanisms of ice in motion, they graduated to calculating world budgets of snow and ice, cataloguing Earth's ice fields, summing up their bulk and turnover, exploring their history and working out their extent in ages past. In these contexts sea ice is no less important than land ice, although it is often the concern of oceanographers rather than glaciologists.

All these studies remain important, for snow and ice are still major forces in the world. More people than ever before make contact with them in daily life. We travel over them, land heavy aircraft on them, drive ships through them. We lay pipelines and build houses on them. Entrepreneurs seek ways of selling large chunks of them to the Arabs or Californians for drinking water. We need to understand how ice and snow work, for the snow and ice fields that dominate the far north in winter, and the far south all the year round, may spread to affect even more of us. The future of much of the human race could depend on our ability to cope with a colder world, where ice and snow are more prominent than at present.

During the past few years glaciologists have placed their discipline in the forefront of studies relating to climatic change. Changes in climate bring about changes in the volume and extent of glaciers, and in the extent of annual sea ice and the thickness of perennial sea ice. Polar glaciologists are now working to discover precisely how climates and ice fields interact. The world's ice sheets contain information about past climates, information we urgently need to know.

These inputs could not have been better timed, for they coincide with a period of universal concern about man-induced climatic changes. Glaciologists are providing readable evidence, and seemingly the most accurate, on two key subjects: climatic variations over the last few tens of thousands of years, and changes in the atmosphere, including those brought about by human activities.

POLAR ECOSYSTEMS AND THEIR MANAGEMENT

Polar ecology is the study of polar organisms and their relationships with each other and with the environments in which they live. The principles of polar ecology are not different from those of ecology elsewhere, but studying and understanding them is often somewhat simpler. For land and freshwater ecosystems at least, fewer species are involved, the environments are less complex, and there are correspondingly fewer relationships and interactions to take into account. Several ecologists who helped to found the science during the 1920s and '30s spent formative weeks or months in polar regions. Alaska, Canada and Svalbard were excellent training grounds.

Simple ecosystems may be good for ecologists, but less good for the plants and animals involved. Simple ecosystems are more readily upset. Severe or hazardous conditions on land favour only a few species, and few species means a limited number of pathways in the food web and instability in the ecosystem as a whole. When snow stays on the ground until late spring, migrant birds arrive to find their nest sites and food supplies unavailable, and they may fail to breed. A bad year for lemmings is a bad year for lemming predators too, for there are not enough alternative kinds of prey to feed them; skuas, owls and foxes must go elsewhere or starve.

Human impact on polar ecosystems can be devastating. If we disturb a complex ecosystem, it usually has the capacity to return to at least an appearance of normalcy. If we clear space in a temperate forest, within months the breach will have started to heal; several dozen species will have moved in to fill the gap, and a succession of plants and dependent animals will replace each other in the ensuing months and years. If we drop rubbish, in time it will rust, rot or simply disappear under a cover of vegetation. Polar ecosystems are more fragile. Cut a hole in tundra, and months or years will pass before there is even a semblance of healing. Leave rubbish and it will degrade very, very slowly, and covering will take longer still. In the polar regions any mark we make, any rubbish we drop, will be there for the span of a human lifetime at least.

Some of the slow processes of polar terrestrial ecosystems were studied in detail during the International Biological Programme (1964–74), a worldwide stock-take of biological ecosystems. The Tundra Biome sub-programme included several Arctic sites and some on the Antarctic fringe. Since then, industrial developments in the north and the opening of more scientific bases in the south have encouraged further studies, relating not only to the biology of these ecosystems but to their management. These have helped to clarify at least one issue on which both scientists and non-scientists hold strong views: if we use polar lands for any purpose, effectively we destroy them. Any disturbance causes irrevocable damage. Instant repairs like landscaping and tree-planting, feasible elsewhere, are simply not possible in polar regions.

Degradation of the polar regions is no more or

■ ■ ■

Oceanographers lower an array of buoys and recording instruments into the Weddell Sea, Antarctica. The array, hundreds of metres long, will record currents, temperatures and other variables at different depths in the ocean for a period of a few weeks. Then it will be recovered and the accumulated data analysed.

less serious than our everyday destruction of temperate grasslands by building roads and cities on them. However, it requires less effort to damage tundra; it is much easier to damage it casually, just by walking on it or driving a truck over it. This realisation has prompted strong reactions and controversy among conservationists. For some it is a clear indication that we must stop using polar lands altogether. Extremists apply this rigorously to Antarctica, and would like to

■ ■ ■

*A polar bear being
weighed, measured,
examined and tagged by
zoologists as part of an
international field study
throughout the Arctic.
The bear has been
tranquillized with a
drugged dart.*

apply it to some of the less spoiled areas of the Arctic
too. If we cannot use these places without destroying
them, they say, let us declare them off limits to the
whole human race and leave them strictly alone.

Others with less extreme views are in favour of
closing large areas of both polar regions but allowing
development in others. Some want to prohibit such
obviously disruptive activities as mining, but allow scientific research. Some want to ban tourists; others recognize the right of anybody to visit the polar regions,
but would like to restrict tourism to particular areas or
routes. A few believe that tourism should be encouraged on the grounds that good tourists are responsible people, perhaps more responsible than scientists
have been, and a positive force in protecting what

they have come a long way to see. Management of
polar regions is a lively field of research and discussion, with many practical consequences.

Polar and sub-polar marine ecosystems are closer
in complexity and stability to their temperate counterparts, which is fortunate, for sealing, whaling and
fishing have already dealt massive insults to them and
further exploitation of them is planned. Marine ecologists are now well aware of the issues, and better
equipped than they once were to draw up sensible
regulations and set realistic catch limits. There is now
backing legislation, both national and international,
to ensure some degree of control over the exploiters.

■ ■ ■

*An array of plastic
sampling bottles
containing sea water.
Lowered by winches into
the ocean, the bottles open
and close on signals from
the ship, capturing samples
of water from different*

*known depths. Analysis of
their chemical content helps
scientists to determine the
origins and history of the
water masses that make up
the polar oceans.*

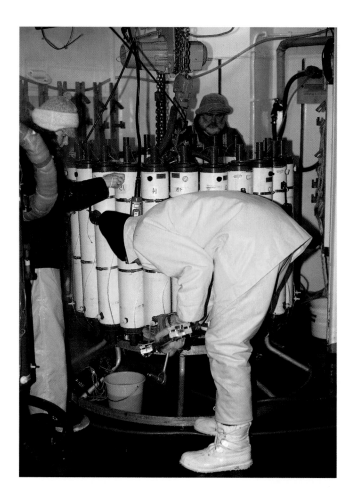

■ ■ ■

Part of a rubbish dump outside a Chilean Antarctic station. Until recently almost every station accumulated rubbish. Now, under pressure from tourists and environmental groups, stations are being encouraged to clean up.

This has not prevented the ecological devastation by over-fishing of some sub-polar seas even in recent times, but the symptoms are clear to all, and there is every hope that they will eventually recover.

A healthy sign of progress is the increasing involvement of local people in protecting their stocks of exploitable animals. In the North American Arctic both terrestrial and marine hunting have for many years been controlled by federal or provincial government agencies. Bringing them more into the the responsibility of local communities is part of a wider policy of involving native peoples in government. Antarctica is less fortunate in this respect. It has no local people, and until recently had little effective legislation to protect its stocks of exploitable animals. The Antarctic Treaty (see Chapter 10) has provided plenty of legislation, well-intentioned but cumbersome in operation. Although it lacks the understanding that local people can bring to management of their own concerns, it may still be the best legislation and the best protection available for a remote and vulnerable continent.

10

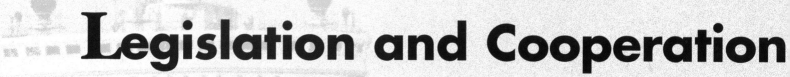

Legislation and Cooperation

Within the span of a human lifetime the role of the polar regions in human affairs has changed dramatically. For many centuries they were the forgotten fringes of the inhabited earth. Now they are regions that nobody with political aspirations or responsibilities can afford to forget. In curious and unexpected ways each has achieved its own political importance. The polar regions have come in from the cold, to play, if not a starring role, at least a substantial supporting part in world affairs.

None of the early polar explorers, even up to the first decades of this century, foresaw political futures for the polar regions. A few visualized air routes across the Arctic and possibly some mineral exploitation. Antarctica was a continent to be explored and, like any other new area, exploited if possible. Some US political commentators during the 1920s and '30s wondered if Antarctica could be internationalized, possibly on the Svalbard pattern. The 'owner' nations would have none of it, and proceeded instead to a full-scale colonial carve-up that left unclaimed only the difficult section south of the Pacific Ocean.

World War II and the Cold War brought the Arctic into the limelight. At the same time more and more nations began to take an interest in Antarctica. Until the mid-1950s Antarctica was still a continent for colonization. In the late 1950s, at the height of the Cold War, it might have become a battleground, or at least a site for testing nuclear weapons. But instead, quite suddenly, it became something different and very much more important. It became a continent for peaceful international cooperation, and a possible model for peace and accord in the Arctic.

INTERNATIONAL GEOPHYSICAL YEAR

The internationalization of Antarctica arose unexpectedly from a routine effort in scientific cooperation, the International Geophysical Year 1957–58. Previous international 'scientific years', for example the first and second International Polar Years of 1882–83 and 1932–33, had come and gone without lasting political effect. They involved several countries setting up polar or sub-polar stations to provide a network of scientific observatories at which matching and simultaneous observations could be

taken. There had been good cooperation, but nothing of permanent international consequence had resulted. Nor was anything unusual or lasting expected in the early 1950s when scientists began planning a new international year.

They chose 1957–58, as a period of lively sunspot activity when the polar regions would become key areas for geophysical research. It was made an 'international year', rather than a third 'polar year', so that the tropical belt and certain meridians outside the polar zones could be included. However, in its planning the International Council of Scientific Unions, which includes all the world's leading scientific institutions, emphasized the importance of Antarctica as a region of great geographical and geophysical interest.

It soon became clear that at least 40 nations would be involved in the IGY, of which about a dozen — including the USA and USSR — would send expeditions to Antarctica. The question arose as to how they might be accommodated in a continent where issues of sovereignty were both unsettled and prickly. Britain, Chile and Argentina were quarrelling over ownership of the Peninsula, and France, Norway, New Zealand and Australia all claimed their swathes of the main continent. The USA and USSR, which at that time agreed on very little, held curiously similar views on Antarctica: neither made claims, nor respected the claims of others, but both declared strong interests arising from earlier exploration. Each was watching the other closely to see that neither gained a strategic advantage in Antarctica. Both were watched with suspicion by 'owner' nations, who felt their claims weakened by American and Soviet free-wheeling.

The sovereignty issue was neatly sidestepped. At the 1955 conference of the planning body, Comité Spécial de l'Année Géophysique Internationale (CSAGI) in Paris, all countries agreed that, in the interests of science, discussions of sovereignty would be suspended for the duration of the IGY. For its time — at the height of the Cold War, and with Argentina, Britain and Chile bristling — this was a remarkable diplomatic achievement.

Furthermore it worked, although it did not entirely disarm suspicion. IGY began officially on 1 July 1957. In the months beforehand the Australians were dismayed to find the Soviets building three substantial bases in 'their' territory. The Americans moved into New Zealand's Ross Dependency, and upstaged everyone politically as well as scientifically by establishing a station at the South Pole. New Zealanders and Australians also opened continental stations. The British, Argentinians, Chileans, Norwegians and French established new stations or refurbished existing ones as IGY observatories. And new Belgian, South African and Japanese stations appeared along the mainland coasts.

Suspicions were forgotten when everyone got down to work. Logistic and scientific cooperation throughout the IGY was excellent, and by every possible standard of science and human relationships it was a resoundingly successful year. When the year ended on 31 December 1958, everyone involved was already saying 'Why not continue?'

THE ANTARCTIC TREATY

Plans for possible continuation had of course been discussed beforehand, particularly when it seemed likely that the Soviet Union was there to stay. While Soviet stations remained, neither the United States nor Australia wanted to leave. Similarly, US stations in the Ross Dependency encouraged New Zealand to stay, and both countries benefited from the many opportunities for cooperation that arose. France was already committed to long-term studies, as were Britain, Chile and Argentina.

The political initiative was American. While the IGY was still in operation, a note from the US government dated 2 May 1958 invited the 11 other governments participating in Antarctic research to join in developing a treaty that would effectively prolong scientific cooperation indefinitely. The response was prompt and positive. An initial meeting was set up in Washington in June 1958, and there followed almost a year of tough, patient bargaining, in which the US delegation, led by Paul Daniels, played a leading role. By May 1959 a treaty had been drafted, and representatives of the 12 governments signed it on 1 December 1959. By 23 June 1961 the last of the governments had ratified it, plus one more — Poland — that already qualified for entry. So the Antarctic Treaty came into force.

A simple document that anyone can follow, the Antarctic Treaty starts with a preamble listing the 12 nations that originally drew it up, and defines a major point of recognition or objective, that Antarctica shall '...continue for ever to be used exclusively for peaceful purposes and shall not become the scene or object of international discord'. There follow 14 articles prescribing many features important for the maintenance of peace and the promotion of science.

Its main points can be summarized as follows. Under Article I the Treaty governments agree to use Antarctica for peaceful purposes only, and to limit the use of military forces to science and logistics. They endorse freedom to pursue science there, subject to

■ ■ ■

RRS Bransfield, *research ship and transport of the British Antarctic Survey, offloading stores at the Signy Island station. Polar stations are usually replenished in summer, where possible by sea.*

The Antarctic Treaty

The Governments of Argentina, Australia, Belgium, Chile, the French Republic, Japan, New Zealand, Norway, the Union of South Africa, the Union of Soviet Socialist Republics, the United Kingdom of Great Britain and Northern Ireland, and the United States of America,

Recognizing that it is in the interest of all mankind that Antarctica shall continue for ever to be used exclusively for peaceful purposes and shall not become the scene or object of international discord;

Acknowledging the substantial contributions to scientific knowledge resulting from international co-operation in scientific investigation in Antarctica;

Convinced that the establishment of a firm foundation for the continuation and development of such co-operation on the basis of freedom of scientific investigation in Antarctica as applied during the International Geophysical Year accords with the interests of science and the progress of all mankind;

Convinced also that a treaty ensuring the use of Antarctica for peaceful purposes only and the continuance of international harmony in Antarctica will further the purposes and principles embodied in the Charter of the United Nations;

Have agreed as follows:

Article I

1. Antarctica shall be used for peaceful purposes only. There shall be prohibited, inter alia, *any measure of a military nature, such as the establishment of military bases and fortifications, the carrying out of military manoeuvres, as well as the testing of any type of weapon.*

2. The present Treaty shall not prevent the use of military personnel or equipment for scientific research or for any other peaceful purpose.

Article II

Freedom of scientific investigation in Antarctica and co-operation toward that end, as applied during the International Geophysical Year, shall continue, subject to the provisions of the present Treaty.

Article III

1. In order to promote international co-operation in scientific investigation in Antarctica, as provided for in Article II of the present Treaty, the Contracting Parties agree that, to the greatest extent feasible and practicable:
(a) information regarding plans for scientific programs in Antarctica shall be exchanged to permit maximum economy of and efficiency of operations;
(b) scientific personnel shall be exchanged in Antarctica between expeditions and stations;
(c) scientific observations and results from Antarctica shall be exchanged and made freely available.

Article IV

1. Nothing contained in the present Treaty shall be interpreted as:
(a) a renunciation by any Contracting Party of previously asserted rights of or claims to territorial sovereignty in Antarctica;
(b) a renunciation or diminution by any Contracting Party of any basis of claim to territorial sovereignty in Antarctica which it may have whether as a result of its activities or those of of its nationals in Antarctica, or otherwise;
(c) prejudicing the position of any Contracting Party as regards its recognition or non-recognition of any other State's rights of or claim or basis of claim to territorial sovereignty in Antarctica.
2. No acts or activities taking place while the present Treaty is in force shall constitute a basis for asserting, supporting or denying a claim to territorial sovereignty in Antarctica or create any rights of sovereignty in

Antarctica. No new claim, or enlargement of an existing claim, to territorial sovereignty in Antarctica shall be asserted while the present Treaty is in force.

Article V

1. Any nuclear explosions in Antarctica and the disposal there of radioactive waste material shall be prohibited.

2. In the event of the conclusion of international agreements concerning the use of nuclear energy, including nuclear explosions and the disposal of radioactive waste material, to which all of the Contracting Parties whose representatives are entitled to participate in the meetings provided for under Article IX are parties, the rules established under such agreements shall apply in Antarctica.

Article VI

The provisions of the present Treaty shall apply to the area south of 60° South Latitude, including all ice shelves, but nothing in the present Treaty shall prejudice or in any way affect the rights, or the exercise of the rights, of any State under international law with regard to the high seas within that area.

Article VII

1. In order to promote the objectives and ensure the observance of the provisions of the present Treaty, each Contracting Party whose representatives are entitled to participate in the meetings referred to in Article IX of the Treaty shall have the right to designate observers to carry out any inspection provided for by the present Article. Observers shall be nationals of the Contracting Parties which designate them. The names of observers shall be communicated to every other Contracting Party having the right to designate observers, and like notice shall be given of the termination of their appointment.

2. Each observer designated in accordance with the provisions of paragraph 1 of this Article shall have complete freedom of access at any time to any or all areas of Antarctica.

3. All areas of Antarctica, including all stations, installations and equipment within those areas, and all ships and aircraft at points of discharging or embarking cargoes or personnel in Antarctica, shall be open at all times to inspection by any observers designated in accordance with paragraph 1 of this Article.

4. Aerial observation may be carried out at any time over any or all areas of Antarctica by any of the Contracting Parties having the right to designate observers.

5. Each Contracting Party shall, at the time when the present Treaty enters into force for it, inform the other Contracting Parties, and thereafter shall give them notice in advance, of

(a) all expeditions to and within Antarctica, on the part of its ships or nationals, and all expeditions to Antarctica organized in or proceeding from its territory;

(b) all stations in Antarctica occupied by its nationals; and

(c) any military personnel or equipment intended to be introduced by it into Antarctica subject to the conditions prescribed in paragraph 2 of Article I of the present Treaty.

Article VIII

1. In order to facilitate the exercise of their functions under the present Treaty, and without prejudice to the respective positions of the Contracting Parties relating to jurisdiction over all other persons in Antarctica, observers designated under paragraph 1 of Article VII and scientific personnel exchanged under subparagraph 1(b) of Article III of the Treaty, and members of the staffs accompanying any such persons, shall be subject only to the jurisdiction of the Contracting Party of which they are nationals in respect of all acts or omissions occurring while they are in Antarctica for the purpose of exercising their functions.

2. Without prejudice to the provisions of paragraph 1 of this Article, and pending the adoption of measures in pursuance of sub-paragraph 1(e) of Article IX, the Contracting Parties concerned in any case of dispute with regard to the exercise of jurisdiction in Antarctica shall immediately consult together with a view to reaching a mutually acceptable solution.

Article IX

1. Representatives of the Contracting Parties named in the preamble to the present Treaty shall meet at the City of Canberra within two months after the date of entry into force of the Treaty, and thereafter at suitable intervals and places, for the purpose of exchanging information, consulting together on matters of common interest pertaining to Antarctica, and formulating and considering, and recommending to their Governments, measures in furtherance of the principles and objectives of the Treaty, including measures regarding:

(a) use of Antarctica for peaceful purposes only;

(b) facilitation of scientific research in Antarctica;

(c) facilitation of international scientific co-operation in Antarctica;

(d) facilitation of the exercise of the rights of inspection provided for in Article VII of the Treaty

(e) questions relating to the exercise of jurisdiction in Antarctica;

(f) preservation and conservation of living resources in Antarctica.

2. Each Contracting Party which has become a party to the present Treaty by accession under Article XIII shall be entitled to appoint representatives to participate in the meetings referred to in paragraph 1 of the present Article, during such times as that Contracting Party demonstrates its interest in Antarctica by conducting substantial research activity there, such as the establishment of a scientific station or the despatch of a scientific expedition.

3. Reports from the observers referred to in Article VII of the present Treaty shall be transmitted to the representatives of the Contracting Parties participating in the meetings referred to in paragraph 1 of the present Article.

4. The measures referred to in paragraph 1 of this Article shall become effective when approved by all the Contracting Parties whose representatives were entitled to participate in the meetings held to consider those measures.

5. Any or all of the rights established in the present Treaty may be exercised as from the date of entry into force of the Treaty whether or not any measures facilitating the exercise of such rights have been proposed, considered or approved as provided in this Article.

Article X

Each of the Contracting Parties undertakes to exert appropriate efforts, consistent with the Charter of the United Nations, to the end that no one engages in any activity in Antarctica contrary to the principles or purposes of the present Treaty.

Article XI

1. If any dispute arises between two or more of the Contracting Parties concerning the interpretation or application of the present Treaty, those Contracting Parties shall consult among themselves with a view to having the dispute resolved by negotiation, inquiry, mediation, conciliation, arbitration, judicial settlement or other peaceful means of their own choice.

2. Any dispute of this character not so resolved shall, with the consent, in each case, of all parties to the dispute, be referred to the International Court of Justice for settlement; but failure to reach agreement on reference to the International Court shall not absolve parties to the dispute from the responsibility of continuing to seek to resolve it by any of the various peaceful means referred to in paragraph 1 of this Article.

Article XII

1. (a) The present Treaty may be modified or amended at any time by unanimous agreement of the

Contracting Parties whose representatives are entitled to participate in the meetings provided for under Article IX. Any such modification or amendment shall enter into force when the depositary Government has received notice from all such Contracting Parties that they have ratified it.

(b) Such modification or amendment shall thereafter enter into force as to any other Contracting Party when notice of ratification by it has been received by the depositary Government. Any such Contracting Party from which no notice of ratification is received within a period of two years from the date of entry into force of the modification or amendment in accordance with the provision of sub-paragraph 1(a) of this Article shall be deemed to have withdrawn from the present Treaty on the date of the expiration of such period.

2. (a) If after the expiration of thirty years from the date of entry into force of the present Treaty, any of the Contracting Parties whose representatives are entitled to participate in the meetings provided for under Article IX so requests by a communication addressed to the depositary Government, a Conference of all the Contracting Parties shall be held as soon as practicable to review the operation of the Treaty.

(b) Any modification or amendment to the present Treaty which is approved at such a Conference by a majority of the Contracting Parties there represented, including a majority of those whose representatives are entitled to participate in the meetings provided for under Article IX, shall be communicated by the depositary Government to all Contracting Parties immediately after the termination of the Conference and shall enter into force in accordance with the provisions of paragraph 1 of the present Article.

(c) If any such modification or amendment has not entered into force in accordance with the provisions of sub-paragraph 1(a) of this Article within a period of two years after the date of its communication to all the Contracting Parties, any Contracting Party may at any time after the expiration of that period give notice to the depositary Government of its withdrawal from the present Treaty; and such withdrawal shall take effect two years after the receipt of the notice by the depositary Government.

Article XIII

1. The present Treaty shall be subject to ratification by the signatory States. It shall be open for accession by any State which is a Member of the United Nations, or by any other State which may be invited to accede to the Treaty with the consent of all the Contracting Parties whose representatives are entitled to participate in the meetings provided for under Article IX of the Treaty.

2. Ratification of or accession to the present Treaty shall be effected by each State in accordance with its constitutional processes.

3. Instruments of ratification and instruments of accession shall be deposited with the Government of the United States of America, hereby designated as the depositary Government.

4. The depositary Government shall inform all signatory and acceding States of the date of each deposit of an instrument of ratification or accession, and the date of entry into force of the Treaty and of any modification or amendment thereto.

5. Upon the deposit of instruments of ratification by all the signatory States, the present Treaty shall enter into force for those States and for States which have deposited instruments of accession. Thereafter the Treaty shall enter into force for any acceding State upon the deposit of its instruments of accession.

6. The present Treaty shall be registered by the depositary Government pursuant to Article 102 of the Charter of the United Nations.

Article XIV

The present Treaty, done in the English, French, Russian and Spanish languages, each version being equally authentic, shall be deposited in the archives of the Government of the United States of America, which shall transmit duly certified copies thereof to the Governments of the signatory and acceding States.

the Treaty (Article II), and agree to free exchanges of plans, information and personnel (Article III). They confirm that membership of the Treaty does not in any way affect their attitudes to their own or to anybody else's claims to ownership of territory, and that new claims will not be made while the Treaty is in force (Article IV).

Article V requires Treaty governments to prohibit nuclear explosions and the dumping of nuclear waste, and confirms that other international agreements about nuclear energy will apply to Antarctica if all consultative parties (see below) agree on them. Article VI limits the Treaty to the area south of 60°S, although the rights of members on the high seas within the Treaty area are unaffected. Article VII provides for members to inspect each other's stations and facilities in Antarctica, and requires them to keep each other informed of plans. Article VIII confirms that observers or scientists visiting other stations remain under the jurisdiction of their own governments.

Article IX provides for periodic meetings of representatives to exchange information and formulate new measures for promoting the aims of the Treaty, which will be recommended to their respective governments. Participation in the meetings is open to any party that 'demonstrates its interest in Antarctica by conducting substantial research activity there, such as the establishment of a scientific station or the despatch of a scientific expedition'. Governments that accede to the Treaty but are not active in Antarctica are 'contracting parties'. Those that qualify by participation become 'consultative parties', and form an inner circle of decision-makers within the Treaty organization.

Article X prohibits activities that are contrary to the Treaty, and Article XI provides ways for resolving disputes under the Treaty. Article XII makes provision for amending the Treaty, specifying that a reviewing conference will be held 30 years from the Treaty's accession if a consultative member so requests, and specifies how modifications or amendments may be made to the Treaty at that time. It also provides ways for members to withdraw from the Treaty.

Article XIII makes it clear that membership is open to any state which is a member of the United Nations, or to non-members by agreement of the consultative parties. Article XIV, the final article, specifies the four languages in which the Treaty is valid, and names the United States of America as the depositary government.

The IGY was followed in 1959 by International Geophysical Cooperation Year (IGCY), a holding operation while the diplomats argued. The Comité Spécial that had steered the IGY became the Special Committee for Antarctic Research, which after 1961 became the permanent Scientific Committee for Antarctic Research (SCAR). A non-government body of scientists with a base in Cambridge, England, SCAR coordinates scientific research in Antarctica and is constantly available to advise the Treaty nations.

AFTER THE TREATY

The Antarctic Treaty was a start. It was sufficient to keep expeditions in the field and diplomats around their tables, backed and prompted by scientists. Among the signatory countries (soon to be joined by more) any initial suspicions of land-grabbing and politicking soon fell away. Between members of the different expeditions there had virtually always been good feeling, cooperation, and a strong professional interest in each other's equipment and ways of coping with the environment. The Treaty did nothing to destroy this and much to encourage it. International cooperation — full, unstinting, unselfconscious and genuine — became completely commonplace.

The first Consultative Meeting was held in Canberra, Australia, in July 1961, and the second in Buenos Aires, Argentina, in July 1962. Since then meetings have been held approximately every other year, working through the countries in alphabetical order. At each meeting, representatives of the consultative parties discuss pre-arranged matters and decide, by concensus, on issues to be recommended to their governments. Once accepted by the governments, these become part of the Treaty system. Each meeting produces a new crop of recommendations, on matters ranging from conservation to facilitation of scientific cooperation, from meteorology and telecommunications to transport and logistics.

Conservation of living resources has provided the Treaty powers with important exercises in management, for these are the most likely resources to be exploited and therefore most urgently in need of management guidelines. 'Agreed measures' within

A party of tourists on the Antarctic Peninsula. Currently, about 3,000 tourists visit Antarctica each year, usually well-organized and controlled by responsible tour operators.

the Treaty were drawn up to cover conservation on land, and in 1972 the Treaty gave rise to a Convention for the Conservation of Antarctic Seals, followed in 1980 by a Convention on the Conservation of Antarctic Marine Living Resources. Between them these provided guidelines and agreed procedures for exploitation and monitoring. Although Southern Ocean seals are not currently exploited, stocks of fish and krill are. The Commission for the Conservation of Antarctic Marine Living Resources, a management body set up under the Convention, maintains a close watch on commercial catches from

its headquarters in Hobart, Tasmania. Whales, and what little whaling remains in Antarctic waters, continue to be monitored by the International Whaling Commission, an unrelated body that predated the Treaty by many years.

A third convention, drawn up in 1988, tackled the more difficult question of mineral resource management. Discussions on this issue began in 1982, and delegates attended eleven meetings, extending over six years, to draw up a Convention on the Regulation of Antarctic Mineral Resource Activities. This convention lays down guidelines and safety regulations that would enable mining or exploitation to occur, but with stringent controls and maximal safeguards for the environment.

During those six years, however, Antarctica became a target for environmental groups, which seek to protect it from the kind of despoliation that has adversely affected every other continent. Strongly opposed to mining or minerals development, the environmentalists regard the Convention on the Regulation of Antarctic Mineral Resource Activities quite simply as an invitation to exploiters. Their arguments have persuaded a number of governments — notably France, Australia and New Zealand — not to ratify it. The Convention is thus unlikely to take its place alongside those relating to seals and marine living resources, and the Treaty system has suffered its first major setback in 30 years of existence.

CRITICISMS OF THE TREATY

The Treaty has both admirers and critics. Admirers marvel that so simple a document could emerge from such unpromising beginnings, and prove so effective in promoting peace and scientific cooperation for three decades and more. Critics write it off as bland and toothless, providing agreement on issues that do not really matter, but avoiding or falling down on the more important, controversial issues, such as mineral exploitation. Admirers see it as an imperfect but evolving system for managing a continent in harmony and peace. Detractors, including the governments of many developing countries, see the Treaty as the manifesto of an exclusive club, and the consultative parties as a neo-colonial clique of rich nations, sullied by the presence among them of the Republic of South Africa and bent on controlling Antarctica exclusively for their own benefit.

Antarctica and the Treaty are debated each year in the General Assembly of the United Nations, when grievances against the Treaty and possible alternative systems of management are aired. The strongest and most consistent view sees Antarctica as part of the heritage of the whole human race, and not to be alienated by a small group of wealthy nations. In reply Treaty supporters point out that any member of the United Nations may join the 'club' as a contracting party, while those that are interested enough have only to send an expedition to the Antarctic to qualify for consultative status and take part in decision-making. Indeed many nations have already done both. At the XVth Consultative Meeting in Paris in December 1989 there were 39 parties to the Treaty, of whom 22 were consultative parties. Treaty supporters may add, if they feel inclined, that the consultative members, far from being a small clique, now represent well over half the world's population. Fortunately for that argument, both China and India are consultative parties.

Conservationists also debate the issues in every public forum, generally expressing dissatisfaction with Treaty management and especially deploring the gradual erosion of Antarctica's pristine qualities. Some, perhaps the majority, would like to see Antarctica declared a 'world park' and kept aloof from development of any kind. When asked what they mean by a world park, who would run it, and with what management objectives and funding, they are usually at a loss to say. The more practical ones favour keeping the Antarctic Treaty organization, but working to strengthen both its sense of purpose and its teeth.

There are other grounds for dissatisfaction with the Treaty and the hegemony given to scientists in Antarctica. Decisions affecting the management and future of the continent are made, often behind closed doors, by scientists or at the behest of scientists, to the exclusion of other interested parties. Antarctica has become 'a continent for science' (an inexcusable phrase that scientists use unblushingly) in which tourists and other visitors are frankly unwelcome. Yet under the impact of scientists and those who support them, Antarctica has deteriorated markedly. The litter of derelict huts, rubbish tips and packing materials that reappears in Antarctica with each spring thaw is a reminder that scientists, just like anyone else, need to be watched.

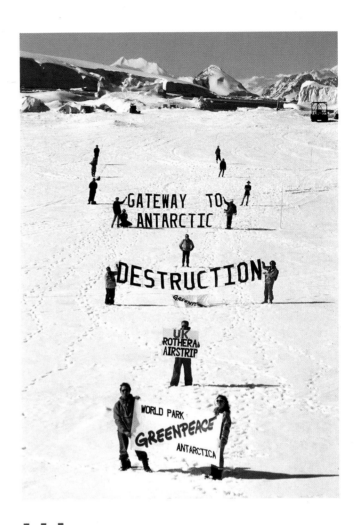

■ ■ ■

Environmentalists protesting against the building of yet another airstrip in Antarctica. Concern about unnecessary destruction and damage comes from tourists as well as environmental groups. Both constituencies keep Antarctic administrators and planners on their toes.

AN ARCTIC TREATY?

The success of the Antarctic Treaty in its two major purposes — keeping the peace and providing a mechanism for close scientific cooperation — has led many to wonder if something of the kind could ever be worked out for the Arctic. Pessimists say no, pointing out that every hectare of the Arctic is unequivocally owned, that no Arctic fringe country would alienate any part of its lands to a common

■ ■ ■

Rubbish-burning at an
Antarctic base. Although
burning rubbish is better
than leaving it to the
vagaries of the wind,
this method of rubbish
disposal is now officially
prohibited.

pool, and that strategic considerations make nonsense of any idea of cooperative science. Optimists say yes. Ownership, they say, means that questions of sovereignty are not an issue, so all that is needed is a Treaty that will provide an encouraging political environment, one that allows scientists to work where they will across the Arctic basin and exchange ideas freely.

Suggesting even the mildest approach to an Arctic accord during the 1950s and '60s would have invited derision. However, even then the scientists tried hard to cooperate, and some succeeded. Soviet, Scandinavian, Canadian and American researchers in several fields of Arctic study occasionally managed to meet and exchange ideas across the Iron Curtain. There were successful international agreements on fisheries and sealing quotas, but both sides suffered from paranoia about security. Information of the slightest strategic value was rigorously kept under wraps and remained unpublished.

A heartening breakthrough was an international study of polar bears, which began with a meeting in Fairbanks, Alaska, in 1965, attended by biologists

from the United States, Canada, Denmark, Norway and the Soviet Union. From this arose separate but closely linked studies of polar bears throughout the Arctic. Information was freely exchanged, and in response to the concern expressed by the scientists, hunting was modified and reduced in each of the five countries. In 1973 came the International Agreement on the Conservation of Polar Bears and their Habitats, the first ever pan-Arctic international agreement on any scientific issue, which all five countries ratified. The agreement was renewed in perpetuity in 1981.

Progress since then has been slow. While the Antarctic Treaty developed, Arctic accord seemed as far away as ever. In 1986 Antarctic scientists at a meeting of the Scientific Committee for Antarctic Research (SCAR) raised the question of whether it would be helpful to have an Arctic equivalent of SCAR. There was a more formal meeting in Oslo in February 1987, from which followed a proposal for an 'International Arctic Science Committee' (IASC) to promote pan-Arctic studies among the Arctic fringe countries. Then in October 1987 came the remarkable policy declaration by Mikhail Gorbachev, which set scientific antennae quivering. Was this perhaps the cue that everyone had been waiting for?

Apparently it was. In March 1988, at a conference in Stockholm, scientists from the United States, Canada, Denmark, Greenland, Finland, Iceland, Norway, Sweden and the Soviet Union announced their firm intention of forming IASC, 'to promote international cooperation and coordination of scientific research in the Arctic, for the benefit of the peoples of the region and for the advancement of world scientific knowledge.' A conference in Leningrad in December that year set the seal on IASC. The Arctic now has its equivalent of SCAR and, with the example of Antarctic before it, has every chance of entering an era of peace and cooperation.

Scientific cooperation is a good thing and scientific and political cooperation can only be better. As we have seen, there are plenty of problems in both polar regions, some that will benefit from science and politics, and others that may not. Foremost in the Arctic are the problems of native peoples displaced in time and location, jolted by progress from their old ways but not yet prepared for the new.

In Antarctica are the problems of a land without native peoples, a workplace for thousands but homeland to no one — a land pulled hither by scientists and thither by environmentalists, but truly cherished by few.

Science, politics, human puzzles and vexations and beyond them the polar regions themselves — the cold Arctic basin ringed by tundra, the vast dome of Antarctica with its fringe of islands. Their beauty touches everyone who sees them. Their presence is commanding, their scale magnificent. They are of immense value to the world. We have gained much and learned much from polar regions, and damaged both in the process. Perhaps now, in maturity, we are learning to care for them. If not, the gains will stop, and we shall learn no more.

FURTHER READING

Armstrong, T. E., Rogers, G. and Rowley, G. 1978.
The Circumpolar North: a political and economic geography of the Arctic and Sub-Arctic.
London, Methuen.

Berton, P. 1988.
The Arctic Grail: the quest for the North West Passage and the North Pole, 1818-1909.
New York, Viking.

Bonner, W. N. and Walton, D. W. H. (editors). 1985.
Antarctica.
Oxford, Pergamon.

Brody, H. 1987.
Living Arctic.
London, Faber & Faber.

Central Intelligence Agency. 1978.
Polar Regions Atlas.
Washington, CIA.

Deacon, G. 1984.
The Antarctic Circumpolar Ocean.
Cambridge, Cambridge University Press.

Hall, S. 1987.
The Fourth World: the heritage of the Arctic and its destruction.
London, Bodley Head.

Headland, R. K. 1990.
Chronological list of Antarctic expeditions and related historical events.
Cambridge, Cambridge University Press.

Imbrie, J. and Imbrie, K. P. 1979.
Ice Ages: solving the mystery.
Short Hills NJ, Enslow Publishers.

Karjanoja, M. (editor). 1988.
Arctic Circle, Rovaniemi-Nuorgam.
Oulu, Finnish National Committee of the European Cultural Foundation.

Karjanoja, M. and Toivanen, L. (editors). 1989.
Arctic Circle 2, Rovaniemi-Kilpisjärvi.
Oulu, Finnish National Committee of the European Cultural Foundation.

Orrego-Vicuna, F. (editor). 1983.
Antarctic Resources Policy.
Cambridge, Cambridge University Press.

Osherenko, G. and Young, O. R. 1989.
The Age of the Arctic.
Cambridge, Cambridge University Press.

Reader's Digest. 1985.
Antarctica: great stories from the frozen continent.
Sydney, Reader's Digest.

Rey, L. and Stonehouse, B. 1982.
The Arctic Ocean: the hydrographic environment and the fate of pollutants.
London, Macmillan.

Sage, B. (editor). 1986.
The Arctic and its Wildlife.
London, Croom Helm.

Stonehouse, B. 1985.
Sea Mammals of the World.
London, Penguin.

Stonehouse, B. (editor). 1986.
Arctic Air Pollution.
Cambridge, Cambridge University Press.

Stonehouse, B. 1989.
Polar Ecology.
Glasgow, Blackie.

Thomson, G. M. 1975.
The North-west Passage.
London, Secker & Warburg.

Triggs, G. D. (editor). 1987.
The Antarctic Treaty Regime: law, environment and resources.
Cambridge, Cambridge University Press.

Young, S. B. 1989.
To the Arctic: an introduction to the far northern world.
New York, Wiley.

PICTURE CREDITS

Bryan & Cherry Alexander endpapers, title page, 6 (inset), 17, 19 bottom, 20, 21 top, 21 bottom, 22, 30, 32, 45, 46, 50–51, 60–61, 76, 81, 82 top, 82 bottom left, 92, 98 left, 98 right, 106, 110, 124, 154, 161, 171, 174, 180, 186, 194 top, front jacket inset • **Bryan & Cherry Alexander – Wayne Lynd** 96 top right • **Heather Angel** 39, 56, 93 top, 97 bottom • **Arctic Camera** 19 top, 24, 52, 80 bottom left, 88 bottom right, 93 bottom right • **Biofotos – Bryn Campbell** 150 • **Biofotos – J. Hoogesteger** 26, 40–41 • **Biofotos – Soames Summerhayes** 62, 83 top • **Bridgeman Art Library** 114–115 • **Bruce Coleman – Erwin & Peggy Bauer** 87, 97 top • **Mary Evans Picture Library** 128, 131, 137, 151 right • **Werner Forman Archive** 113, 116 • **M. R. Gorman** 18 top, 42, 182 • **Greenpeace** 195, 205 • **Michael Holford** 142–143 • **Eric Kay** 6 (background), 18 bottom, 29, 48, 54, 88 top, 89, 93 bottom left, 94, 164, front jacket background • **Mansell Collection** 144, 149, 151 left, 157, 160 • **NHPA – ANT** 14 bottom, 187 • **NHPA – Melvin Grey** 96 top left • **NHPA – Brian Hawkes** 96 bottom left, 96 bottom right, 99 • **NHPA – Tony Howard** 101 top left • **NHPA – Stephen Krasemann** 57, 80 top, 82 bottom right • **NHPA – Tsuneo Nakamura** 70, 83 bottom • **NHPA – Haroldo Palo** 146–147 • **NHPA – View A/S** 159 • **Mark Nuttall** 109 • **Ann Ronan Picture Library** 117, 119, 120, 123 top, 125 • **David Rootes** 7, 16, 80 bottom, 91, 101 bottom left, 188, 198, 206, 207 • **Royal Geographical Society** 121 • **Science Photo Library** 191 • **Scott Polar Research Institute** 34, 35, 36, 37, 69, 126 • **Bernard Stonehouse** contents page, 12, 15, 23, 25, 28, 38, 59, 64, 66, 67, 68, 72, 73 top, 73 bottom, 75, 79, 84 top, 84 bottom, 86 left, 86 right, 90, 100 top, 100 bottom, 101 bottom, 102, 135, 138, 193, 194 bottom, 204 back jacket right • **P. Stonehouse** 177 • **Charles Swithinbank** 14 top, 190 • **TASS** 123 bottom, 152, 168, 170, 196 back jacket left • **P. Vitebsky** 162.

MAPS AND DIAGRAMS CREDITS

Malcolm Porter 8–9, 10–11, 44, 55, 78, 132, 140, 158, 165, 169, 172, 178.